SOLUTIONS MANUAL

Statistics for Business and Economics

Eighth Edition

David R. Anderson
University of Cincinnati

Dennis J. Sweeney
University of Cincinnati

Thomas A. Williams
Rochester Institute of Technology

SOUTH-WESTERN
★
™
THOMSON LEARNING

Australia · Canada · Mexico · Singapore · Spain · United Kingdom · United States

Solutions Manual for Statistics for Business and Economics 8e
by Anderson, Sweeney, and Williams

Publisher: Dave Shaut
Sr. Acquisitions Editor: Charles E. McCormick, Jr.
Sr. Developmental Editor: Alice C. Denny
Sr. Marketing Manager: Joseph A. Sabatino
Sr. Production Editor: Deanna R. Quinn
Manufacturing Coordinator: Doug Wilke
Printer: Webcom

Printed in Canada
1 2 3 4 5 04 03 02 01

For more information contact South-Western, 5101 Madison Road, Cincinnati, Ohio, 45227 or
find us on the Internet at http://www.swcollege.com

For permission to use material from this text or product, contact us by
• **telephone: 1-800-730-2214**
• **fax: 1-800-730-2215**
• **web: http://www.thomsonrights.com**

ISBN 0-324-06675-9

Contents

Chapter

Preface

The purpose of *Statistics for Business and Economics* is to provide students, primarily in the fields of business administration and economics, with a sound conceptual introduction to the field of statistics and its many applications. The text is applications-oriented and has been written with the needs of the nonmathematician in mind.

The solutions manual furnishes assistance by identifying learning objectives and providing detailed solutions for all exercises in the text.

Note: The solutions to the case problems are included in the Instructor's Manual.

Acknowledgements

We would like to provide special recognition to Catherine J. Williams for her efforts in preparing the solutions manual.

David R. Anderson
Dennis J. Sweeney
Thomas A. Williams

Chapter 1
Data and Statistics

Learning Objectives

1. Obtain an appreciation for the breadth of statistical applications in business and economics.

2. Understand the meaning of the terms elements, variables, and observations as they are used in statistics.

3. Obtain an understanding of the difference between qualitative, quantitative, crossectional and time series data.

4. Learn about the sources of data for statistical analysis both internal and external to the firm.

5. Be aware of how errors can arise in data.

6. Know the meaning of descriptive statistics and statistical inference.

7. Be able to distinguish between a population and a sample.

8. Understand the role a sample plays in making statistical inferences about the population.

Solutions:

1. Statistics can be referred to as numerical facts. In a broader sense, statistics is the field of study dealing with the collection, analysis, presentation and interpretation of data.

2. a. 9

    b. 4

    c. Country and room rate are qualitative variables; number of rooms and the overall score are quantitative variables.

    d. Country is nominal; room rate is ordinal; number of rooms and overall score are ratio.

3. a. Average number of rooms = 808/9 = 89.78 or approximately 90 rooms

    b. 2 of 9 are located in England; approximately 22%

    c. 4 of 9 have a room rate of $$; approximately 44%

4. a. 10

    b. <u>Fortune</u> 500 largest U.S. industrial corporations

    c. Average revenue = $142,275.9/10 = $14,227.59 million

    d. Using the sample average, statistical inference would let us estimate the average revenue for the population of 500 corporations as $14,227.59 million.

5. a. 3

    b. Industry code is qualitative; revenues and profit are quantitative.

    c. Average profit = 10,652.1/10 = $1065.21 million

    d. 8 of 10 had a profit over $100 million; 80%

    e. 1 of 10 had an industry code of 3; 10%

6. Questions a, c, and d are quantitative.

    Questions b and e are qualitative.

7. a. The data are numeric and the variable is qualitative.

    b. Nominal

8. a. 2,013

    b. Qualitative

    c. Percentages since we have qualitative data

    d. (0.28)(2013) = 563.64 Must have been 563 or 564.

9. a. Qualitative

    b. 30 of 71; 42.3%

10. a. Quantitative; ratio

    b. Qualitative; nominal

    c. Qualitative (Note: Rank is a numeric label that identifies the position of a student in the class. Rank does not indicate how much or how many and is not quantitative.); ordinal

    d. Qualitative; nominal

    e. Quantitative; ratio

11. a. Quantitative; ratio

    b. Qualitative; ordinal

    c. Qualitative; ordinal (assuming employees can be ranked by classification)

    d. Quantitative; ratio

    e. Qualitative; nominal

12. a. The population is all visitors coming to the state of Hawaii.

    b. Since airline flights carry the vast majority of visitors to the state, the use of questionnaires for passengers during incoming flights is a good way to reach this population. The questionnaire actually appears on the back of a mandatory plants and animals declaration form that passengers must complete during the incoming flight. A large percentage of passengers complete the visitor information questionnaire.

    c. Questions 1 and 4 provide quantitative data indicating the number of visits and the number of days in Hawaii. Questions 2 and 3 provide qualitative data indicating the categories of reason for the trip and where the visitor plans to stay.

13. a. Quantitative

    b. Time series with 7 observations

    c. Number of riverboat casinos.

    d. Time series shows a rapid increase; an increase would be expected in 1998, but it appears that the rate of increase is slowing.

14. a. 4

    b. All four variables are quantitative.

    c. Time series data for 1993 to 1996.

15.   Crossectional data. It is based on the 1996 performance data that was available April 1997.

16. a. We would like to see data from product taste tests and test marketing the product.

    b. Such data would be obtained from specially designed statistical studies.

17.   Internal data on salaries of other employees can be obtained from the personnel department. External data might be obtained from the Department of Labor or industry associations.

18. a. (48/120)100% = 40% in the sample died from some form of heart disease. This can be used as an estimate of the percentage of all males 60 or older who die of heart disease.

    b. The data on cause of death is qualitative.

19. a. All subscribers of Business Week at the time the 1996 survey was conducted.

    b. Quantitative

    c. Qualitative (yes or no)

    d. Crossectional - 1996 was the time of the survey.

    e. Using the sample results, we could infer or estimate 59% of the population of subscribers have an annual income of $75,000 or more and 50% of the population of subscribers have an American Express credit card.

20. a. 56% of market belonged to A.C. Nielsen
        $387,325 is the average amount spent per category

    b. 3.73

    c. $387,325

21. a. The two populations are the population of women whose mothers took the drug DES during pregnancy and the population of women whose mothers did not take the drug DES during pregnancy.

    b. It was a survey.

    c. 63 / 3.980 = 15.8 women out of each 1000 developed tissue abnormalities.

    d. The article reported "twice" as many abnormalities in the women whose mothers had taken DES during pregnancy. Thus, a rough estimate would be 15.8/2 = 7.9 abnormalities per 1000 women whose mothers had *not* taken DES during pregnancy.

    e. In many situations, disease occurrences are rare and affect only a small portion of the population. Large samples are needed to collect data on a reasonable number of cases where the disease exists.

22. a. All adult viewers reached by the Denver, Colorado television station.

    b. The viewers contacted in the telephone survey.

    c. A sample. It would clearly be too costly and time consuming to try to contact all viewers.

23. a. Percent of television sets that were tuned to a particular television show and/or total viewing audience.

    b. All television sets in the United States which are available for the viewing audience. Note this would not include television sets in store displays.

    c. A portion of these television sets. Generally, individual households would be contacted to determine which programs were being viewed.

    d. The cancellation of programs, the scheduling of programs, and advertising cost rates.

24. a. This is a statistically correct descriptive statistic for the sample.

    b. An incorrect generalization since the data was not collected for the entire population.

    c. An acceptable statistical inference based on the use of the word "estimate."

    d. While this statement is true for the sample, it is not a justifiable conclusion for the entire population.

    e. This statement is not statistically supportable. While it is true for the particular sample observed, it is entirely possible and even very likely that at least some students will be outside the 65 to 90 range of grades.

Chapter 2
Descriptive Statistics: Tabular and Graphical Methods

Learning Objectives

1.   Learn how to construct and interpret summarization procedures for qualitative data such as : frequency and relative frequency distributions, bar graphs and pie charts.

2.   Learn how to construct and interpret tabular summarization procedures for quantitative data such as: frequency and relative frequency distributions, cumulative frequency and cumulative relative frequency distributions.

3.   Learn how to construct a dot plot, a histogram, and an ogive as graphical summaries of quantitative data.

4.   Be able to use and interpret the exploratory data analysis technique of a stem-and-leaf display.

5.   Learn how to construct and interpret cross tabulations and scatter diagrams of bivariate data.

Solutions:

1.

Class	Frequency	Relative Frequency
A	60	60/120 = 0.50
B	24	24/120 = 0.20
C	36	36/120 = 0.30
	120	1.00

2. a. $1 - (.22 + .18 + .40) = .20$

    b. $.20(200) = 40$

    c/d

Class	Frequency	Percent Frequency
A	.22(200) = 44	22
B	.18(200) = 36	18
C	.40(200) = 80	40
D	.20(200) = 40	20
Total	200	100

3. a. $360° \times 58/120 = 174°$

    b. $360° \times 42/120 = 126°$

    c.

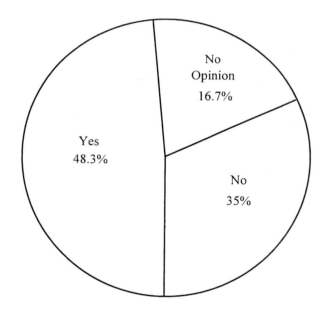

d.

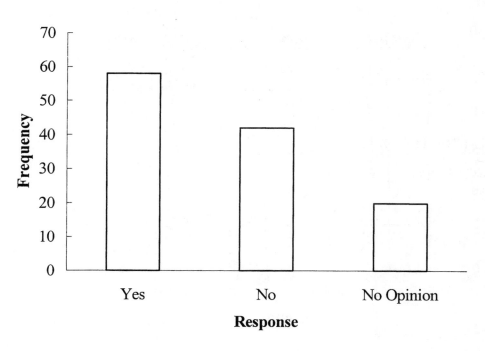

4. a. The data are qualitative.

    b.

TV Show	Frequency	Percent Frequency
Millionaire	24	48
Frasier	15	30
Chicago Hope	7	14
Charmed	4	8
Total:	50	100

c.

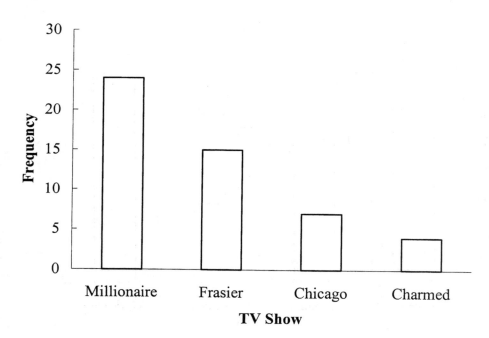

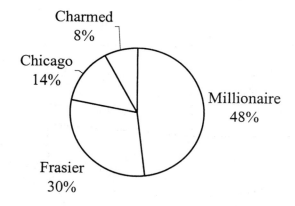

d. Millionaire has the largest market share. Frasier is second.

5. a.

Major	Relative Frequency	Percent Frequency
Management	55/216 = 0.25	25
Accounting	51/216 = 0.24	24
Finance	28/216 = 0.13	13
Marketing	82/216 = 0.38	38
Total	1.00	100

b.

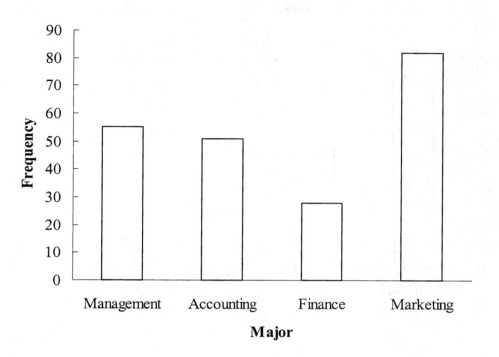

c.   Pie Chart

6.   a.

Book	Frequency	Percent Frequency
7 Habits	10	16.66
Millionaire	16	26.67
Motley	9	15.00
Dad	13	21.67
WSJ Guide	6	10.00
Other	6	10.00
Total:	60	100.00

The Ernst & Young Tax Guide 2000 with a frequency of 3, *Investing for Dummies* with a frequency of 2, and *What Color is Your Parachute? 2000* with a frequency of 1 are grouped in the "Other" category.

b. The rank order from first to fifth is: Millionaire, Dad, 7 Habits, Motley, and WSJ Guide.

c. The percent of sales represented by *The Millionaire Next Door* and *Rich Dad, Poor Dad* is 48.33%.

7.

Rating	Frequency	Relative Frequency
Outstanding	19	0.38
Very Good	13	0.26
Good	10	0.20
Average	6	0.12
Poor	2	0.04
	50	1.00

Management should be pleased with these results. 64% of the ratings are very good to outstanding. 84% of the ratings are good or better. Comparing these ratings with previous results will show whether or not the restaurant is making improvements in its ratings of food quality.

8. a.

Position	Frequency	Relative Frequency
Pitcher	17	0.309
Catcher	4	0.073
1st Base	5	0.091
2nd Base	4	0.073
3rd Base	2	0.036
Shortstop	5	0.091
Left Field	6	0.109
Center Field	5	0.091
Right Field	7	0.127
	55	1.000

b. Pitchers (Almost 31%)

c. 3rd Base (3 - 4%)

d. Right Field (Almost 13%)

e. Infielders (16 or 29.1%) to Outfielders (18 or 32.7%)

9. a/b.

Starting Time	Frequency	Percent Frequency
7:00	3	15
7:30	4	20
8:00	4	20
8:30	7	35
9:00	2	10
	20	100

c. Bar Graph

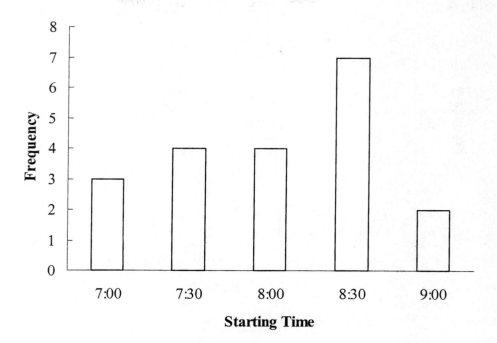

Starting Time

d.

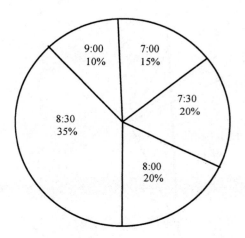

e. The most preferred starting time is 8:30 a.m.. Starting times of 7:30 and 8:00 a.m. are next.

10. a. The data refer to quality levels of poor, fair, good, very good and excellent.

b.

Rating	Frequency	Relative Frequency
Poor	2	0.03
Fair	4	0.07
Good	12	0.20
Very Good	24	0.40
Excellent	18	0.30
	60	1.00

c. Bar Graph

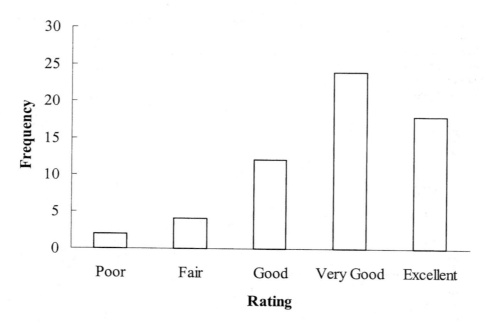

Pie Chart

d. The course evaluation data indicate a high quality course. The most common rating is very good with the second most common being excellent.

11.

Class	Frequency	Relative Frequency	Percent Frequency
12-14	2	0.050	5.0
15-17	8	0.200	20.0
18-20	11	0.275	27.5
21-23	10	0.250	25.5
24-26	9	0.225	22.5
Total	40	1.000	100.0

12.

Class	Cumulative Frequency	Cumulative Relative Frequency
less than or equal to 19	10	.20
less than or equal to 29	24	.48
less than or equal to 39	41	.82
less than or equal to 49	48	.96
less than or equal to 59	50	1.00

13.

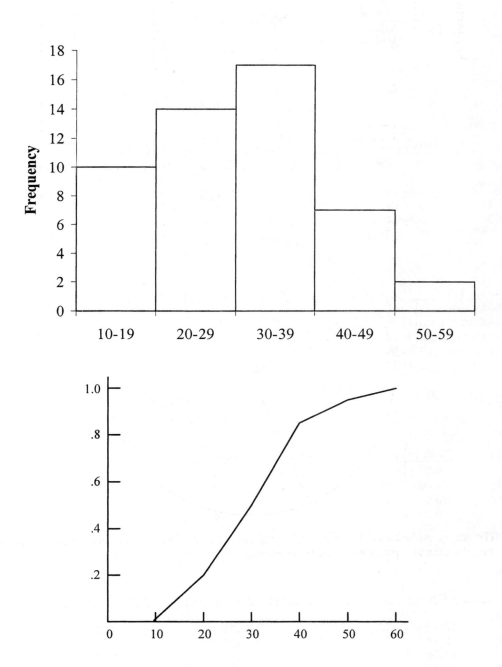

14. a.

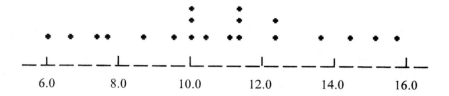

b/c.

Class	Frequency	Percent Frequency
6.0 - 7.9	4	20
8.0 - 9.9	2	10
10.0 - 11.9	8	40
12.0 - 13.9	3	15
14.0 - 15.9	3	15
	20	100

15. a/b.

Waiting Time	Frequency	Relative Frequency
0 - 4	4	0.20
5 - 9	8	0.40
10 - 14	5	0.25
15 - 19	2	0.10
20 - 24	1	0.05
Totals	20	1.00

c/d.

Waiting Time	Cumulative Frequency	Cumulative Relative Frequency
Less than or equal to 4	4	0.20
Less than or equal to 9	12	0.60
Less than or equal to 14	17	0.85
Less than or equal to 19	19	0.95
Less than or equal to 24	20	1.00

e. $12/20 = 0.60$

16. a.

Stock Price ($)	Frequency	Relative Frequency	Percent Frequency
10.00 - 19.99	10	0.40	40
20.00 - 29.99	4	0.16	16
30.00 - 39.99	6	0.24	24
40.00 - 49.99	2	0.08	8
50.00 - 59.99	1	0.04	4
60.00 - 69.99	2	0.08	8
Total	25	1.00	100

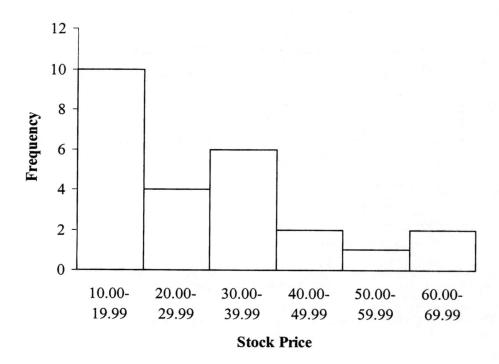

Many of these are low priced stocks with the greatest frequency in the $10.00 to $19.99 range.

b.

Earnings per Share ($)	Frequency	Relative Frequency	Percent Frequency
-3.00 to -2.01	2	0.08	8
-2.00 to -1.01	0	0.00	0
-1.00 to -0.01	2	0.08	8
0.00 to 0.99	9	0.36	36
1.00 to 1.99	9	0.36	36
2.00 to 2.99	3	0.12	12
Total	25	1.00	100

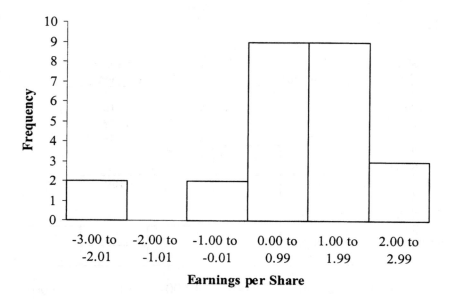

The majority of companies had earnings in the $0.00 to $2.00 range. Four of the companies lost money.

17.

Call Duration	Frequency	Relative Frequency
2 - 3.9	5	0.25
4 - 5.9	9	0.45
6 - 7.9	4	0.20
8 - 9.9	0	0.00
10 - 11.9	2	0.10
Totals	20	1.00

Histogram

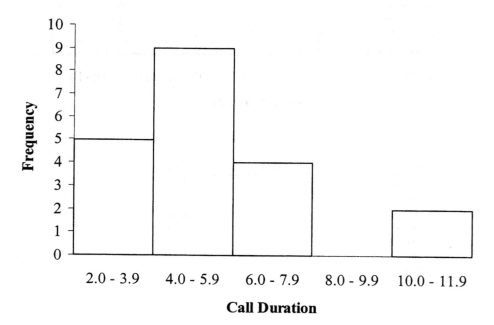

18. a. Lowest salary: $93,000
       Highest salary: $178,000

    b.

Salary ($1000s)	Frequency	Relative Frequency	Percent Frequency
91-105	4	0.08	8
106-120	5	0.10	10
121-135	11	0.22	22
136-150	18	0.36	36
151-165	9	0.18	18
166-180	3	0.06	6
Total	50	1.00	100

    c. Proportion $135,000 or less: 20/50.

    d. Percentage *more than* $150,000: 24%

    e.

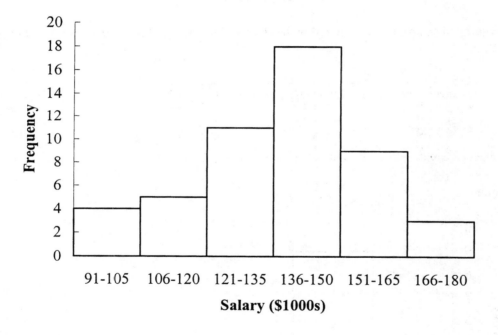

19. a/b.

Number	Frequency	Relative Frequency
140 - 149	2	0.10
150 - 159	7	0.35
160 - 169	3	0.15
170 - 179	6	0.30
180 - 189	1	0.05
190 - 199	1	0.05
Totals	20	1.00

c/d.

Number	Cumulative Frequency	Cumulative Relative Frequency
Less than or equal to 149	2	0.10
Less than or equal to 159	9	0.45
Less than or equal to 169	12	0.60
Less than or equal to 179	18	0.90
Less than or equal to 189	19	0.95
Less than or equal to 199	20	1.00

e.

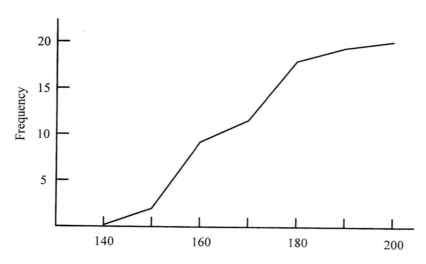

20. a. The percentage of people 34 or less is $20.0 + 5.7 + 9.6 + 13.6 = 48.9$.

   b. The percentage of the population that is between 25 and 54 years old inclusively is $13.6 + 16.3 + 13.5 = 43.4$

   c. The percentage of the population over 34 years old is $16.3 + 13.5 + 8.7 + 12.6 = 51.1$

   d. The percentage less than 25 years old is $20.0 + 5.7 + 9.6 = 35.3$.
   So there are $(.353)(275) = 97.075$ million people less than 25 years old.

   e. An estimate of the number of retired people is $(.5)(.087)(275) + (.126)(275) = 46.6125$ million.

21. a/b.

Computer Usage (Hours)			Frequency	Relative Frequency
0.0	-	2.9	5	0.10
3.0	-	5.9	28	0.56
6.0	-	8.9	8	0.16
9.0	-	11.9	6	0.12
12.0	-	14.9	3	0.06
		Total	50	1.00

c.

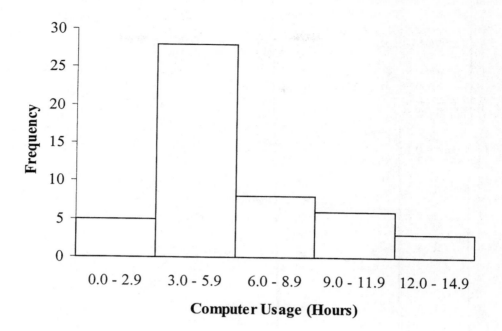

d.

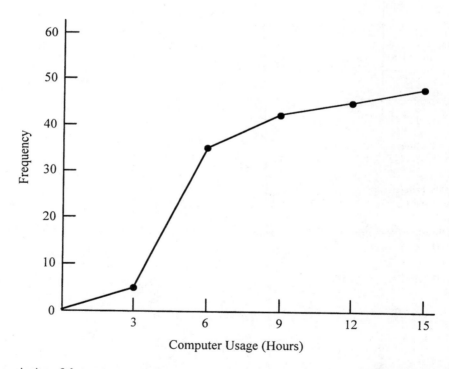

e. The majority of the computer users are in the 3 to 6 hour range. Usage is somewhat skewed toward the right with 3 users in the 12 to 15 hour range.

22.

```
5 | 7  8
6 | 4  5  8
7 | 0  2  2  5  5  6  8
8 | 0  2  3  5
```

23.   Leaf Unit = 0.1

```
 6 | 3
 7 | 5  5  7
 8 | 1  3  4  8
 9 | 3  6
10 | 0  4  5
11 | 3
```

24.   Leaf Unit = 10

```
11 | 6
12 | 0  2
13 | 0  6  7
14 | 2  2  7
15 | 5
16 | 0  2  8
17 | 0  2  3
```

25.

```
 9 | 8 9
10 | 2 4 6 6
11 | 4 5 7 8 8 9
12 | 2 4 5 7
13 | 1 2
14 | 4
15 | 1
```

26.   Leaf Unit = 0.1

```
0 | 4 7 8 9 9
1 | 1 2 9
2 | 0 0 1 3 5 5 6 8
3 | 4 9
4 | 8
5 |
6 |
7 | 1
```

27.

```
4 | 1  3  6  6  7
5 | 0  0  3  8  9
6 | 0  1  1  4  4  5  7  7  9  9
7 | 0  0  0  1  3  4  4  5  5  6  6  6  7  8  8
8 | 0  1  1  3  4  4  5  7  7  8  9
9 | 0  2  2  7
```

or

```
4 | 1  3
4 | 6  6  7
5 | 0  0  3
5 | 8  9
6 | 0  1  1  4  4
6 | 5  7  7  9  9
7 | 0  0  0  1  3  4  4
7 | 5  5  6  6  6  7  8  8
8 | 0  1  1  3  4  4
8 | 5  7  7  8  9
9 | 0  2  2
9 | 7
```

28. a.

```
0 | 5  8
1 | 1  1  3  3  4  4
1 | 5  6  7  8  9  9
2 | 2  3  3  3  5  5
2 | 6  8
3 |
3 | 6  7  7  9
4 | 0
4 | 7  8
5 |
5 |
6 | 0
```

b.

2000 P/E Forecast	Frequency	Percent Frequency
5 - 9	2	6.7
10 - 14	6	20.0
15 - 19	6	20.0
20 - 24	6	20.0
25 - 29	2	6.7
30 - 34	0	0.0
35 - 39	4	13.3
40 - 44	1	3.3
45 - 49	2	6.7
50 - 54	0	0.0
55 - 59	0	0.0
60 - 64	1	3.3
Total	30	100.0

29. a.

		y		
		1	2	Total
	A	5	0	5
x	B	11	2	13
	C	2	10	12
	Total	18	12	30

b.

	y		
	1	2	Total
A	100.0	0.0	100.0
x B	84.6	15.4	100.0
C	16.7	83.3	100.0

c.

	y	
	1	2
A	27.8	0.0
x B	61.1	16.7
C	11.1	83.3
Total	100.0	100.0

d. Category A values for x are always associated with category 1 values for y. Category B values for x are usually associated with category 1 values for y. Category C values for x are usually associated with category 2 values for y.

30. a.

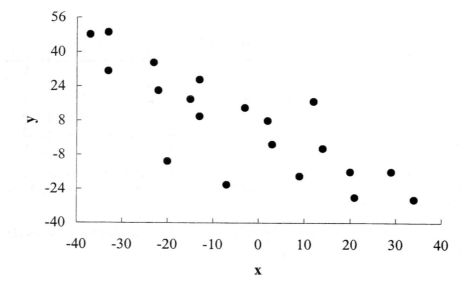

b.   There is a negative relationship between x and y; y decreases as x increases.

31.

Quality Rating	Meal Price ($)			
	10-19	20-29	30-39	40-49
Good	53.8	33.9	2.7	0.0
Very Good	43.6	54.2	60.5	21.4
Excellent	2.6	11.9	36.8	78.6
Total	100.0	100.0	100.0	100.0

As the meal price goes up, the percentage of high quality ratings goes up. A positive relationship between meal price and quality is observed.

32. a.

Sales/Margins/ROE	EPS Rating					Total
	0-19	20-39	40-59	60-79	80-100	
A				1	8	9
B		1	4	5	2	12
C	1		1	2	3	7
D	3	1		1		5
E		2	1			3
Total	4	4	6	9	13	36

b.

Sales/Margins/ROE	EPS Rating					Total
	0-19	20-39	40-59	60-79	80-100	
A				11.11	88.89	100
B		8.33	33.33	41.67	16.67	100
C	14.29		14.29	28.57	42.86	100
D	60.00	20.00		20.00		100
E		66.67	33.33			100

Higher EPS ratings seem to be associated with higher ratings on Sales/Margins/ROE. Of those companies with an "A" rating on Sales/Margins/ROE, 88.89% of them had an EPS Rating of 80 or higher. Of the 8 companies with a "D" or "E" rating on Sales/Margins/ROE, only 1 had an EPS rating above 60.

33. a.

Sales/Margins/ROE	Industry Group Relative Strength					Total
	A	B	C	D	E	
A	1	2	2	4		9
B	1	5	2	3	1	12
C	1	3		2	1	7
D	1		1	1	2	5
E		1	2			3
Total	4	11	7	10	4	36

b/c. The frequency distributions for the Sales/Margins/ROE data is in the rightmost column of the crosstabulation. The frequency distribution for the Industry Group Relative Strength data is in the bottom row of the crosstabulation.

d.   Once the crosstabulation is complete, the individual frequency distributions are available in the margins.

34. a.

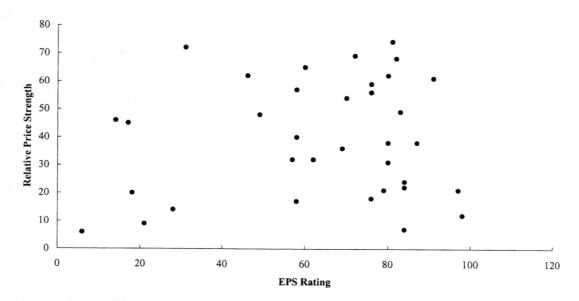

b. One might expect stocks with higher EPS ratings to show greater relative price strength. However, the scatter diagram using this data does not support such a relationship.

The scatter diagram appears similar to the one showing "No Apparent Relationship" in Figure 2.19.

35. a.

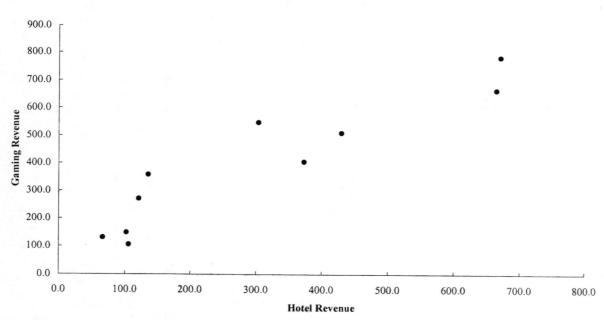

b. There appears to be a positive relationship between hotel revenue and gaming revenue. Higher values of hotel revenue are associated with higher values of gaming revenue.

36. a.

Vehicle	Frequency	Percent Frequency
F-Series	17	34
Silverado	12	24
Taurus	8	16
Camry	7	14
Accord	6	12
Total	50	100

b. The two top selling vehicles are the Ford F-Series Pickup and the Chevrolet Silverado.

c.

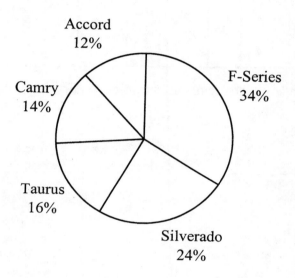

37. a/b.

Industry	Frequency	Percent Frequency
Beverage	2	10
Chemicals	3	15
Electronics	6	30
Food	7	35
Aerospace	2	10
Totals:	20	100

c.

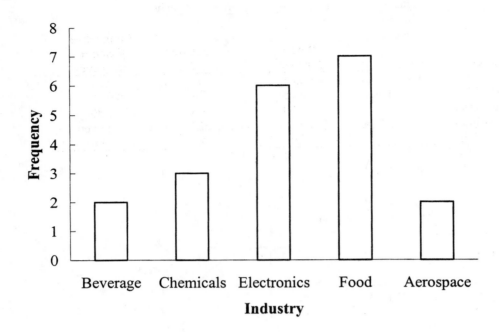

38. a.

Movie	Frequency	Percent Frequency
Blair Witch Project	159	36.0
Phantom Menace	89	20.2
Beloved	85	19.3
Primary Colors	57	12.9
Truman Show	51	11.6
Total	441	100.0

b.

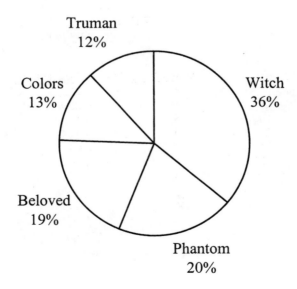

c. The percent of mail pertaining to 1999 cover stories is 36.0 + 20.2 = 56.2%

39. a-d.

Sales	Frequency	Relative Frequency	Cumulative Frequency	Cumulative Relative Frequency
0 - 499	13	0.65	13	0.65
500 - 999	3	0.15	16	0.80
1000 - 1499	0	0.00	16	0.80
1500 - 1999	3	0.15	19	0.95
2000 - 2499	1	0.05	20	1.00
Total	20	1.00		

e.

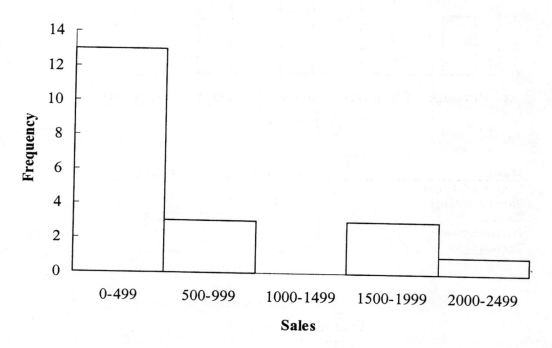

40. a.

Closing Price	Frequency	Relative Frequency
0 - 9 7/8	9	0.225
10 - 19 7/8	10	0.250
20 - 29 7/8	5	0.125
30 - 39 7/8	11	0.275
40 - 49 7/8	2	0.050
50 - 59 7/8	2	0.050
60 - 69 7/8	0	0.000
70 - 79 7/8	1	0.025
Totals	40	1.000

b.

Closing Price	Cumulative Frequency	Cumulative Relative Frequency
Less than or equal to 9 7/8	9	0.225
Less than or equal to 19 7/8	19	0.475
Less than or equal to 29 7/8	24	0.600
Less than or equal to 39 7/8	35	0.875
Less than or equal to 49 7/8	37	0.925
Less than or equal to 59 7/8	39	0.975
Less than or equal to 69 7/8	39	0.975
Less than or equal to 79 7/8	40	1.000

c.

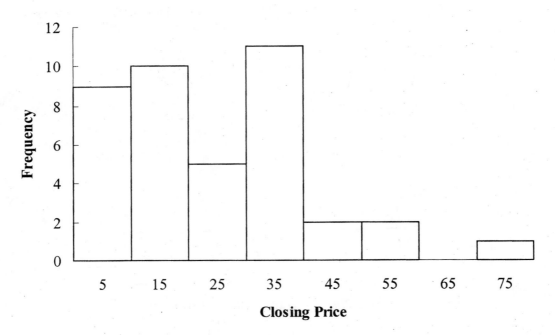

d. Over 87% of common stocks trade for less than $40 a share and 60% trade for less than $30 per share.

41. a.

Exchange	Frequency	Relative Frequency
American	3	0.15
New York	2	0.10
Over the Counter	15	0.75
	20	1.00

b.

Earnings Per Share	Frequency	Relative Frequency
0.00 - 0.19	7	0.35
0.20 - 0.39	7	0.35
0.40 - 0.59	1	0.05
0.60 - 0.79	3	0.15
0.80 - 0.99	2	0.10
	20	1.00

Seventy percent of the shadow stocks have earnings per share less than $0.40. It looks like low EPS should be expected for shadow stocks.

Price-Earning Ratio	Frequency	Relative Frequency
0.00 - 9.9	3	0.15
10.0 - 19.9	7	0.35
20.0 - 29.9	4	0.20
30.0 - 39.9	3	0.15
40.0 - 49.9	2	0.10
50.0 - 59.9	1	0.05
	20	1.00

P-E Ratios vary considerably, but there is a significant cluster in the 10 - 19.9 range.

42.

Income ($)	Frequency	Relative Frequency
18,000-21,999	13	0.255
22,000-25,999	20	0.392
26,000-29,999	12	0.235
30,000-33,999	4	0.078
34,000-37,999	2	0.039
Total	51	1.000

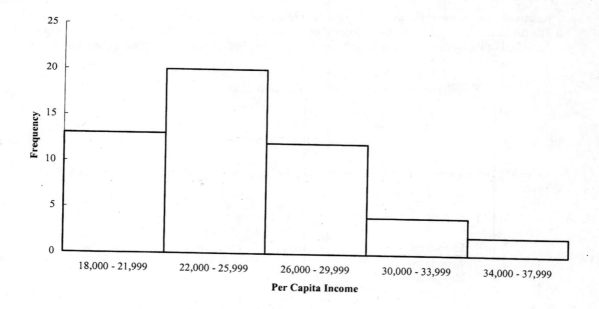

43. a.

0	8 9
1	0 2 2 2 3 4 4 4
1	5 5 6 6 6 6 7 7 8 8 8 8 9 9 9
2	0 1 2 2 2 3 4 4 4
2	5 6 8
3	0 1 3

b/c/d.

Number Answered Correctly	Frequency	Relative Frequency	Cumulative Frequency
5 - 9	2	0.050	2
10 - 14	8	0.200	10
15 - 19	15	0.375	25
20 - 24	9	0.225	34
25 - 29	3	0.075	37
30 - 34	3	0.075	40
Totals	40	1.000	

e. Relatively few of the students (25%) were able to answer 1/2 or more of the questions correctly. The data seem to support the Joint Council on Economic Education's claim. However, the degree of difficulty of the questions needs to be taken into account before reaching a final a conclusion.

44. a/b.

High Temperature		Low Temperature	
	3	3	9
	4	4	3 6 8
7	5	5	0 0 0 2 4 4 5 5 7 9
1 4 4 4 4 6 8	6	6	1 8
3 5 7 9	7	7	2 4 5 5
0 1 1 4 6	8	8	
0 2 3	9	9	

c. It is clear that the range of low temperatures is below the range of high temperatures. Looking at the stem-and-leaf displays side by side, it appears that the range of low temperatures is about 20 degrees below the range of high temperatures.

d. There are two stems showing high temperatures of 80 degrees or higher. They show 8 cities with high temperatures of 80 degrees or higher.

e.

Temperature	Frequency High Temp.	Frequency Low. Temp.
30-39	0	1
40-49	0	3
50-59	1	10
60-69	7	2
70-79	4	4
80-89	5	0
90-99	3	0
Total	20	20

45. a.

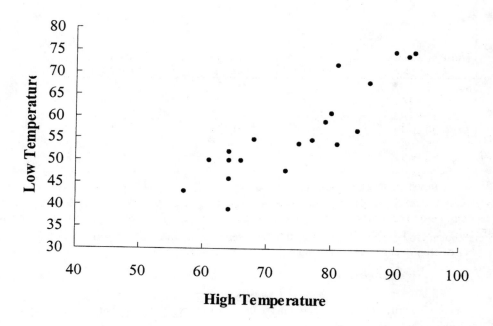

b. There is clearly a positive relationship between high and low temperature for cities. As one goes up so does the other.

46. a.

Occupation	30-39	40-49	Satisfaction Score 50-59	60-69	70-79	80-89	Total
Cabinetmaker			2	4	3	1	10
Lawyer	1	5	2	1	1		10
Physical Therapist			5	2	1	2	10
Systems Analyst		2	1	4	3		10
Total	1	7	10	11	8	3	40

b.

Occupation	30-39	40-49	Satisfaction Score 50-59	60-69	70-79	80-89	Total
Cabinetmaker			20	40	30	10	100
Lawyer	10	50	20	10	10		100
Physical Therapist			50	20	10	20	100
Systems Analyst		20	10	40	30		100

c. Each row of the percent crosstabulation shows a percent frequency distribution for an occupation. Cabinet makers seem to have the higher job satisfaction scores while lawyers seem to have the lowest. Fifty percent of the physical therapists have mediocre scores but the rest are rather high.

47. a.

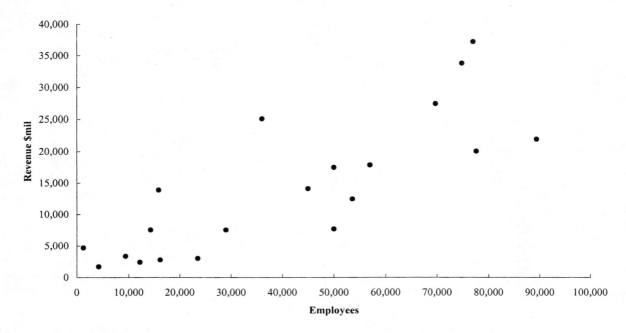

b. There appears to be a positive relationship between number of employees and revenue. As the number of employees increases, annual revenue increases.

48. a.

| Year Constructed | Elec | Fuel Type | | | | Total |
		Nat. Gas	Oil	Propane	Other	
1973 or before	40	183	12	5	7	247
1974-1979	24	26	2	2	0	54
1980-1986	37	38	1	0	6	82
1987-1991	48	70	2	0	1	121
Total	149	317	17	7	14	504

b.

Year Constructed	Frequency	Fuel Type	Frequency
1973 or before	247	Electricity	149
1974-1979	54	Nat. Gas	317
1980-1986	82	Oil	17
1987-1991	121	Propane	7
Total	504	Other	14
		Total	504

c. Crosstabulation of Column Percentages

Year Constructed	Elec	Nat. Gas	Oil	Propane	Other
		Fuel Type			
1973 or before	26.9	57.7	70.5	71.4	50.0
1974-1979	16.1	8.2	11.8	28.6	0.0
1980-1986	24.8	12.0	5.9	0.0	42.9
1987-1991	32.2	22.1	11.8	0.0	7.1
Total	100.0	100.0	100.0	100.0	100.0

d. Crosstabulation of row percentages.

Year Constructed	Elec	Nat. Gas	Oil	Propane	Other	Total
		Fuel Type				
1973 or before	16.2	74.1	4.9	2.0	2.8	100.0
1974-1979	44.5	48.1	3.7	3.7	0.0	100.0
1980-1986	45.1	46.4	1.2	0.0	7.3	100.0
1987-1991	39.7	57.8	1.7	0.0	0.8	100.0

e. <u>Observations from the column percentages crosstabulation</u>

For those buildings using electricity, the percentage has not changed greatly over the years. For the buildings using natural gas, the majority were constructed in 1973 or before; the second largest percentage was constructed in 1987-1991. Most of the buildings using oil were constructed in 1973 or before. All of the buildings using propane are older.

<u>Observations from the row percentages crosstabulation</u>

Most of the buildings in the CG&E service area use electricity or natural gas. In the period 1973 or before most used natural gas. From 1974-1986, it is fairly evenly divided between electricity and natural gas. Since 1987 almost all new buildings are using electricity or natural gas with natural gas being the clear leader.

49. a. Crosstabulation for stockholder's equity and profit.

Stockholders' Equity ($000)	0-200	200-400	400-600	600-800	800-1000	1000-1200	Total
			Profits ($000)				
0-1200	10	1				1	12
1200-2400	4	10			2		16
2400-3600	4	3	3	1	1	1	13
3600-4800					1	2	3
4800-6000		2	3	1			6
Total	18	16	6	2	4	4	50

b. Crosstabulation of Row Percentages.

Stockholders' Equity ($1000s)	0-200	200-400	400-600	600-800	800-1000	1000-1200	Total
			Profits ($000)				
0-1200	83.33	8.33	0.00	0.00	0.00	8.33	100
1200-2400	25.00	62.50	0.00	0.00	12.50	0.00	100
2400-3600	30.77	23.08	23.08	7.69	7.69	7.69	100
3600-4800		0.00	0.00	0.00	33.33	66.67	100
4800-6000	0.00	33.33	50.00	16.67	0.00	0.00	100

c. Stockholder's equity and profit seem to be related. As profit goes up, stockholder's equity goes up. The relationship, however, is not very strong.

50. a. Crosstabulation of market value and profit.

Market Value ($1000s)	Profit ($1000s) 0-300	300-600	600-900	900-1200	Total
0-8000	23	4			27
8000-16000	4	4	2	2	12
16000-24000		2	1	1	4
24000-32000		1	2	1	4
32000-40000		2	1		3
Total	27	13	6	4	50

b. Crosstabulation of Row Percentages.

Market Value ($1000s)	Profit ($1000s) 0-300	300-600	600-900	900-1200	Total
0-8000	85.19	14.81	0.00	0.00	100
8000-16000	33.33	33.33	16.67	16.67	100
16000-24000	0.00	50.00	25.00	25.00	100
24000-32000	0.00	25.00	50.00	25.00	100
32000-40000	0.00	66.67	33.33	0.00	100

c. There appears to be a positive relationship between Profit and Market Value. As profit goes up, Market Value goes up.

51. a. Scatter diagram of Profit vs. Stockholder's Equity.

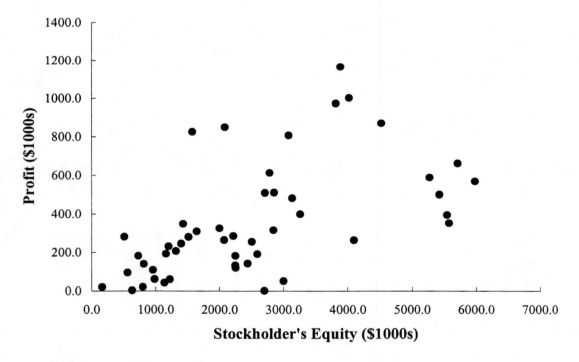

b. Profit and Stockholder's Equity appear to be positively related.

52. a. Scatter diagram of Market Value and Stockholder's Equity.

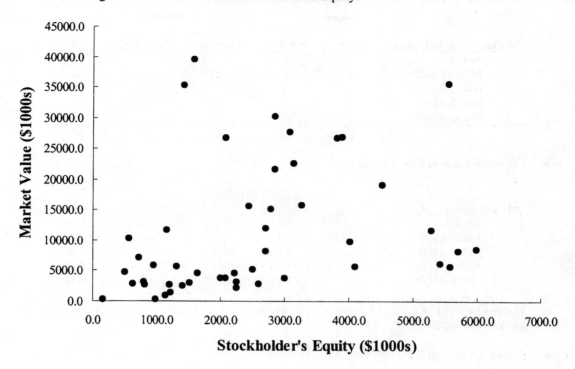

b. There is a positive relationship between Market Value and Stockholder's Equity.

Chapter 3
Descriptive Statistics: Numerical Methods

Learning Objectives

1. Understand the purpose of measures of location.

2. Be able to compute the mean, median, mode, quartiles, and various percentiles.

3. Understand the purpose of measures of variability.

4. Be able to compute the range, interquartile range, variance, standard deviation, and coefficient of variation.

5. Understand how z scores are computed and how they are used as a measure of relative location of a data value.

6. Know how Chebyshev's theorem and the empirical rule can be used to determine the percentage of the data within a specified number of standard deviations from the mean.

7. Learn how to construct a 5-number summary and a box plot.

8. Be able to compute and interpret covariance and correlation as measures of association between two variables.

9. Be able to compute a weighted mean.

Solutions:

1. $$\bar{x} = \frac{\Sigma x_i}{n} = \frac{75}{5} = 15$$

    10, 12, 16, 17, 20

    Median = 16 (middle value)

2. $$\bar{x} = \frac{\Sigma x_i}{n} = \frac{96}{6} = 16$$

    10, 12, 16, 17, 20, 21

    $$\text{Median} = \frac{16+17}{2} = 16.5$$

3. 15, 20, 25, 25, 27, 28, 30, 32

    $$i = \frac{20}{100}(8) = 1.6 \qquad \text{2nd position} = 20$$

    $$i = \frac{25}{100}(8) = 2 \qquad \frac{20+25}{2} = 22.5$$

    $$i = \frac{65}{100}(8) = 5.2 \qquad \text{6th position} = 28$$

    $$i = \frac{75}{100}(8) = 6 \qquad \frac{28+30}{2} = 29$$

4. $$\text{Mean} = \frac{\Sigma x_i}{n} = \frac{657}{11} = 59.727$$

    Median = 57   6th item

    Mode = 53   It appears 3 times

5. a. $$\bar{x} = \frac{\Sigma x_i}{n} = \frac{1106.4}{30} = 36.88$$

    b. There are an even number of items. Thus, the median is the average of the 15th and 16th items after the data have been placed in rank order.

    $$\text{Median} = \frac{36.6+36.7}{2} = 36.65$$

    c. Mode = 36.4 This value appears 4 times

    d. First Quartile $i = \left(\frac{25}{100}\right)30 = 7.5$

Rounding up, we see that Q_1 is at the 8th position.

$Q_1 = 36.2$

e. Third Quartile $\quad i = \left(\dfrac{75}{100}\right)30 = 22.5$

Rounding up, we see that Q_3 is at the 23rd position.

$Q_3 = 37.9$

6. a. $\bar{x} = \dfrac{\Sigma x_i}{n} = \dfrac{1845}{20} = 92.25$

Median is average of 10th and 11th values after arranging in ascending order.

Median $= \dfrac{66+95}{2} = 80.5$

Data are multimodal

b. $\bar{x} = \dfrac{\Sigma x_i}{n} = \dfrac{1334}{20} = 66.7$

Median $= \dfrac{66+70}{2} = 68$

Mode $= 70$ (4 brokers charge $70)

c. Comparing all three measures of central location (mean, median and mode), we conclude that it costs more, on average, to trade 500 shares at $50 per share.

d. Yes, trading 500 shares at $50 per share is a transaction value of $25,000 whereas trading 1000 shares at $5 per share is a transaction value of $5000.

7. a. $\bar{x} = \dfrac{\Sigma x_i}{n} = \dfrac{1380}{30} = 46$

b. Yes, the mean here is 46 minutes. The newspaper reported on average of 45 minutes.

c. Median $= \dfrac{45+52.9}{2} = 48.95$

d. $Q_1 = 7$ (value of 8th item in ranked order)

$Q_3 = 70.4$ (value of 23rd item in ranked list)

e. Find position $i = \left(\dfrac{40}{100}\right)30 = 12$; 40th percentile is average of values in 12th and 13th positions.

40th percentile $= \dfrac{28.8 + 29.1}{2} = 28.95$

8. a. $\Sigma x_i = 775$

$$\bar{x} = \frac{\Sigma x_i}{n} = \frac{775}{20} = 38.75$$

The modal age is 29; it appears 3 times.

b. Median is average of 10th and 11th items.

$$\text{Median} = \frac{37 + 40}{2} = 38.5$$

Data suggest at - home workers are slightly younger.

c. For Q_1,

$$i = \left(\frac{25}{100}\right)20 = 5$$

Since i is integer,

$$Q_1 = \frac{29 + 30}{2} = 29.5$$

For Q_3,

$$i = \left(\frac{75}{100}\right)20 = 15$$

Since i is integer,

$$Q_3 = \frac{46 + 49}{2} = 47.5$$

d. $i = \left(\dfrac{32}{100}\right)20 = 6.4$

Since i is not an integer, we round up to the 7th position.

32nd percentile = 31

9. a. $\bar{x} = \dfrac{\Sigma x_i}{n} = \dfrac{270,377}{25} = 10,815.08$ Median (Position 13) = 8296

b. Median would be better because of large data values.

c. $i = (25 / 100)\, 25 = 6.25$

Q_1 (Position 7) = 5984

$i = (75 / 100)\,25 = 18.75$

Q_3 (Position 19) $= 14{,}330$

d. $i = (85/100)\,25 = 21.25$

85th percentile (position 22) $= 15{,}593$. Approximately 85% of the websites have less than 15,593 unique visitors.

10. a. $\Sigma x_i = 435$

$$\overline{x} = \frac{\Sigma x_i}{n} = \frac{435}{9} = 48.33$$

Data in ascending order:

28 42 45 48 49 50 55 58 60

Median $= 49$

Do not report a mode; each data value occurs once.

The index could be considered good since both the mean and median are less than 50.

b. $i = \left(\dfrac{25}{100}\right)9 = 2.25$

Q_1 (3rd position) $= 45$

$i = \left(\dfrac{75}{100}\right)9 = 6.75$

Q_3 (7th position) $= 55$

11. $\overline{x} = \dfrac{526}{20} = 26.3$

15 16 18 19 20 21 22 22 24 <u>24 26</u> 26 27 27 30 31 33 33 34 58

Median $= 25$

Do not report a mode since five values appear twice.

For Q_1,

$i = \left(\dfrac{25}{100}\right)20 = 5$

$Q_1 = \dfrac{20 + 21}{2} = 20.5$

For Q_3,

$$i = \left(\frac{75}{100}\right)20 = 15$$

$$Q_3 = \frac{30+31}{2} = 30.5$$

12.   Using the mean we get $\bar{x}_{city} = 15.58$, $\bar{x}_{country} = 18.92$

For the samples we see that the mean mileage is better in the country than in the city.

<u>City</u>

    13.2 14.4 15.2 15.3 15.3 15.3 15.9 16 16.1 16.2 16.2 16.7 16.8
                                    ↑
                                 Median

Mode: 15.3

<u>Country</u>

    17.2 17.4 18.3 18.5 18.6 18.6 18.7 19.0 19.2 19.4 19.4 20.6 21.1
                                    ↑
                                 Median

Mode: 18.6, 19.4

The median and modal mileages are also better in the country than in the city.

13. a.   Mean = 261/15 = 17.4

            14 15 15 15 16 16 17 18 18 18 18 19 20 21 21
                                    ↑
                                 Median

Mode is 18 (occurs 4 times)

Interpretation: the average number of credit hours taken was 17.4. At least 50% of the students took 18 or more hours; at least 50% of the students took 18 or fewer hours. The most frequently occurring number of credit hours taken was 18.

     b.   For Q_1,

$$i = \left(\frac{25}{100}\right)15 = 3.75$$

Q_1 (4th position) = 15

For Q_3,

$$i = \left(\frac{75}{100}\right)15 = 11.25$$

Q_3 (12th position) = 19

c. For the 70th percentile,

$$i = \left(\frac{70}{100}\right)15 = 10.5$$

Rounding up we see the 70th percentile is in position 11.

70th percentile = 18

14. a. $\bar{x} = \dfrac{\Sigma x_i}{n} = \dfrac{12,780}{20} = \$639$

b. $\bar{x} = \dfrac{\Sigma x_i}{n} = \dfrac{1976}{20} = 98.8$ pictures

c. $\bar{x} = \dfrac{\Sigma x_i}{n} = \dfrac{2204}{20} = 110.2$ minutes

d. This is not an easy choice because it is a multicriteria problem. If price was the only criterion, the lowest price camera (Fujifilm DX-10) would be preferred. If maximum picture capacity was the only criterion, the maximum picture capacity camera (Kodak DC280 Zoom) would be preferred. But, if battery life was the only criterion, the maximum battery life camera (Fujifilm DX10) would be preferred. There are many approaches used to select the best choice in a multicriteria situation. These approaches are discussed in more specialized books on decision analysis.

15. Range 20 - 10 = 10

10, 12, 16, 17, 20

$$i = \frac{25}{100}(5) = 1.25$$

Q_1 (2nd position) = 12

$$i = \frac{75}{100}(5) = 3.75$$

Q_3 (4th position) = 17

IQR = Q_3 - Q_1 = 17 - 12 = 5

16. $\bar{x} = \dfrac{\Sigma x_i}{n} = \dfrac{75}{5} = 15$

$s^2 = \dfrac{\Sigma(x_i - \bar{x})^2}{n-1} = \dfrac{64}{4} = 16$

$s = \sqrt{16} = 4$

17.   15, 20, 25, 25, 27, 28, 30, 34   Range = 34 - 15 = 19

$i = \dfrac{25}{100}(8) = 2$ $Q_1 = \dfrac{20 + 25}{2} = 22.5$

$i = \dfrac{75}{100}(8) = 6$ $Q_1 = \dfrac{28 + 30}{2} = 29$

IQR = Q_3 - Q_1 = 29 - 22.5 = 6.5

$\bar{x} = \dfrac{\Sigma x_i}{n} = \dfrac{204}{8} = 25.5$

$s^2 = \dfrac{\Sigma(x_i - \bar{x})^2}{n-1} = \dfrac{242}{7} = 34.57$

$s = \sqrt{34.57} = 5.88$

18. a.   Range = 190 - 168 = 22

b. $\Sigma(x_i - \bar{x})^2 = 376$

$s^2 = \dfrac{376}{5} = 75.2$

c. $s = \sqrt{75.2} = 8.67$

d.   Coefficient of Variation $= \left(\dfrac{8.67}{178}\right)100 = 4.87$

19.   Range = 92 - 67 = 25

IQR = Q_3 - Q_1 = 80 - 77 = 3

$\bar{x} = 78.4667$

$\sum(x_i - \bar{x})^2 = 411.7333$

$s^2 = \dfrac{\sum(x_i - \bar{x})^2}{n-1} = \dfrac{411.7333}{14} = 29.4095$

$s = \sqrt{29.4095} = 5.4231$

20. a. Range = 60 - 28 = 32

    IQR = $Q_3 - Q_1$ = 55 - 45 = 10

    b. $\bar{x} = \dfrac{435}{9} = 48.33$

    $\Sigma(x_i - \bar{x})^2 = 742$

    $s^2 = \dfrac{\Sigma(x_i - \bar{x})^2}{n-1} = \dfrac{742}{8} = 92.75$

    $s = \sqrt{92.75} = 9.63$

    c. The average air quality is about the same. But, the variability is greater in Anaheim.

21. $\bar{x} = \dfrac{2000}{5} = 400$

x_i	$\bar{x}$	$x_i - \bar{x}$	$(x_i - \bar{x})^2$
410	400	10	100
420	400	20	400
390	400	-10	100
400	400	0	0
380	400	-20	400
2000			1000

$s^2 = \dfrac{\Sigma(x_i - \bar{x})^2}{n-1} = \dfrac{1000}{4} = 250$

$s = \sqrt{250} = 15.81$

22. Dawson Supply: Range = 11 - 9 = 2

    $s = \sqrt{\dfrac{4.1}{9}} = 0.67$

    J.C. Clark: Range = 15 - 7 = 8

    $s = \sqrt{\dfrac{60.1}{9}} = 2.58$

23. a. Winter

    Range = 21 - 12 = 9
    IQR = $Q_3 - Q_1$ = 20-16 = 4

    Summer

    Range = 38 - 18 = 20
    IQR = $Q_3 - Q_1$ = 29-18 = 11

b.

	Variance	Standard Deviation
Winter	8.2333	2.8694
Summer	44.4889	6.6700

c. Winter

$$\text{Coefficient of Variation} = \left(\frac{s}{\overline{x}}\right)100 = \left(\frac{2.8694}{17.7}\right)100 = 16.21$$

Summer

$$\text{Coefficient of Variation} = \left(\frac{s}{\overline{x}}\right)100 = \left(\frac{6.6700}{25.6}\right)100 = 26.05$$

d. More variability in the summer months.

24. a. <u>500 Shares at $50</u>

Min Value = 34   Max Value = 195

Range = 195 - 34 = 161

$$Q_1 = \frac{45+50}{2} = 47.5 \qquad Q_3 = \frac{140+140}{2} = 140$$

Interquartile range = 140 - 47.5 = 92.5

<u>1000 Shares at $5</u>

Min Value = 34   Max Value = 90

Range = 90 - 34 = 56

$$Q_1 = \frac{60+60.5}{2} = 60.25 \qquad Q_3 = \frac{79.5+80}{2} = 79.75$$

Interquartile range = 79.75 - 60.25 = 19.5

b. <u>500 Shares at $50</u>

$$s^2 = \frac{\Sigma(x_i - \overline{x})^2}{n-1} = \frac{51,402.25}{19} = 2705.3816$$
$$s = \sqrt{2705.3816} = 52.01$$

<u>1000 Shares at $5</u>

$$s^2 = \frac{\Sigma(x_i - \overline{x})^2}{n-1} = \frac{5526.2}{19} = 290.8526$$
$$s = \sqrt{290.8526} = 17.05$$

c. <u>500 Shares at $50</u>

   Coefficient of Variation $= \dfrac{s}{\bar{x}}(100) = \dfrac{52.01}{92.25}(100) = 56.38$

   <u>1000 Shares at $5</u>

   Coefficient of Variation $= \dfrac{s}{\bar{x}}(100) = \dfrac{17.05}{66.70}(100) = 25.56$

d. The variability is greater for the trade of 500 shares at $50 per share. This is true whether we use the standard deviation or the coefficient of variation as a measure.

25. $s^2 = 0.0021$ Production should not be shut down since the variance is less than .005.

26. <u>Quarter milers</u>

   $s = 0.0564$

   Coefficient of Variation $= (s/\bar{x})100 = (0.0564/0.966)100 = 5.8$

   <u>Milers</u>

   $s = 0.1295$

   Coefficient of Variation $= (s/\bar{x})100 = (0.1295/4.534)100 = 2.9$

   Yes; the coefficient of variation shows that as a percentage of the mean the quarter milers' times show more variability.

27. a. $z = \dfrac{40-30}{5} = 2 \left(1 - \dfrac{1}{2^2}\right) = 0.75$ At least 75%

   b. $z = \dfrac{45-30}{5} = 3 \left(1 - \dfrac{1}{3^2}\right) = 0.89$ At least 89%

   c. $z = \dfrac{38-30}{5} = 1.6 \left(1 - \dfrac{1}{1.6^2}\right) = 0.61$ At least 61%

   d. $z = \dfrac{42-30}{5} = 2.4 \left(1 - \dfrac{1}{2.4^2}\right) = 0.83$ At least 83%

   e. $z = \dfrac{48-30}{5} = 3.6 \left(1 - \dfrac{1}{3.6^2}\right) = 0.92$ At least 92%

28. a.   Approximately 95%

   b.   Almost all

   c.   Approximately 68%

29.
$$\bar{x} = \frac{\Sigma x_i}{n} = \frac{75}{5} = 15$$

$$s^2 = \sqrt{\frac{\Sigma(x_i - \bar{x})^2}{n-1}} = \sqrt{\frac{64}{4}} = 4$$

10    $z = \dfrac{10-15}{4} = -1.25$

20    $z = \dfrac{20-15}{4} = +1.25$

12    $z = \dfrac{12-15}{4} = -0.75$

17    $z = \dfrac{17-15}{4} = +.50$

16    $z = \dfrac{16-15}{4} = +.25$

30.
$$z = \frac{520-500}{100} = +.20$$

$$z = \frac{650-500}{100} = +1.50$$

$$z = \frac{500-500}{100} = 0.00$$

$$z = \frac{450-500}{100} = -0.50$$

$$z = \frac{280-500}{100} = -2.20$$

31. a.   This is from 2 standard deviations below the mean to 2 standard deviations above the mean.

With $z = 2$, Chebyshev's theorem gives:

$$1 - \frac{1}{z^2} = 1 - \frac{1}{2^2} = 1 - \frac{1}{4} = \frac{3}{4}$$

Therefore, at least 75% of adults sleep between 4.5 and 9.3 hours per day.

b.   This is from 2.5 standard deviations below the mean to 2.5 standard deviations above the mean.

With $z = 2.5$, Chebyshev's theorem gives:

$$1 - \frac{1}{z^2} = 1 - \frac{1}{2.5^2} = 1 - \frac{1}{6.25} = .84$$

Therefore, at least 84% of adults sleep between 3.9 and 9.9 hours per day.

c. With $z = 2$, the empirical rule suggests that 95% of adults sleep between 4.5and 9.3 hours per day. The probability obtained using the empirical rule is greater than the probability obtained using Chebyshev's theorem.

32. a. 2 hours is 1 standard deviation below the mean. Thus, the empirical rule suggests that 68% of the kids watch television between 2 and 4 hours per day. Since a bell-shaped distribution is symmetric, approximately, 34% of the kids watch television between 2 and 3 hours per day.

b. 1 hour is 2 standard deviations below the mean. Thus, the empirical rule suggests that 95% of the kids watch television between 1 and 5 hours per day. Since a bell-shaped distribution is symmetric, approximately, 47.5% of the kids watch television between 1 and 3 hours per day. In part (a) we concluded that approximately 34% of the kids watch television between 2 and 3 hours per day; thus, approximately 34% of the kids watch television between 3 and 4 hours per day. Hence, approximately 47.5% + 34% = 81.5% of kids watch television between 1 and 4 hours per day.

c. Since 34% of the kids watch television between 3 and 4 hours per day, 50% - 34% = 16% of the kids watch television more than 4 hours per day.

33. a. Approximately 68% of scores are within 1 standard deviation from the mean.

b. Approximately 95% of scores are within 2 standard deviations from the mean.

c. Approximately (100% - 95%) / 2 = 2.5% of scores are over 130.

d. Yes, almost all IQ scores are less than 145.

34. a. $z = \dfrac{71.00 - 90.06}{20} = -0.95$

b. $z = \dfrac{168 - 90.06}{20} = 3.90$

c. The z-score in part a indicates that the value is 0.95 standard deviations below the mean. The z-score in part b indicates that the value is 3.90 standard deviations above the mean.

The labor cost in part b is an outlier and should be reviewed for accuracy.

35. a. $\overline{x}$ is approximately 63 or $63,000, and s is 4 or $4000

b. This is from 2 standard deviations below the mean to 2 standard deviations above the mean.

With $z = 2$, Chebyshev's theorem gives:

$$1 - \dfrac{1}{z^2} = 1 - \dfrac{1}{2^2} = 1 - \dfrac{1}{4} = \dfrac{3}{4}$$

Therefore, at least 75% of benefits managers have an annual salary between $55,000 and $71,000.

c. The histogram of the salary data is shown below:

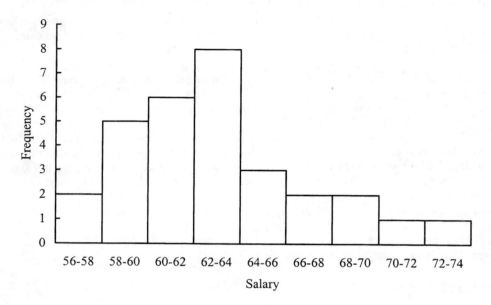

Although the distribution is not perfectly bell shaped, it does appear reasonable to assume that the distribution of annual salary can be approximated by a bell-shaped distribution.

d. With $z = 2$, the empirical rule suggests that 95% of benefits managers have an annual salary between $55,000 and $71,000. The probability is much higher than obtained using Chebyshev's theorem, but requires the assumption that the distribution of annual salary is bell shaped.

e. There are no outliers because all the observations are within 3 standard deviations of the mean.

36. a. $\overline{x}$ is 100 and s is 13.88 or approximately 14

b. If the distribution is bell shaped with a mean of 100 points, the percentage of NBA games in which the winning team scores more than 100 points is 50%. A score of 114 points is $z = 1$ standard deviation above the mean. Thus, the empirical rule suggests that 68% of the winning teams will score between 86 and 114 points. In other words, 32% of the winning teams will score less than 86 points or more than 114 points. Because a bell-shaped distribution is symmetric, approximately 16% of the winning teams will score more than 114 points.

c. For the winning margin, $\overline{x}$ is 11.1 and s is 10.77. To see if there are any outliers, we will first compute the z-score for the winning margin that is farthest from the sample mean of 11.1, a winning margin of 32 points.

$$z = \frac{x - \overline{x}}{s} = \frac{32 - 11.1}{10.77} = 1.94$$

Thus, a winning margin of 32 points is not an outlier ($z = 1.94 < 3$). Because a winning margin of 32 points is farthest from the mean, none of the other data values can have a z-score that is less than 3 or greater than 3 and hence we conclude that there are no outliers

37. a. $\overline{x} = \frac{\Sigma x_i}{n} = \frac{79.86}{20} = 3.99$

$$\text{Median} = \frac{4.17 + 4.20}{2} = 4.185 \text{ (average of 10th and 11th values)}$$

b. $Q_1 = 4.00$ (average of 5th and 6th values)

$Q_3 = 4.50$ (average of 15th and 16th values)

c. $s = \sqrt{\dfrac{\Sigma(x_i - \bar{x})^2}{n-1}} = \sqrt{\dfrac{12.5080}{19}} = 0.8114$

d. Allison One: $z = \dfrac{4.12 - 3.99}{0.8114} \approx 0.16$

Omni Audio SA 12.3: $z = \dfrac{2.32 - 3.99}{0.8114} \approx -2.06$

e. The lowest rating is for the Bose 501 Series. It's z-score is:

$$z = \frac{2.14 - 3.99}{0.8114} \approx -2.28$$

This is not an outlier so there are no outliers.

38.   15, 20, 25, 25, 27, 28, 30, 34

Smallest = 15

$i = \dfrac{25}{100}(8) = 2$ 　　　　$Q_1 = \dfrac{20 + 25}{2} = 22.5$

$\text{Median} = \dfrac{25 + 27}{2} = 26$

$i = \dfrac{75}{100}(8) = 8$ 　　　　$Q_3 = \dfrac{28 + 30}{2} = 29$

Largest = 34

39.

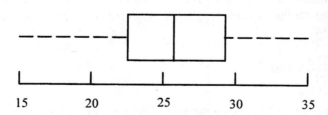

40.   5, 6, 8, 10, 10, 12, 15, 16, 18

Smallest = 5

$i = \dfrac{25}{100}(9) = 2.25 \quad Q_1 = 8 \text{ (3rd position)}$

Median = 10

$$i = \frac{75}{100}(9) = 6.75 \quad Q_3 = 15 \text{ (7th position)}$$

Largest = 18

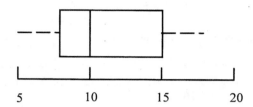

41.   IQR = 50 - 42 = 8

Lower Limit: Q_1 - 1.5 IQR = 42 - 12 = 30
Upper Limit: Q_3 + 1.5 IQR = 50 + 12 = 62

68 is an outlier

42. a.   Five number summary: 5 9.6 14.5 19.2 52.7

b.   IQR = Q_3 - Q_1 = 19.2 - 9.6 = 9.6

Lower Limit: Q_1 - 1.5 (IQR) = 9.6 - 1.5(9.6) = -4.8
Upper Limit: Q_3 + 1.5(IQR) = 19.2 + 1.5(9.6) = 33.6

c.   The data value 41.6 is an outlier (larger than the upper limit) and so is the data value 52.7. The financial analyst should first verify that these values are correct. Perhaps a typing error has caused 25.7 to be typed as 52.7 (or 14.6 to be typed as 41.6). If the outliers are correct, the analyst might consider these companies with an unusually large return on equity as good investment candidates.

d.

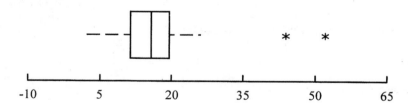

43. a.   Median (11th position) 4019

$$i = \frac{25}{100}(21) = 5.25$$

Q_1 (6th position) = 1872

$$i = \frac{75}{100}(21) = 15.75$$

Q_3 (16th position) = 8305

608, 1872, 4019, 8305, 14138

b.   Limits:

      IQR $= Q_3 - Q_1 = 8305 - 1872 = 6433$

      Lower Limit: $Q_1 - 1.5$ (IQR) $= -7777$

      Upper Limit: $Q_3 + 1.5$ (IQR) $= 17955$

c.   There are no outliers, all data are within the limits.

d.   Yes, if the first two digits in Johnson and Johnson's sales were transposed to 41,138, sales would have shown up as an outlier. A review of the data would have enabled the correction of the data.

e.

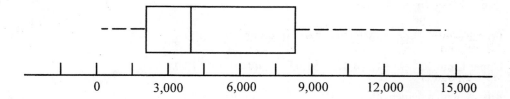

44. a.   Mean = 105.7933 Median = 52.7

b. $Q_1 = 15.7$ $Q_3 = 78.3$

c.   IQR $= Q_3 - Q_1 = 78.3 - 15.7 = 62.6$

      Lower limit for box plot $= Q_1 - 1.5$(IQR) $= 15.7 - 1.5(62.6) = -78.2$

      Upper limit for box plot $= Q_3 + 1.5$ (IQR) $= 78.3 + 1.5(62.6) = 172.2$

      Note: Because the number of shares covered by options grants cannot be negative, the lower limit for the box plot is set at 0. This, outliers are value in the data set greater than 172.2.

      Outliers: Silicon Graphics (188.8) and ToysRUs (247.6)

d.   Mean percentage = 26.73. The current percentage is much greater.

45. a.   Five Number Summary (Midsize)

                 51   71.5   81.5   96.5   128

      Five Number Summary (Small)

                 73   101   108.5   121   140

b.   Box Plots

      <u>Midsize</u>

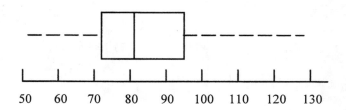

Small Size

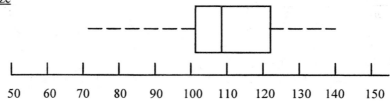

c. The midsize cars appear to be safer than the small cars.

46. a. $\bar{x} = 37.48$ Median = 23.67

    b. $Q_1 = 7.91$ $Q_3 = 51.92$

    c. IQR = 51.92 - 7.91 = 44.01

       Lower Limit: $Q_1 - 1.5(\text{IQR}) = 7.91 - 1.5(44.01) = -58.11$

       Upper Limit: $Q_3 + 1.5(\text{IQR}) = 51.92 + 1.5(44.01) = 117.94$

       Russia, with a percent change of 125.89, is an outlier.

       Turkey, with a percent change of 254.45 is another outlier.

    d. With a percent change of 22.64, the United States is just below the 50th percentile - the median.

47. a.

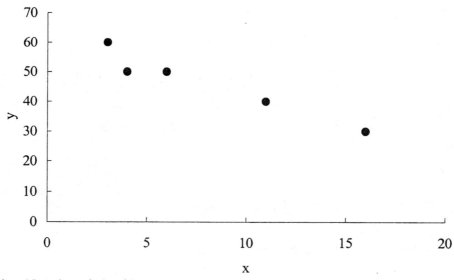

    b. Negative relationship

    c/d. $\Sigma x_i = 40$ $\bar{x} = \dfrac{40}{5} = 8$ $\Sigma y_i = 230$ $\bar{y} = \dfrac{230}{5} = 46$

    $\Sigma(x_i - \bar{x})(y_i - \bar{y}) = -240$ $\Sigma(x_i - \bar{x})^2 = 118$ $\Sigma(y_i - \bar{y})^2 = 520$

$$s_{xy} = \frac{\Sigma(x_i - \bar{x})(y_i - \bar{y})}{n-1} = \frac{-240}{5-1} = -60$$

$$s_x = \sqrt{\frac{\Sigma(x_i - \bar{x})^2}{n-1}} = \sqrt{\frac{118}{5-1}} = 5.4314$$

$$s_y = \sqrt{\frac{\Sigma(y_i - \bar{y})^2}{n-1}} = \sqrt{\frac{520}{5-1}} = 11.4018$$

$$r_{xy} = \frac{s_{xy}}{s_x s_y} = \frac{-60}{(5.4314)(11.4018)} = -0.969$$

There is a strong negative linear relationship.

48. a.

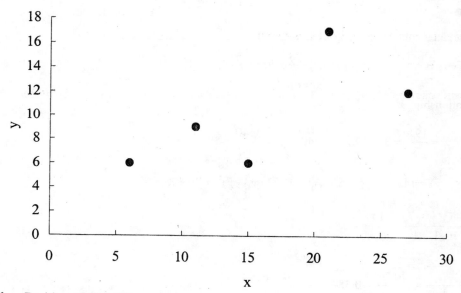

b. Positive relationship

c/d. $\Sigma x_i = 80 \quad \bar{x} = \frac{80}{5} = 16 \quad \Sigma y_i = 50 \quad \bar{y} = \frac{50}{5} = 10$

$\Sigma(x_i - \bar{x})(y_i - \bar{y}) = 106 \quad \Sigma(x_i - \bar{x})^2 = 272 \quad \Sigma(y_i - \bar{y})^2 = 86$

$$s_{xy} = \frac{\Sigma(x_i - \bar{x})(y_i - \bar{y})}{n-1} = \frac{106}{5-1} = 26.5$$

$$s_x = \sqrt{\frac{\Sigma(x_i - \bar{x})^2}{n-1}} = \sqrt{\frac{272}{5-1}} = 8.2462$$

$$s_y = \sqrt{\frac{\Sigma(y_i - \bar{y})^2}{n-1}} = \sqrt{\frac{86}{5-1}} = 4.6368$$

$$r_{xy} = \frac{s_{xy}}{s_x s_y} = \frac{26.5}{(8.2462)(4.6368)} = 0.693$$

A positive linear relationship

49. a.

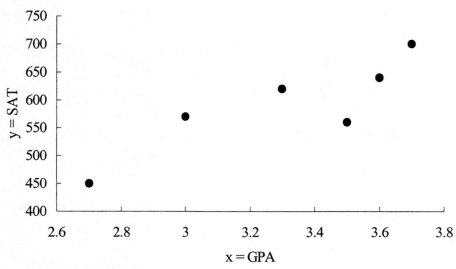

b. Positive relationship

c/d. $\Sigma x_i = 19.8 \quad \bar{x} = \dfrac{19.8}{6} = 3.3 \quad \Sigma y_i = 3540 \quad \bar{y} = \dfrac{3540}{6} = 590$

$\Sigma(x_i - \bar{x})(y_i - \bar{y}) = 143 \quad \Sigma(x_i - \bar{x})^2 = 0.74 \quad \Sigma(y_i - \bar{y})^2 = 36,400$

$$s_{xy} = \frac{\Sigma(x_i - \bar{x})(y_i - \bar{y})}{n-1} = \frac{143}{6-1} = 28.6$$

$$s_x = \sqrt{\frac{\Sigma(x_i - \bar{x})^2}{n-1}} = \sqrt{\frac{0.74}{6-1}} = 0.3847$$

$$s_y = \sqrt{\frac{\Sigma(y_i - \bar{y})^2}{n-1}} = \sqrt{\frac{36,400}{6-1}} = 85.3229$$

$$r_{xy} = \frac{s_{xy}}{s_x s_y} = \frac{28.6}{(0.3847)(85.3229)} = 0.8713$$

A positive linear relationship

50.   Let x = driving speed and y = mileage

$\Sigma x_i = 420 \quad \bar{x} = \dfrac{420}{10} = 42 \quad \Sigma y_i = 270 \quad \bar{y} = \dfrac{270}{10} = 27$

$$\Sigma(x_i - \overline{x})(y_i - \overline{y}) = -475 \qquad \Sigma(x_i - \overline{x})^2 = 1660 \qquad \Sigma(y_i - \overline{y})^2 = 164$$

$$s_{xy} = \frac{\Sigma(x_i - \overline{x})(y_i - \overline{y})}{n-1} = \frac{-475}{10-1} = -52.7778$$

$$s_x = \sqrt{\frac{\Sigma(x_i - \overline{x})^2}{n-1}} = \sqrt{\frac{1660}{10-1}} = 13.5810$$

$$s_y = \sqrt{\frac{\Sigma(y_i - \overline{y})^2}{n-1}} = \sqrt{\frac{164}{10-1}} = 4.2687$$

$$r_{xy} = \frac{s_{xy}}{s_x s_y} = \frac{-52.7778}{(13.5810)(4.2687)} = -.91$$

A strong negative linear relationship

51. a. The sample correlation coefficient is .78.

    b. There is a positive linear relationship between the performance score and the overall rating.

52. a. The sample correlation coefficient is .92.

    b. There is a strong positive linear relationship between the two variables.

53. The sample correlation coefficient is .88. This indicates a strong positive linear relationship between the daily high and low temperatures.

54. a. $\overline{x} = \dfrac{\Sigma w_i x_i}{\Sigma w_i} = \dfrac{6(3.2) + 3(2) + 2(2.5) + 8(5)}{6+3+2+8} = \dfrac{70.2}{19} = 3.69$

    b. $\dfrac{3.2 + 2 + 2.5 + 5}{4} = \dfrac{12.7}{4} = 3.175$

55.

f_i	M_i	$f_i M_i$
4	5	20
7	10	70
9	15	135
5	20	100
25		325

$$\overline{x} = \frac{\Sigma f_i M_i}{n} = \frac{325}{25} = 13$$

f_i	M_i	$M_i - \overline{x}$	$(M_i - \overline{x})^2$	$f_i(M_i - \overline{x})^2$
4	5	-8	64	256
7	10	-3	9	63
9	15	+2	4	36
5	20	+7	49	245
				600

$$s^2 = \frac{\Sigma f_i (M_i - \overline{x})^2}{n-1} = \frac{600}{24} = 25$$

$$s = \sqrt{25} = 5$$

56. a.

Grade x_i	Weight W_i
4 (A)	9
3 (B)	15
2 (C)	33
1 (D)	3
0 (F)	0
	60 Credit Hours

$$\overline{x} = \frac{\Sigma w_i x_i}{\Sigma w_i} = \frac{9(4) + 15(3) + 33(2) + 3(1)}{9 + 15 + 33 + 3} = \frac{150}{60} = 2.50$$

b. Yes; satisfies the 2.5 grade point average requirement

57. We use the weighted mean formula with the weights being the amounts invested.

$$\Sigma w_i x_i = 37,830(0.00) + 27,667(2.98) + 31,037(2.77) + 27,336(2.65) + 37,553(1.58)$$
$$+ 17,812(0.57) + 32,660(2.00) + 17,775(0.00)$$

$$= 375,667.1$$

Σw_i $= 37,830 + 27,667 + \cdots + 17,775$

$= 229,670$

$$\overline{x} = \frac{\Sigma w_i x_i}{\Sigma w_i} = \frac{375,667.1}{229,670} = 1.64$$

58.

M_i	f_i	$f_i M_i$	$M_i - \overline{x}$	$(M_i - \overline{x})^2$	$f_i(M_i - \overline{x})^2$
74	2	148	-8.742647	76.433877	5,656.1069
192	7	1,344	-3.742647	14.007407	2,689.4221
280	12	3,360	1.257353	1.580937	442.6622
105	17	1,785	6.257353	39.154467	4,111.2190
23	22	506	11.257353	126.728000	2,914.7439
6	27	162	16.257353	264.301530	1,585.8092
680		7,305			17,399.9630

Estimate of total gallons sold: $(10.74)(120) = 1288.8$

$$\overline{x} = \frac{7305}{680} = 10.74$$

$$s^2 = \frac{17,399.9630}{679} = 25.63$$

$$s = 5.06$$

59. a.

Class	f_i	M_i	$f_i M_i$
0	15	0	0
1	10	1	10
2	40	2	80
3	85	3	255
4	350	4	1400
Totals	500		1745

$$\bar{x} = \frac{\Sigma_i f M_i}{n} = \frac{1745}{500} = 3.49$$

b.

$M_i - \bar{x}$	$(M_i - \bar{x})^2$	$f_i(M_i - \bar{x})^2$
-3.49	12.18	182.70
-2.49	6.20	62.00
-1.49	2.22	88.80
-0.49	0.24	20.41
+0.51	0.26	91.04
	Total	444.95

$$s^2 = \frac{\Sigma(M_i - \bar{x})^2 f_i}{n-1} = \frac{444.95}{499} = 0.8917 \qquad s = \sqrt{0.8917} = 0.9443$$

60. a. $\bar{x} = \dfrac{\Sigma x_i}{n} = \dfrac{3463}{25} = 138.52$

Median = 129 (13th value)

Mode = 0 (2 times)

b. It appears that this group of young adults eats out much more than the average American. The mean and median are much higher than the average of $65.88 reported in the newspaper.

c. $Q_1 = 95$ (7th value)

$Q_3 = 169$ (19th value)

d. Min = 0   Max = 467

Range = 467 - 0 = 467

IQR = Q_3 - Q_1 = 169 - 95 = 74

e. $s^2 = 9271.01$ $s = 96.29$

f. The z - score for the largest value is:

$$z = \frac{467 - 138.52}{96.29} = 3.41$$

It is the only outlier and should be checked for accuracy.

61. a. $\Sigma x_i = 760$

$$\bar{x} = \frac{\Sigma x_i}{n} = \frac{760}{20} = 38$$

Median is average of 10th and 11th items.

$$\text{Median} = \frac{36+36}{2} = 36$$

The modal cash retainer is 40; it appears 4 times.

b. For Q_1,
c.

$$i = \left(\frac{25}{100}\right)20 = 5$$

Since i is integer,

$$Q_1 = \frac{28+30}{2} = 29$$

For Q_3,

$$i = \left(\frac{75}{100}\right)20 = 15$$

Since i is integer,

$$Q_3 = \frac{40+50}{2} = 45$$

c   Range $= 64 - 15 = 49$

Interquartile range $= 45 - 29 = 16$

d. $s^2 = \dfrac{\Sigma(x_i - \bar{x})^2}{n-1} = \dfrac{3318}{20-1} = 174.6316$

$$s = \sqrt{s^2} = \sqrt{174.6316} = 13.2148$$

e. Coefficient of variation $= \left(\dfrac{s}{\bar{x}}\right)100 = \left(\dfrac{13.2148}{38}\right)100 = 34.8$

62. a. $\bar{x} = \dfrac{\Sigma x_i}{n} = \dfrac{260}{14} = 18.57$

Median $= 16.5$ (Average of 7th and 8th values)

b. $s^2 = 53.49$ $s = 7.31$

c. Quantex has the best record: 11 Days

d. $z = \dfrac{27 - 18.57}{7.31} = 1.15$

Packard-Bell is 1.15 standard deviations slower than the mean.

e. $z = \dfrac{12 - 18.57}{7.31} = -0.90$

IBM is 0.9 standard deviations faster than the mean.

f. Check Toshiba:

$z = \dfrac{37 - 18.57}{7.31} = 2.52$

On the basis of z - scores, Toshiba is not an outlier, but it is 2.52 standard deviations slower than the mean.

63. $\bar{x} = 1890.2/30 = 63$

Median (15th and 16th positions) is $(63 + 63.5)/2 = 63.25$

Mode: 60.5 and 63.5 both occur twice

b. $i = (25 / 100)30 = 7.5$ (8th position)

$Q_1 = 55.9$

$i = (75 / 100)30 = 22.5$ (23rd position)

$Q_3 = 69.0$

64. Sample mean = 7195.5

Median = 7019 (average of positions 5 and 6)

Sample variance = 7,165,941

Sample standard deviation = 2676.93

65. a. The sample mean is 83.135 and the sample standard deviation is 16.173.

b. With $z = 2$, Chebyshev's theorem gives:

$1 - \dfrac{1}{z^2} = 1 - \dfrac{1}{2^2} = 1 - \dfrac{1}{4} = \dfrac{3}{4}$

Therefore, at least 75% of household incomes are within 2 standard deviations of the mean. Using the sample mean and sample standard deviation computed in part (a), the range within 75% of household incomes must fall is $83.135 \pm 2(16.173) = 83.135 \pm 32.346$; thus, 75% of household incomes must fall between 50.789 and 115.481, or \$50,789 to \$115,481.

c. With $z = 2$, the empirical rule suggests that 95% of household incomes must fall between $50,789 to $115,481. For the same range, the probability obtained using the empirical rule is greater than the probability obtained using Chebyshev's theorem.

d. The z-score for Danbury, CT is 3.04; thus, the Danbury, CT observation is an outlier.

66. a. Public Transportation: $\bar{x} = \dfrac{320}{10} = 32$

   Automobile: $\bar{x} = \dfrac{320}{10} = 32$

b. Public Transportation: $s = 4.64$

   Automobile: $s = 1.83$

c. Prefer the automobile. The mean times are the same, but the auto has less variability.

d. Data in ascending order:

   Public: 25 28 29 29 32 32 33 34 37 41

   Auto: 29 30 31 31 32 32 33 33 34 35

   Five number Summaries

   Public: 25 29 32 34 41

   Auto: 29 31 32 33 35

   Box Plots:

   Public:

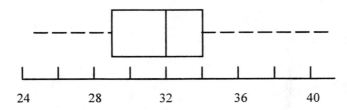

   Auto:

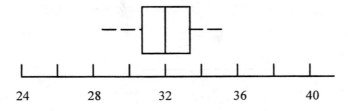

The box plots do show lower variability with automobile transportation and support the conclusion in part c.

67.   Data in ascending order:

42 44 53 56 58 61 62 62 75 76
77 78 79 82 84 84 85 88 89 89
93 95 96 97 98

a.   Five Number Summary

42 62 79 89 98

b.   Box Plot

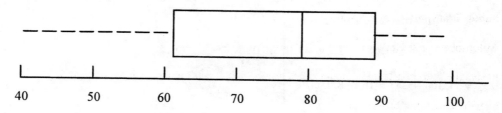

68.   Data in ascending order:

400	451	511	576	596	652	711	744
809	820	852	907	941	971	975	1023
1112	1174	1251	1278				

$i = (25/100)20 = 5$

$i = (75/100)20 = 15$

$i = (50/100)20 = 10$

$$Q_1 = \frac{596 + 652}{2} = 624$$

$$Q_3 = \frac{975 + 1023}{2} = 999$$

$$\text{Median} = \frac{820 + 852}{2} = 836$$

a.   Five Number Summary

400 624 836 999 1278

b.

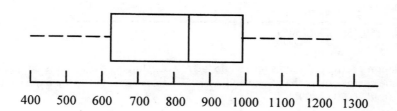

c. There are no values outside the limits. Thus no outliers are identified.

Lower limit = 624 - 1.5(999 - 624) = 61.5

Upper limit = 999 + 1.5(999 - 624) = 1561.5

69. a. The sample covariance is 477.5365. Because the sample covariance is positive, there is a positive linear relationship between income and home price.

b. The sample correlation coefficient is .933; this indicates a strong linear relationship between income and home price.

70. a. The scatter diagram indicates a positive relationship

b. $\Sigma x_i = 798 \quad \Sigma y_i = 11,688 \quad \Sigma x_i y_i = 1,058,019$

$\Sigma x_i^2 = 71,306 \quad \Sigma y_i^2 = 16,058,736$

$$r_{xy} = \frac{\Sigma x_i y_i - (\Sigma x_i \Sigma y_i)/n}{\sqrt{\Sigma x_i^2 - (\Sigma x_i)^2 / n} \sqrt{\Sigma y_i^2 - (\Sigma y_i)^2 / n}} = \frac{1,058,019 - (798)(11,688)/9}{\sqrt{71,306 - (798)^2 /9}\sqrt{16,058,736 - (11,688)^2 /9}} = .9856$$

Strong positive relationship

71. Let x_i = commission on 500 shares trade for broker i
  y_i = commission on 1000 shares trade for broker i

$\Sigma x_i = 1829 \quad \overline{x} = \dfrac{1829}{20} = 91.45 \quad \Sigma y_i = 1326 \quad \overline{y} = \dfrac{1326}{20} = 66.3$

$\Sigma(x_i - \overline{x})(y_i - \overline{y}) = 11,853.3 \quad \Sigma(x_i - \overline{x})^2 = 48,370.95 \quad \Sigma(y_i - \overline{y})^2 = 8506.2$

$$s_{xy} = \frac{\Sigma(x_i - \overline{x})(y_i - \overline{y})}{n-1} = \frac{11,853.3}{19} = 623.8579$$

The covariance shows there is a positive relationship.

$$s_x = \sqrt{\frac{\Sigma(x_i - \overline{x})^2}{n-1}} = \sqrt{\frac{48,370.95}{19}} = 50.4563$$

$$s_y = \sqrt{\frac{\Sigma(y_i - \overline{y})^2}{n-1}} = \sqrt{\frac{8506.2}{19}} = 21.1588$$

$$r_{xy} = \frac{s_{xy}}{s_x s_y} = \frac{623.8579}{(50.4563)(21.1588)} = 0.5844$$

The correlation coefficient shows that while the relationship is positive, it is not real strong. Note that Max Ule charges more than Schwab for the 500 share trade ($195 vs. $155) but less for the 1000 share trade ($70 vs. $90).

72. a. The scatter diagram is shown below:

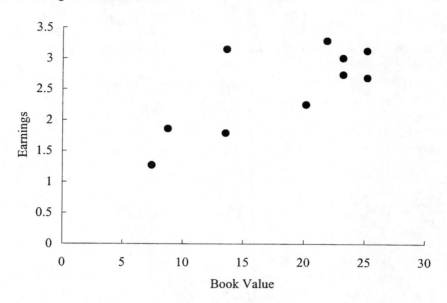

   b. The sample correlation coefficient is .75; this indicates a linear relationship between book value and earnings.

73. $\bar{x} = \dfrac{\Sigma w_i x_i}{\Sigma w_i} = \dfrac{20(20) + 30(12) + 10(7) + 15(5) + 10(6)}{20 + 30 + 10 + 15 + 10} = \dfrac{965}{85} = 11.4 \text{ days}$

74. a. $(800 + 750 + 900)/3 = 817$

   b.
Month	January	February	March
Weight	1	2	3

   $x = \dfrac{\Sigma w_i x_i}{\Sigma w_i} = \dfrac{1(800) + 2(750) + 3(900)}{1 + 2 + 3} = \dfrac{5000}{6} = 833$

75.

f_i	M_i	$f_i M_i$	$M_i - \bar{x}$	$(M_i - \bar{x})^2$	$f_i(M_i - \bar{x})^2$
4	5.5	22.0	-6.8	46.24	184.96
5	9.5	47.5	-2.8	7.84	39.20
7	13.5	94.5	1.2	1.44	10.08
2	17.5	35.0	5.2	27.04	54.08
1	21.5	21.5	9.2	84.64	84.64
1	25.5	25.5	13.2	174.24	174.24
20		246.0			547.20

   $\bar{x} = \dfrac{246}{20} = 12.3$

   $s^2 = \dfrac{547.20}{19} = 28.8$

   $s = 5.37$

76.

f_i	M_i	f_iM_i	$M_i - \overline{x}$	$(M_i - \overline{x})^2$	$f_i(M_i - \overline{x})^2$
2	29.5	59.0	-22	484	968
6	39.5	237.0	-12	144	864
4	49.5	198.0	-2	4	16
4	59.5	238.0	8	64	256
2	69.5	139.0	18	324	648
2	79.5	159.0	28	784	1568
20		1,030.0			4320

$$\overline{x} = \frac{1030}{20} = 51.5$$

$$s = \frac{4320}{19} = 227.37$$

$$s = 15.08$$

77.

f_i	M_i	f_iM_i	$M_i - \overline{x}$	$(M_i - \overline{x})^2$	$f_i(M_i - \overline{x})^2$
10	47	470	-13.68	187.1424	1871.42
40	52	2080	-8.68	75.3424	3013.70
150	57	8550	-3.68	13..5424	2031.36
175	62	10850	+1.32	1.7424	304.92
75	67	5025	+6.32	39.9424	2995.68
15	72	1080	+11.32	128.1424	1922.14
10	77	770	+16.32	266.3424	2663.42
475		28,825			14,802.64

a. $$\overline{x} = \frac{28,825}{475} = 60.68$$

b. $$s^2 = \frac{14,802.64}{474} = 31.23$$

$$s = \sqrt{31.23} = 5.59$$

Chapter 4
Introduction to Probability

Learning Objectives

1. Obtain an appreciation of the role probability information plays in the decision making process.

2. Understand probability as a numerical measure of the likelihood of occurrence.

3. Know the three methods commonly used for assigning probabilities and understand when they should be used.

4. Know how to use the laws that are available for computing the probabilities of events.

5. Understand how new information can be used to revise initial (prior) probability estimates using Bayes' theorem.

Solutions:

1.   Number of experimental Outcomes $= (3)(2)(4) = 24$

2. $\binom{6}{3} = \dfrac{6!}{3!3!} = \dfrac{6\cdot5\cdot4\cdot3\cdot2\cdot1}{(3\cdot2\cdot1)(3\cdot2\cdot1)} = 20$

ABC	ACE	BCD	BEF
ABD	ACF	BCE	CDE
ABE	ADE	BCF	CDF
ABF	ADF	BDE	CEF
ACD	AEF	BDF	DEF

3. $P_3^6 = \dfrac{6!}{(6-3)!} = (6)(5)(4) = 120$

      BDF BFD DBF DFB FBD FDB

4.   a.

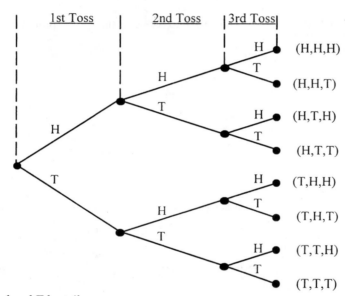

    b. Let: H be head and T be tail

        (H,H,H) (T,H,H)
        (H,H,T) (T,H,T)
        (H,T,H) (T,T,H)
        (H,T,T) (T,T,T)

    c. The outcomes are equally likely, so the probability of each outcomes is 1/8.

5. $P(E_i) = 1/5$ for $i = 1, 2, 3, 4, 5$

      $P(E_i) \geq 0$ for $i = 1, 2, 3, 4, 5$
      $P(E_1) + P(E_2) + P(E_3) + P(E_4) + P(E_5) = 1/5 + 1/5 + 1/5 + 1/5 + 1/5 = 1$

      The classical method was used.

6. $P(E_1) = .40$, $P(E_2) = .26$, $P(E_3) = .34$

   The relative frequency method was used.

7. No. Requirement (4.3) is not satisfied; the probabilities do not sum to 1. $P(E_1) + P(E_2) + P(E_3) + P(E_4) = .10 + .15 + .40 + .20 = .85$

8. a. There are four outcomes possible for this 2-step experiment; planning commission positive - council approves; planning commission positive - council disapproves; planning commission negative - council approves; planning commission negative - council disapproves.

   b. Let   p = positive, n = negative, a = approves, and d = disapproves

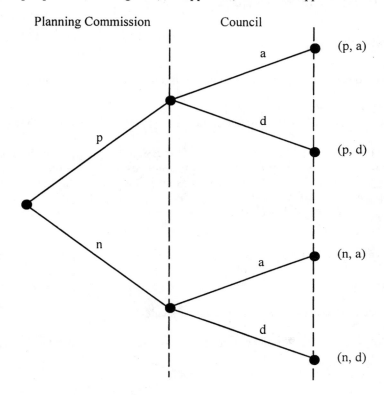

9. $$\binom{50}{4} = \frac{50!}{4!46!} = \frac{50 \cdot 49 \cdot 48 \cdot 47}{4 \cdot 3 \cdot 2 \cdot 1} = 230,300$$

10. a. Use the relative frequency approach:

    P(California) = 1,434/2,374 = .60

    b. Number not from 4 states = 2,374 - 1,434 - 390 - 217 - 112 = 221

    P(Not from 4 States) = 221/2,374 = .09

    c. P(Not in Early Stages) = 1 - .22 = .78

    d. Estimate of number of Massachusetts companies in early stage of development - (.22)390 ≈ 86

    e. If we assume the size of the awards did not differ by states, we can multiply the probability an award went to Colorado by the total venture funds disbursed to get an estimate.

Estimate of Colorado funds = (112/2374)($32.4) = $1.53 billion

Authors' Note: The actual amount going to Colorado was $1.74 billion.

11. a. No, the probabilities do not sum to one. They sum to .85.

    b. Owner must revise the probabilities so they sum to 1.00.

12. a. Use the counting rule for combinations:

$$\binom{49}{5} = \frac{49!}{5!44!} = \frac{(49)(48)(47)(46)(45)}{(5)(4)(3)(2)(1)} = 1,906,884$$

    b. Very small: 1/1,906,884 = 0.0000005

    c. Multiply the answer to part (a) by 42 to get the number of choices for the six numbers.

No. of Choices = (1,906,884)(42) = 80,089,128
Probability of Winning = 1/80,089,128 = 0.0000000125

13. Initially a probability of .20 would be assigned if selection is equally likely. Data does not appear to confirm the belief of equal consumer preference. For example using the relative frequency method we would assign a probability of 5 / 100 = .05 to the design 1 outcome, .15 to design 2, .30 to design 3, .40 to design 4, and .10 to design 5.

14. a. $P(E_2) = 1/4$

    b. P(any 2 outcomes) = 1 / 4 + 1 / 4 = 1 / 2

    c. P(any 3 outcomes) = 1 / 4 + 1 / 4 + 1 / 4 = 3 / 4

15. a. S = {ace of clubs, ace of diamonds, ace of hearts, ace of spades}

    b. S = {2 of clubs, 3 of clubs, . . . , 10 of clubs, J of clubs, Q of clubs, K of clubs, A of clubs}

    c. There are 12; jack, queen, or king in each of the four suits.

    d. For a: 4 / 52 = 1 / 13 = .08

For b: 13 / 52 = 1 / 4 = .25

For c: 12 / 52 = .23

16. a. (6) (6) = 36 sample points

b.

Die 2

	1	2	3	4	5	6
1	2	3	4	5	6	7
2	3	4	5	6	7	8
3	4	5	6	7	8	9
4	5	6	7	8	9	10
5	6	7	8	9	10	11
6	7	8	9	10	11	12

Die 1

← Total for Both

c. 6 / 36 = 1 / 6

d. 10 / 36 = 5 / 18

e. No. P(odd) = 18 / 36 = P(even) = 18 / 36 or 1 / 2 for both.

f. Classical. A probability of 1 / 36 is assigned to each experimental outcome.

17. a. (4, 6), (4, 7), (4 , 8)

b. .05 + .10 + .15 = .30

c. (2, 8), (3, 8), (4, 8)

d. .05 + .05 + .15 = .25

e. .15

18. a. 0; probability is .05

b. 4, 5; probability is .10 + .10 = .20

c. 0, 1, 2; probability is .05 + .15 + .35 = .55

19. a. Yes, the probabilities are all greater than or equal to zero and they sum to one.

b. P(A) = P(0) + P(1) + P(2) = .08 + .18 + .32

= .58

c. $P(B) = P(4) = .12$

20. a. $P(N) = 56/500 = .112$

b. $P(T) = 43/500 = .086$

c. Total in 6 states $= 56 + 53 + 43 + 37 + 28 + 28 = 245$

$P(B) = 245/500 = .49$

Almost half the Fortune 500 companies are headquartered in these states.

21. a. $P(A) = P(1) + P(2) + P(3) + P(4) + P(5)$

$$= \frac{20}{50} + \frac{12}{50} + \frac{6}{50} + \frac{3}{50} + \frac{1}{50}$$

$$= .40 + .24 + .12 + .06 + .02$$

$$= .84$$

b. $P(B) = P(3) + P(4) + P(5)$

$$= .12 + .06 + .02$$

$$= .20$$

c. $P(2) = 12 / 50 = .24$

22. a. $P(A) = .40$, $P(B) = .40$, $P(C) = .60$

b. $P(A \cup B) = P(E_1, E_2, E_3, E_4) = .80$. Yes $P(A \cup B) = P(A) + P(B)$.

c. $A^c = \{E_3, E_4, E_5\}$ $C^c = \{E_1, E_4\}$ $P(A^c) = .60$ $P(C^c) = .40$

d. $A \cup B^c = \{E_1, E_2, E_5\}$ $P(A \cup B^c) = .60$

e. $P(B \cup C) = P(E_2, E_3, E_4, E_5) = .80$

23. a. $P(A) = P(E_1) + P(E_4) + P(E_6) = .05 + .25 + .10 = .40$

$P(B) = P(E_2) + P(E_4) + P(E_7) = .20 + .25 + .05 = .50$

$P(C) = P(E_2) + P(E_3) + P(E_5) + P(E_7) = .20 + .20 + .15 + .05 = .60$

b. $A \cup B = \{E_1, E_2, E_4, E_6, E_7\}$

$P(A \cup B) = P(E_1) + P(E_2) + P(E_4) + P(E_6) + P(E_7)$
$= .05 + .20 + .25 + .10 + .05$
$= .65$

c. $A \cap B = \{E_4\}$ $P(A \cap B) = P(E_4) = .25$

d. Yes, they are mutually exclusive.

e. $B^c = \{E_1, E_3, E_5, E_6\}$; $P(B^c) = P(E_1) + P(E_3) + P(E_5) + P(E_6)$
$$= .05 + .20 + .15 + .10$$
$$= .50$$

24. P(Crash Not Likely) $= 1 - .14 - .43 = .43$

25. Let Y = high one-year return
M = high five-year return

a. $P(Y) = 15/30 = .50$

$P(M) = 12/30 = .40$

$P(Y \cap M) = 6/30 = .20$

b. $P(Y \cup M) = P(Y) + P(M) - P(Y \cap M)$
$$= .50 + .40 - .20 = .70$$

c. $1 - P(Y \cup M) = 1 - .70 = .30$

26. Let Y = high one-year return
M = high five-year return

a. $P(Y) = 9/30 = .30$

$P(M) = 7/30 = .23$

b. $P(Y \cap M) = 5/30 = .17$

c. $P(Y \cup M) = .30 + .23 - .17 = .36$

$P(\text{Neither}) = 1 - .36 = .64$

27. Let: D = consumes or serves domestic wine
I = consumes or serves imported wine

We are given $P(D) = 0.57$, $P(I) = 0.33$, $P(D \cup I) = 0.63$

$P(D \cap I) = P(D) + P(I) - P(D \cup I)$

$$= 0.57 + 0.33 - 0.63 = 0.27$$

28. Let: B = rented a car for business reasons
P = rented a car for personal reasons

a. $P(B \cup P) = P(B) + P(P) - P(B \cap P)$
$$= .54 + .458 - .30 = .698$$

b. $P(\text{Neither}) = 1 - .698 = .302$

29. a. $P(H) = \dfrac{725,790}{2,425,000} \approx 0.299$

$P(C) = \dfrac{537,390}{2,425,000} \approx 0.222$

$$P(S) = \frac{159,877}{2,425,000} \approx 0.066$$

b. A person can have only one primary cause of death listed on a death certificate. So, they are mutually exclusive.

c. $P(H \cup C) = 0.299 + 0.222 = 0.521$

d. $P(C \cup S) = 0.222 + 0.066 = 0.288$

e. $1 - 0.299 - 0.222 - 0.066 = 0.413$

30. a. $P(A|B) = \dfrac{P(A \cap B)}{P(B)} = \dfrac{.40}{.60} = .6667$

b. $P(B|A) = \dfrac{P(A \cap B)}{P(A)} = \dfrac{.40}{.50} = .80$

c. No because $P(A \mid B) \neq P(A)$

31. a. $P(A \cap B) = 0$

b. $P(A|B) = \dfrac{P(A \cap B)}{P(B)} = \dfrac{0}{.4} = 0$

c. No. $P(A \mid B) \neq P(A)$; $\therefore$ the events, although mutually exclusive, are not independent.

d. Mutually exclusive events are dependent.

32. a.

	Single	Married	Total
Under 30	.55	.10	.65
30 or over	.20	.15	.35
Total	.75	.25	1.00

b. 65% of the customers are under 30.

c. The majority of customers are single: $P(\text{single}) = .75$.

d. .55

e. Let: A = event under 30
B = event single

$$P(B|A) = \frac{P(A \cap B)}{P(A)} = \frac{.55}{.65} = .8462$$

f. $P(A \cap B) = .55$

$$P(A)P(B) = (.65)(.75) = .49$$

Since $P(A \cap B) \neq P(A)P(B)$, they cannot be independent events; or, since $P(A \mid B) \neq P(B)$, they cannot be independent.

33. a.

Reason for Applying

	Quality	Cost/Convenience	Other	Total
Full Time	.218	.204	.039	.461
Part Time	.208	.307	.024	.539
	.426	.511	.063	1.00

b. It is most likely a student will cite cost or convenience as the first reason - probability = .511. School quality is the first reason cited by the second largest number of students - probability = .426.

c. P(Quality | full time) = .218 / .461 = .473

d. P(Quality | part time) = .208 / .539 = .386

e. For independence, we must have $P(A)P(B) = P(A \cap B)$.

From the table, $P(A \cap B) = .218$, $P(A) = .461$, $P(B) = .426$

$$P(A)P(B) = (.461)(.426) = .196$$

Since $P(A)P(B) \neq P(A \cap B)$, the events are not independent.

34. a. P(O) = 0.38 + 0.06 = 0.44

b. P(Rh-) = 0.06 + 0.02 + 0.01 + 0.06 = 0.15

c. P(both Rh-) = P(Rh-) P(Rh-) = (0.15)(0.15) = 0.0225

d. P(both AB) = P(AB) P(AB) = (0.05)(0.05) = 0.0025

e. $P(Rh-|O) = \dfrac{P(Rh- \cap O)}{P(O)} = \dfrac{.06}{.44} = .136$

f. $P(Rh+) = 1 - P(Rh-) = 1 - 0.15 = 0.85$

$$P(B|Rh+) = \frac{P(B \cap Rh+)}{P(Rh+)} = \frac{.09}{.85} = .106$$

35. a. $P(\text{Up for January}) = 31 / 48 = 0.646$

b. $P(\text{Up for Year}) = 36 / 48 = 0.75$

c. $P(\text{Up for Year} \cap \text{Up for January}) = 29 / 48 = 0.604$

$P(\text{Up for Year} | \text{Up for January}) = 0.604 / 0.646 = 0.935$

d. They are not independent since

$P(\text{Up for Year}) \neq P(\text{Up for Year} | \text{Up for January})$

$0.75 \neq 0.935$

36. a.

Occupation	Under 50	50-59	Satisfaction Score 60-69	70-79	80-89	Total
Cabinetmaker	.000	.050	.100	.075	.025	.250
Lawyer	.150	.050	.025	.025	.000	.250
Physical Therapist	.000	.125	.050	.025	.050	.250
Systems Analyst	.050	.025	.100	.075	.000	.250
Total	.200	.250	.275	.200	.075	1.000

b. $P(80s) = .075$ (a marginal probability)

c. $P(80s | PT) = .050/.250 = .20$ (a conditional probability)

d. $P(L) = .250$ (a marginal probability)

e. $P(L \cap \text{Under 50}) = .150$ (a joint probability)

f. $P(\text{Under 50} | L) = .150/.250 = .60$ (a conditional probability)

g. $P(70 \text{ or higher}) = .275$ (Sum of marginal probabilities)

37. a. $P(A \cap B) = P(A)P(B) = (.55)(.35) = .19$

b. $P(A \cup B) = P(A) + P(B) - P(A \cap B) = .55 + .35 - .19 = .71$

c. $P(\text{shutdown}) = 1 - P(A \cup B) = 1 - .71 = .29$

38. a. $P(\text{Telephone}) = \dfrac{52}{190} \approx 0.2737$

b. This is an intersection of two events. It seems reasonable to assume the next two messages will be independent; we use the multiplication rule for independent events.

$$P(\text{E-mail} \cap \text{Fax}) = P(\text{E-mail}) \, P(\text{Fax}) = \left(\frac{30}{190}\right)\left(\frac{15}{190}\right) \approx 0.0125$$

c. This is a union of two mutually exclusive events.

P(Telephone $\cup$ Interoffice Mail) = P(Telephone) + P(Interoffice Mail)

$$= \frac{52}{190} + \frac{18}{190} = \frac{70}{190} \approx 0.7368$$

39. a. Yes, since $P(A_1 \cap A_2) = 0$

b. $P(A_1 \cap B) = P(A_1)P(B \mid A_1) = .40(.20) = .08$

$P(A_2 \cap B) = P(A_2)P(B \mid A_2) = .60(.05) = .03$

c. $P(B) = P(A_1 \cap B) + P(A_2 \cap B) = .08 + .03 = .11$

d. $P(A_1 \mid B) = \dfrac{.08}{.11} = .7273$

$P(A_2 \mid B) = \dfrac{.03}{.11} = .2727$

40. a. $P(B \cap A_1) = P(A_1)P(B \mid A_1) = (.20)\,(.50) = .10$

$P(B \cap A_2) = P(A_2)P(B \mid A_2) = (.50)\,(.40) = .20$
$P(B \cap A_3) = P(A_3)P(B \mid A_3) = (.30)\,(.30) = .09$

b. $P(A_2 \mid B) = \dfrac{.20}{.10 + .20 + .09} = .51$

c.

Events	$P(A_i)$	$P(B \mid A_i)$	$P(A_i \cap B)$	$P(A_i \mid B)$
A_1	.20	.50	.10	.26
A_2	.50	.40	.20	.51
A_3	.30	.30	.09	.23
	1.00		.39	1.00

41. S_1 = successful, S_2 = not successful and B = request received for additional information.

a. $P(S_1) = .50$

b. $P(B \mid S_1) = .75$

c. $P(S_1 \mid B) = \dfrac{(.50)(.75)}{(.50)(.75) + (.50)(.40)} = \dfrac{.375}{.575} = .65$

42. M = missed payment

D_1 = customer defaults
D_2 = customer does not default

$P(D_1) = .05 \quad P(D_2) = .95 \quad P(M \mid D_2) = .2 \quad P(M \mid D_1) = 1$

a. $P(D_1 | M) = \dfrac{P(D_1)P(M|D_1)}{P(D_1)P(M|D_1) + P(D_2)P(M|D_2)} = \dfrac{(.05)(1)}{(.05)(1) + (.95)(.2)} = \dfrac{.05}{.24} = .21$

b. Yes, the probability of default is greater than .20.

43.   Let: S = small car
          S^c = other type of vehicle
          F = accident leads to fatality for vehicle occupant

We have P(S) = .18, so $P(S^c)$ = .82. Also P(F | S) = .128 and $P(F | S^c)$ = .05. Using the tabular form of Bayes Theorem provides:

Events	Prior Probabilities	Conditional Probabilities	Joint Probabilities	Posterior Probabilities
S	.18	.128	.023	.36
S^c	.82	.050	.041	.64
	1.00		.064	1.00

From the posterior probability column, we have P(S | F) = .36. So, if an accident leads to a fatality, the probability a small car was involved is .36.

44.   Let A_1 = Story about Basketball Team
         A_2 = Story about Hockey Team
         W = "We Win" headline

$P(A_1)$ = .60 $P(W | A_1)$ = .641

$P(A_2)$ = .40 $P(W | A_2)$ = .462

A_i	$P(A_i)$	$P(W | A_1)$	$P(W \cap A_i)$	$P(A_i | M)$	
A_1	.60	.641	.3846	.3846/.5694	= .6754
A_2	.40	.462	.1848	.1848/.5694	= .3246
			.5694		1.0000

The probability the story is about the basketball team is .6754.

45. a.

Events	$P(D_i)$	$P(S_1 | D_i)$	$P(D_i \cap S_1)$	$P(D_i | S_1)$
D_1	.60	.15	.090	.2195
D_2	.40	.80	.320	.7805
	1.00		$P(S_1) = .410$	1.000

$P(D_1 | S_1)$ = .2195

$P(D_2 | S_1)$ = .7805

b.

Events	$P(D_i)$	$P(S_2 | D_i)$	$P(D_i \cap S_2)$	$P(D_i | S_2)$
D_1	.60	.10	.060	.500
D_2	.40	.15	.060	.500
	1.00		$P(S_2) = .120$	1.000

$P(D_1 | S_2)$ = .50

$P(D_2 | S_2)$ = .50

c.

Events	$P(D_i)$	$P(S_3 \mid D_i)$	$P(D_i \cap S_3)$	$P(D_i \mid S_3)$
D_1	.60	.15	.090	.8824
D_2	.40	.03	.012	.1176
	1.00		$P(S_3) = .102$	1.0000

$P(D_1 \mid S_3) = .8824$

$P(D_2 \mid S_3) = .1176$

d. Use the posterior probabilities from part (a) as the prior probabilities here.

Events	$P(D_i)$	$P(S_2 \mid Di)$	$P(D_i \cap S_2)$	$P(D_i \mid S_2)$
D_1	.2195	.10	.0220	.1582
D_2	.7805	.15	.1171	.8418
	1.0000		.1391	1.0000

$P(D_1 \mid S_1 \text{ and } S_2) = .1582$

$P(D_2 \mid S_1 \text{ and } S_2) = .8418$

46. a. P(Excellent) = .18
    P(Pretty Good) = .50

    P(Pretty Good $\cup$ Excellent) = .18 + .50 = .68

    Note: Events are mutually exclusive since a person may only choose one rating.

b. 1035 (.05) = 51.75

    We estimate 52 respondents rated US companies poor.

c. 1035 (.01) = 10.35

    We estimate 10 respondents did not know or did not answer.

47. a. (2) (2) = 4

b. Let   s = successful
           u = unsuccessful

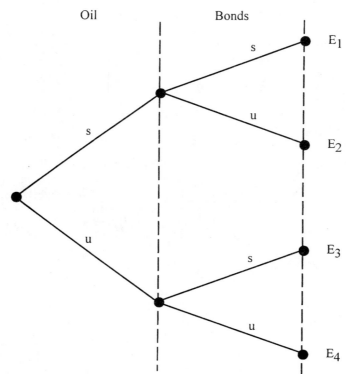

c. $O = \{E_1, E_2\}$

   $M = \{E_1, E_3\}$

d. $O \cup M = \{E_1, E_2, E_3\}$

e. $O \cap M = \{E_1\}$

f.   No; since $O \cap M$ has a sample point.

48. a.   P(satisfied) = 0.61

   b.   The 18 - 34 year old group (64% satisfied) and the 65 and over group (70% satisfied).

   c.   P(not satisfied) = 0.26 + 0.04 = 0.30

49.   Let   I = treatment-caused injury
              D = death from injury
              N = injury caused by negligence
              M = malpractice claim filed
              $ = payment made in claim

      We are given P(I) = 0.04, P(N | I) = 0.25, P(D | I) = 1/7, P(M | N) = 1/7.5 = 0.1333, and P($ | M) = 0.50

   a.   P(N) = P(N | I) P(I) + P(N | I^c) P(I^c)
              = (0.25)(0.04) + (0)(0.96)
              = 0.01

b. $P(D) = P(D \mid I) P(I) + P(D \mid I^c) P(I^c)$
$= (1/7)(0.04) + (0)(0.96)$
$= 0.006$

c. $P(M) = P(M \mid N) P(N) + P(M \mid N^c) P(N^c)$
$= (0.1333)(0.01) + (0)(0.99)$
$= 0.001333$

$P(\$) = P(\$ \mid M) P(M) + P(\$ \mid M^c) P(M^c)$
$= (0.5)(0.001333) + (0)(0.9987)$
$= 0.00067$

50. a. Probability of the event $= P(\text{average}) + P(\text{above average}) + P(\text{excellent})$

$$= \frac{11}{50} + \frac{14}{50} + \frac{13}{50}$$

$$= .22 + .28 + .26$$

$$= .76$$

b. Probability of the event $= P(\text{poor}) + P(\text{below average})$

$$= \frac{4}{50} + \frac{8}{50} = .24$$

51. a. $P(\text{leases 1}) = 168 / 932 = 0.18$

b. $P(\text{2 or fewer}) = 401 / 932 + 242 / 932 + 65 / 932 = 708 / 932 = 0.76$

c. $P(\text{3 or more}) = 186 / 932 + 112 / 932 = 298 / 932 = 0.32$

d. $P(\text{no cars}) = 19 / 932 = 0.02$

52. a.

	Yes	No	Total
23 and Under	.1026	.0996	.2022
24 - 26	.1482	.1878	.3360
27 - 30	.0917	.1328	.2245
31 - 35	.0327	.0956	.1283
36 and Over	.0253	.0837	.1090
Total	.4005	.5995	1.0000

b. .2022

c. .2245 + .1283 + .1090 = .4618

d. .4005

53. a. P(24 to 26 | Yes) = .1482 / .4005 = .3700

b. P(Yes | 36 and over) = .0253 / .1090 = .2321

c. .1026 + .1482 + .1878 + .0917 + .0327 + .0253 = .5883

d. P(31 or more | No) = (.0956 + .0837) / .5995 = .2991

e. No, because the conditional probabilities do not all equal the marginal probabilities. For instance,

$$P(24 \text{ to } 26 \mid \text{Yes}) = .3700 \neq P(24 \text{ to } 26) = .3360$$

54.   Let   I = important or very important
              M = male
              F = female

a. P(I) = .49 (a marginal probability)

b. P(I | M) = .22/.50 = .44 (a conditional probability)

c. P(I | F) = .27/.50 = .54 (a conditional probability)

d. It is not independent

$$P(I) = .49 \neq P(I \mid M) = .44$$
and
$$P(I) = .49 \neq P(I \mid F) = .54$$

e. Since level of importance is dependent on gender, we conclude that male and female respondents have different attitudes toward risk.

55. a. $P(B|S) = \dfrac{P(B \cap S)}{P(S)} = \dfrac{.12}{.40} = .30$

We have P(B | S) > P(B).

Yes, continue the ad since it increases the probability of a purchase.

b. Estimate the company's market share at 20%. Continuing the advertisement should increase the market share since P(B | S) = .30.

c. $P(B|S) = \dfrac{P(B \cap S)}{P(S)} = \dfrac{.10}{.30} = .333$

The second ad has a bigger effect.

56. a. P(A) = 200/800 = .25

b. P(B) = 100/800 = .125

c. $P(A \cap B) = 10/800 = .0125$

d. $P(A \mid B) = P(A \cap B) / P(B) = .0125 / .125 = .10$

e. No, $P(A \mid B) \neq P(A) = .25$

57. Let $A =$ lost time accident in current year
$B =$ lost time accident previous year

Given: $P(B) = .06, P(A) = .05, P(A \mid B) = .15$

a. $P(A \cap B) = P(A \mid B)P(B) = .15(.06) = .009$

b. $P(A \cup B) = P(A) + P(B) - P(A \cap B)$

$\qquad = .06 + .05 - .009 = .101$ or 10.1%

58. Let: $A =$ return is fraudulent
$B =$ exceeds IRS standard for deductions

Given: $P(A \mid B) = .20, P(A \mid B^c) = .02, P(B) = .08$, find $P(A) = .3$.
Note $P(B^c) = 1 - P(B) = .92$

$$P(A) = P(A \cap B) + P(A \cap B^c)$$
$$= P(B)P(A \mid B) + P(B^c)P(A \mid B^c)$$
$$= (.08)(.20) + (.92)(.02) = .0344$$

We estimate 3.44% will be fraudulent.

59. a. $P(Oil) = .50 + .20 = .70$

b. Let S = Soil test results

Events	$P(A_i)$	$P(S \mid A_i)$	$P(A_i \cap S)$	$P(A_i \mid S)$
High Quality (A_1)	.50	.20	.10	.31
Medium Quality (A_2)	.20	.80	.16	.50
No Oil (A_3)	.30	.20	.06	.19
	1.00		$P(S) = .32$	1.00

$P(Oil) = .81$ which is good; however, probabilities now favor medium quality rather than high quality oil.

60. a. $A_1 =$ field will produce oil

$A_2 =$ field will not produce oil

$W =$ well produces oil

Events	$P(A_i)$	$P(W^c \mid A_i)$	$P(W^c \cap A_i)$	$P(A_i \mid W^c)$
Oil in Field	.25	.20	.05	.0625
No Oil in Field	.75	1.00	.75	.9375
	1.00		.80	1.0000

The probability the field will produce oil given a well comes up dry is .0625.

b.

Events	$P(A_i)$	$P(W^c \mid A_i)$	$P(W^c \cap A_i)$	$P(A_i \mid W^c)$
Oil in Field	.0625	.20	.0125	.0132
No Oil in Field	.9375	1.00	.9375	.9868
	1.0000		.9500	1.0000

The probability the well will produce oil drops further to .0132.

c. Suppose a third well comes up dry. The probabilities are revised as follows:

Events	$P(A_i)$	$P(W^c \mid A_i)$	$P(W^c \cap A_i)$	$P(A_i \mid W^c)$
Oil in Field	.0132	.20	.0026	.0026
Incorrect Adjustment	.9868	1.00	.9868	.9974
	1.0000		.9894	1.0000

Stop drilling and abandon field if three consecutive wells come up dry.

Chapter 5
Discrete Probability Distributions

Learning Objectives

1. Understand the concepts of a random variable and a probability distribution.

2. Be able to distinguish between discrete and continuous random variables.

3. Be able to compute and interpret the expected value, variance, and standard deviation for a discrete random variable.

4. Be able to compute and work with probabilities involving a binomial probability distribution.

5. Be able to compute and work with probabilities involving a Poisson probability distribution.

6. Know when and how to use the hypergeometric probability distribution.

Solutions:

1. a. Head, Head (H,H)
   Head, Tail (H,T)
   Tail, Head (T,H)
   Tail, Tail (T,T)

   b. x = number of heads on two coin tosses

   c.

Outcome	Values of x
(H,H)	2
(H,T)	1
(T,H)	1
(T,T)	0

   d. Discrete. It may assume 3 values: 0, 1, and 2.

2. a. Let x = time (in minutes) to assemble the product.

   b. It may assume any positive value: $x > 0$.

   c. Continuous

3. Let Y = position is offered
   N = position is not offered

   a. S = {(Y,Y,Y), (Y,Y,N), (Y,N,Y), (Y,N,N), (N,Y,Y), (N,Y,N), (N,N,Y), (N,N,N)}

   b. Let N = number of offers made; N is a discrete random variable.

   c.

Experimental Outcome	(Y,Y,Y)	(Y,Y,N)	(Y,N,Y)	(Y,N,N)	(N,Y,Y)	(N,Y,N)	(N,N,Y)	(N,N,N)
Value of N	3	2	2	1	2	1	1	0

4. x = 0, 1, 2, . . ., 12.

5. a. S = {(1,1), (1,2), (1,3), (2,1), (2,2), (2,3)}

   b.

Experimental Outcome	(1,1)	(1,2)	(1,3)	(2,1)	(2,2)	(2,3)
Number of Steps Required	2	3	4	3	4	5

6. a. values: 0,1,2,...,20
      discrete
   b. values: 0,1,2,...
      discrete
   c. values: 0,1,2,...,50
      discrete

   d. values: $0 \leq x \leq 8$
      continuous

e. values: $x > 0$
        continuous

7. a. $f(x) \geq 0$ for all values of x.

    $\Sigma f(x) = 1$ Therefore, it is a proper probability distribution.

   b. Probability $x = 30$ is $f(30) = .25$

   c. Probability $x \leq 25$ is $f(20) + f(25) = .20 + .15 = .35$

   d. Probability $x > 30$ is $f(35) = .40$

8. a.

x	$f(x)$
1	3/20 = .15
2	5/20 = .25
3	8/20 = .40
4	4/20 = .20
	Total 1.00

   b.

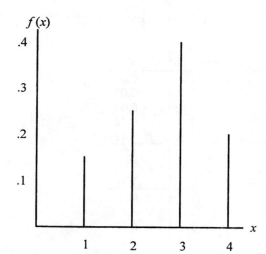

   c. $f(x) \geq 0$ for $x = 1,2,3,4$.

     $\Sigma f(x) = 1$

9. a.

x	$f(x)$
1	15/462 = 0.032
2	32/462 = 0.069
3	84/462 = 0.182
4	300/462 = 0.650
5	31/462 = 0.067

b.

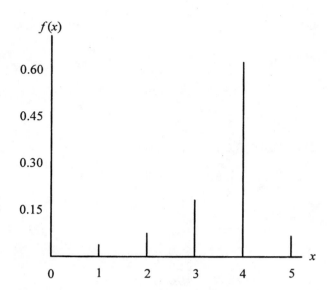

c.   All $f(x) \geq 0$

$\Sigma f(x) = 0.032 + 0.069 + 0.182 + 0.650 + 0.067 = 1.000$

10. a.

x	f(x)
1	0.05
2	0.09
3	0.03
4	0.42
5	0.41
	1.00

b.

x	f(x)
1	0.04
2	0.10
3	0.12
4	0.46
5	0.28
	1.00

c. $P(4 \text{ or } 5) = f(4) + f(5) = 0.42 + 0.41 = 0.83$

d.   Probability of very satisfied: 0.28

e.   Senior executives appear to be more satisfied than middle managers. 83% of senior executives have a score of 4 or 5 with 41% reporting a 5. Only 28% of middle managers report being very satisfied.

11. a.

Duration of Call

x	f(x)
1	0.25
2	0.25
3	0.25
4	0.25
	1.00

b.

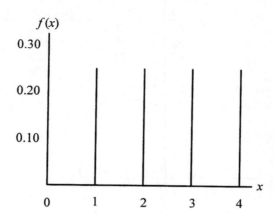

c. $f(x) \geq 0$ and $f(1) + f(2) + f(3) + f(4) = 0.25 + 0.25 + 0.25 + 0.25 = 1.00$

d. $f(3) = 0.25$

e. P(overtime) $= f(3) + f(4) = 0.25 + 0.25 = 0.50$

12. a. Yes; $f(x) \geq 0$ for all x and $\Sigma f(x) = .15 + .20 + .30 + .25 + .10 = 1$

b. P(1200 or less) $= f(1000) + f(1100) + f(1200)$
$= .15 + .20 + .30$
$= .65$

13. a. Yes, since $f(x) \geq 0$ for $x = 1,2,3$ and $\Sigma f(x) = f(1) + f(2) + f(3) = 1/6 + 2/6 + 3/6 = 1$

b. $f(2) = 2/6 = .333$

c. $f(2) + f(3) = 2/6 + 3/6 = .833$

14. a. $f(200) = 1 - f(-100) - f(0) - f(50) - f(100) - f(150)$
$= 1 - .95 = .05$

This is the probability MRA will have a \$200,000 profit.

b. P(Profit) $= f(50) + f(100) + f(150) + f(200)$
$= .30 + .25 + .10 + .05 = .70$

c. P(at least 100) $= f(100) + f(150) + f(200)$
$= .25 + .10 + .05 = .40$

15. a.

x	$f(x)$	$xf(x)$
3	.25	.75
6	.50	3.00
9	.25	2.25
	1.00	6.00

$E(x) = \mu = 6.00$

b.

x	x - μ	(x - μ)2	f(x)	(x - μ)2 f(x)
3	-3	9	.25	2.25
6	0	0	.50	0.00
9	3	9	.25	2.25
				4.50

Var $(x) = \sigma^2 = 4.50$

c. $\sigma = \sqrt{4.50} = 2.12$

16. a.

y	f(y)	y f(y)
2	.20	.40
4	.30	1.20
7	.40	2.80
8	.10	.80
	1.00	5.20

E(y) = μ = 5.20

b.

y	y - μ	(y - μ)²	f(y)	(y - μ)² f(y)
2	-3.20	10.24	.20	2.048
4	-1.20	1.44	.30	.432
7	1.80	3.24	.40	1.296
8	2.80	7.84	.10	.784
				4.560

Var $(y) = 4.56$

$\sigma = \sqrt{4.56} = 2.14$

17. a/b.

x	f(x)	x f(x)	x - μ	(x - μ)²	(x - μ)² f(x)
0	.10	.00	-2.45	6.0025	.600250
1	.15	.15	-1.45	2.1025	.315375
2	.30	.60	- .45	.2025	.060750
3	.20	.60	.55	.3025	.060500
4	.15	.60	1.55	2.4025	.360375
5	.10	.50	2.55	6.5025	.650250
		2.45			2.047500

$E(x) = \mu = 2.45$

$\sigma^2 = 2.0475$

$\sigma = 1.4309$

18. a/b.

x	f(x)	x f(x)	x - μ	(x - μ)²	(x - μ)² f(x)
0	.01	0	-2.3	5.29	0.0529
1	.23	.23	-1.3	1.69	0.3887
2	.41	.82	-0.3	0.09	0.0369
3	.20	.60	0.7	0.49	0.098
4	.10	.40	1.7	2.89	0.289
5	.05	.25	2.7	7.29	0.3645
		2.3			1.23

$$E(x) = 2.3 \qquad \text{Var}(x) = 1.23$$
$$\sigma = \sqrt{1.23} = 1.11$$

The expected value, $E(x) = 2.3$, of the probability distribution is the same as that reported in the *1997 Statistical Abstract of the United States*.

19. a. $E(x) = \Sigma \, xf(x) = 0\,(.50) + 2\,(.50) = 1.00$

    b. $E(x) = \Sigma \, xf(x) = 0\,(.61) + 3\,(.39) = 1.17$

    c. The expected value of a 3 - point shot is higher. So, if these probabilities hold up, the team will make more points in the long run with the 3 - point shot.

20. a.

x	$f(x)$	$xf(x)$
0	.90	0.00
400	.04	16.00
1000	.03	30.00
2000	.01	20.00
4000	.01	40.00
6000	.01	60.00
	1.00	166.00

$E(x) = 166$. If the company charged a premium of \$166.00 they would break even.

    b.

Gain to Policy Holder	f(Gain)	(Gain) f(Gain)
-260.00	.90	-234.00
140.00	.04	5.60
740.00	.03	22.20
1,740.00	.01	17.40
3,740.00	.01	37.40
5,740.00	.01	57.40
		-94.00

E (gain) = -94.00. The policy holder is more concerned that the big accident will break him than with the expected annual loss of \$94.00.

21. a. $E(x) = \Sigma \, xf(x) = 0.05(1) + 0.09(2) + 0.03(3) + 0.42(4) + 0.41(5)$
    $= 4.05$

    b. $E(x) = \Sigma \, xf(x) = 0.04(1) + 0.10(2) + 0.12(3) + 0.46(4) + 0.28(5)$
    $= 3.84$

    c. Executives: $\sigma^2 = \Sigma \,(x - \mu)^2 f(x) = 1.2475$

       Middle Managers: $\sigma^2 = \Sigma \,(x - \mu)^2 f(x) = 1.1344$

    d. Executives: $\sigma = 1.1169$

       Middle Managers: $\sigma = 1.0651$

    e. The senior executives have a higher average score: 4.05 vs. 3.84 for the middle managers. The executives also have a slightly higher standard deviation.

22. a. $E(x) = \Sigma\, x f(x)$

      $= 300\,(.20) + 400\,(.30) + 500\,(.35) + 600\,(.15) = 445$

   The monthly order quantity should be 445 units.

   b. Cost: 445 @ \$50 = \$22,250
      Revenue: 300 @ \$70 = 21,000
      $\quad\quad\quad\quad\quad\quad\quad\quad$ \$ 1,250 Loss

23. a. Laptop: $E(x) = .47(0) + .45(1) + .06(2) + .02(3) = .63$

   Desktop: $E(x) = .06(0) + .56(1) + .28(2) + .10(3) = 1.42$

   b. Laptop: $\text{Var}(x) = .47(-.63)^2 + .45(.37)^2 + .06(1.37)^2 + .02(2.37)^2 = .4731$

   Desktop: $\text{Var}(x) = .06(-1.42)^2 + .56(-.42)^2 + .28(.58)^2 + .10(1.58)^2 = .5636$

   c. From the expected values in part (a), it is clear that the typical subscriber has more desktop computers than laptops. There is not much difference in the variances for the two types of computers.

24. a. Medium $E(x) = \Sigma\, x f(x)$

      $= 50\,(.20) + 150\,(.50) + 200\,(.30) = 145$

   Large: $E(x) = \Sigma\, x f(x)$

      $= 0\,(.20) + 100\,(.50) + 300\,(.30) = 140$

   Medium preferred.

   b. <u>Medium</u>

x	$f(x)$	$x - \mu$	$(x - \mu)^2$	$(x - \mu)^2 f(x)$
50	.20	-95	9025	1805.0
150	.50	5	25	12.5
200	.30	55	3025	907.5
				$\sigma^2 = 2725.0$

   <u>Large</u>

y	$f(y)$	$y - \mu$	$(y - \mu)^2$	$(y - \mu)^2 f(y)$
0	.20	-140	19600	3920
100	.50	-40	1600	800
300	.30	160	25600	7680
				$\sigma^2 = 12,400$

   Medium preferred due to less variance.

25. a.

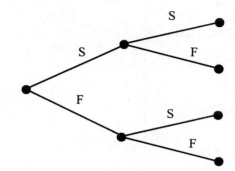

b. $f(1) = \binom{2}{1}(.4)^1(.6)^1 = \dfrac{2!}{1!1!}(.4)(.6) = .48$

c. $f(0) = \binom{2}{0}(.4)^0(.6)^2 = \dfrac{2!}{0!2!}(1)(.36) = .36$

d. $f(2) = \binom{2}{2}(.4)^2(.6)^0 = \dfrac{2!}{2!0!}(.16)(1) = .16$

e. $P(x \geq 1) = f(1) + f(2) = .48 + .16 = .64$

f. $E(x) = np = 2(.4) = .8$

$\text{Var}(x) = np(1-p) = 2(.4)(.6) = .48$

$\sigma = \sqrt{.48} = .6928$

26. a. $f(0) = .3487$

b. $f(2) = .1937$

c. $P(x \leq 2) = f(0) + f(1) + f(2) = .3487 + .3874 + .1937 = .9298$

d. $P(x \geq 1) = 1 - f(0) = 1 - .3487 = .6513$

e. $E(x) = np = 10(.1) = 1$

f. $\text{Var}(x) = np(1-p) = 10(.1)(.9) = .9$

$\sigma = \sqrt{.9} = .9487$

27. a. $f(12) = .1144$

b. $f(16) = .1304$

c. $P(x \geq 16) = f(16) + f(17) + f(18) + f(19) + f(20)$
$= .1304 + .0716 + .0278 + .0068 + .0008$
$= .2374$

d. $P(x \leq 15) = 1 - P(x \geq 16) = 1 - .2374 = .7626$

e. $E(x) = np = 20(.7) = 14$

f. $\text{Var}(x) = np(1-p) = 20(.7)(.3) = 4.2$

$\sigma = \sqrt{4.2} = 2.0494$

28. a. $f(2) = \binom{6}{2}(.33)^2(.67)^4 = .3292$

b. P(at least 2) $= 1 - f(0) - f(1)$

$$= 1 - \binom{6}{0}(.33)^0(.67)^6 - \binom{6}{1}(.33)^1(.67)^5$$

$$= 1 - .0905 - .2673 = .6422$$

c. $f(10) = \binom{10}{0}(.33)^0(.67)^{10} = .0182$

29. P(At Least 5) $= 1 - f(0) - f(1) - f(2) - f(3) - f(4)$
$= 1 - .0000 - .0005 - .0031 - .0123 - .0350$
$= .9491$

30. a. Probability of a defective part being produced must be .03 for each trial; trials must be independent.

b. Let: D = defective
   G = not defective

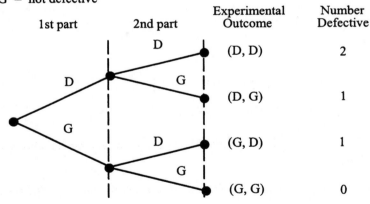

		Experimental Outcome	Number Defective
1st part	2nd part		
		(D, D)	2
		(D, G)	1
		(G, D)	1
		(G, G)	0

c. 2 outcomes result in exactly one defect.

d. P (no defects) = (.97) (.97) = .9409

   P (1 defect) = 2 (.03) (.97) = .0582

   P (2 defects) = (.03) (.03) = .0009

31. Binomial $n = 10$ and $p = .05$

$$f(x) = \frac{10!}{x!(10-x)!}(.05)^x(.95)^{10-x}$$

a. Yes. Since they are selected randomly, p is the same from trial to trial and the trials are independent.

b. $f(2) = .0746$

c. $f(0) = .5987$

d. $P(\text{At least } 1) = 1 - f(0) = 1 - .5987 = .4013$

32. a. .90

b. $P(\text{at least } 1) = f(1) + f(2)$

$$f(1) = \frac{2!}{1! \, 1!} (.9)^1 (.1)^1$$

$$= 2(.9)(.1) = .18$$

$$f(2) = \frac{2!}{2! \, 0!} (.9)^2 (.1)^0$$

$$= 1(.81)(1) = .81$$

$$\therefore P(\text{at least } 1) = .18 + .81 = .99$$

Alternatively

$$P(\text{at least } 1) = 1 - f(0)$$

$$f(0) = \frac{2!}{0! \, 2!} (.9)^0 (.1)^2 = .01$$

Therefore, $P(\text{at least } 1) = 1 - .01 = .99$

c. $P(\text{at least } 1) = 1 - f(0)$

$$f(0) = \frac{3!}{0! \, 3!} (.9)^0 (.1)^3 = .001$$

Therefore, $P(\text{at least } 1) = 1 - .001 = .999$

d. Yes; $P(\text{at least } 1)$ becomes very close to 1 with multiple systems and the inability to detect an attack would be catastrophic.

33. a. Using the binomial formula or the table of binomial probabilities with $p = .5$ and $n = 20$, we find:

x	$f(x)$
12	0.1201
13	0.0739
14	0.0370
15	0.0148
16	0.0046
17	0.0011
18	0.0002
19	0.0000
20	0.0000
	0.2517

The probability 12 or more will send representatives is 0.2517.

b. Using the binomial formula or the tables, we find:

x	$f(x)$
0	0.0000
1	0.0000
2	0.0002
3	0.0011
4	0.0046
5	0.0148
	0.0207

c. $E(x) = n\,p = 20(0.5) = 10$

d. $\sigma^2 = n\,p\,(1 - p) = 20(0.5)(0.5) = 5$

$\sigma = \sqrt{5} = 2.2361$

34. a. $f(3) = .0634$ (from tables)

b. The answer here is the same as part (a). The probability of 12 failures with $p = .60$ is the same as the probability of 3 successes with $p = .40$.

c. $f(3) + f(4) + \cdots + f(15) = 1 - f(0) - f(1) - f(2)$
$= 1 - .0005 - .0047 - .0219$
$= .9729$

35. a. $f(0) + f(1) + f(2) = .0115 + .0576 + .1369 = .2060$

b. $f(4) = .2182$

c. $1 - [\,f(0) + f(1) + f(2) + f(3)\,] = 1 - .2060 - .2054 = .5886$

d. $\mu = n\,p = 20\,(.20) = 4$

36.

x	$f(x)$	$x - \mu$	$(x - \mu)^2$	$(x - \mu)^2 f(x)$
0	.343	-.9	.81	.27783
1	.441	.1	.01	.00441
2	.189	1.1	1.21	.22869
3	.027	2.1	4.41	.11907
	1.000			$\sigma^2 = .63000$

37. $E(x) = n\,p = 30(0.29) = 8.7$

$\sigma^2 = n\,p\,(1 - p) = 30(0.29)(0.71) = 6.177$

$\sigma = \sqrt{6.177} = 2.485$

38. a. $f(x) = \dfrac{3^x e^{-3}}{x!}$

b. $f(2) = \dfrac{3^2 e^{-3}}{2!} = \dfrac{9(.0498)}{2} = .2241$

c. $f(1) = \dfrac{3^1 e^{-3}}{1!} = 3(.0498) = .1494$

d. $P(x \geq 2) = 1 - f(0) - f(1) = 1 - .0498 - .1494 = .8008$

39. a. $f(x) = \dfrac{2^x e^{-2}}{x!}$

b. $\mu = 6$ for 3 time periods

c. $f(x) = \dfrac{6^x e^{-6}}{x!}$

d. $f(2) = \dfrac{2^2 e^{-2}}{2!} = \dfrac{4(.1353)}{2} = .2706$

e. $f(6) = \dfrac{6^6 e^{-6}}{6!} = .1606$

f. $f(5) = \dfrac{4^5 e^{-4}}{5!} = .1563$

40. a. $\mu = 48\,(5/60) = 4$

$f(3) = \dfrac{4^3 e^{-4}}{3!} = \dfrac{(64)(.0183)}{6} = .1952$

b. $\mu = 48\,(15/60) = 12$

$f(10) = \dfrac{12^{10} e^{-12}}{10!} = .1048$

c. $\mu = 48\,(5/60) = 4$ I expect 4 callers to be waiting after 5 minutes.

$f(0) = \dfrac{4^0 e^{-4}}{0!} = .0183$

The probability none will be waiting after 5 minutes is .0183.

d. $\mu = 48\,(3/60) = 2.4$

$f(0) = \dfrac{2.4^0 e^{-2.4}}{0!} = .0907$

The probability of no interruptions in 3 minutes is .0907.

41. a. 30 per hour

 b. $\mu = 1\,(5/2) = 5/2$

$$f(3) = \frac{(5/2)^3\,e^{-(5/2)}}{3!} = .2138$$

 c. $f(0) = \frac{(5/2)^0\,e^{-(5/2)}}{0!} = e^{-(5/2)} = .0821$

42. a. $f(x) = \frac{\mu^x e^{-\mu}}{x!}$

$$f(2) = \frac{4^2 e^{-4}}{2!} = \frac{16(0.0183)}{2} = 8(0.0183) = 0.1465$$

 b. For a 3-month period: $\mu = 1$

 c. For a 6-month period: $\mu = 2$

$$f(0) = \frac{2^0 e^{-2}}{0!} = e^{-2} = 0.1353$$

 The probability of 1 or more flights $= 1 - f(0) = 1 - 0.1353 = 0.8647$

43. a. $f(0) = \frac{10^0 e^{-10}}{0!} = e^{-10} = .000045$

 b. $f(0) + f(1) + f(2) + f(3)$

 $f(0) = .000045$ (part a)

$$f(1) = \frac{10^1 e^{-10}}{1!} = .00045$$

 Similarly, $f(2) = .00225, f(3) = .0075$

 and $f(0) + f(1) + f(2) + f(3) = .010245$

 c. 2.5 arrivals / 15 sec. period   Use $\mu = 2.5$

$$f(0) = \frac{2.5^0 e^{-2.5}}{0!} = .0821$$

 d. $1 - f(0) = 1 - .0821 = .9179$

44. Poisson distribution applies

 a. $\mu = 1.25$ per month

b. $f(0) = \dfrac{1.25^0 e^{-1.25}}{0!} = 0.2865$

c. $f(1) = \dfrac{1.25^1 e^{-1.25}}{1!} = 0.3581$

d. P (More than 1) $= 1 - f(0) - f(1) = 1 - 0.2865 - 0.3581 = 0.3554$

45. a. For 1 week, $\mu = 450 / 52 = 8.65$

b. $f(0) = \dfrac{8.65^1 e^{-8.65}}{0!} = e^{-8.65} = 0.0002$

c. For a 1-day period: $\mu = 450 / 365 = 1.23$

$$f(0) = \frac{1.23^0 e^{-1.23}}{0!} = e^{-1.23} = 0.2923$$

$$f(1) = \frac{1.23^1 e^{-1.23}}{1} = 1.23(0.2923) = 0.3595$$

Probability of 2 or more deaths $= 1 - f(0) - f(1) = 1 - 0.2923 - 0.3595 = 0.3482$

46. a. $f(1) = \dfrac{\binom{3}{1}\binom{10-3}{4-1}}{\binom{10}{4}} = \dfrac{\left(\dfrac{3!}{1!2!}\right)\left(\dfrac{7!}{3!4!}\right)}{\dfrac{10!}{4!6!}} = \dfrac{(3)(35)}{210} = .50$

b. $f(2) = \dfrac{\binom{3}{2}\binom{10-3}{2-2}}{\binom{10}{2}} = \dfrac{(3)(1)}{45} = .067$

c. $f(0) = \dfrac{\binom{3}{0}\binom{10-3}{2-0}}{\binom{10}{2}} = \dfrac{(1)(21)}{45} = .4667$

d. $f(2) = \dfrac{\binom{3}{2}\binom{10-3}{4-2}}{\binom{10}{4}} = \dfrac{(3)(21)}{210} = .30$

47. $f(3) = \dfrac{\binom{4}{3}\binom{15-4}{10-3}}{\binom{15}{10}} = \dfrac{(4)(330)}{3003} = .4396$

48.   Hypergeometric with $N = 10$ and $r = 6$

a. $f(2) = \dfrac{\binom{6}{2}\binom{4}{1}}{\binom{10}{3}} = \dfrac{(15)(4)}{120} = .50$

b.   Must be 0 or 1 prefer Coke Classic.

$f(1) = \dfrac{\binom{6}{1}\binom{4}{2}}{\binom{10}{3}} = \dfrac{(6)(6)}{120} = .30$

$f(0) = \dfrac{\binom{6}{0}\binom{4}{3}}{\binom{10}{3}} = \dfrac{(1)(4)}{120} = .0333$

$P\text{ (Majority Pepsi) } = f\,(1) + f\,(0) = .3333$

49.   Parts a, b & c involve the hypergeometric distribution with $N = 52$ and $n = 2$

a. $r = 20, x = 2$

$f(2) = \dfrac{\binom{20}{2}\binom{32}{0}}{\binom{52}{2}} = \dfrac{(190)(1)}{1326} = .1433$

b. $r = 4, x = 2$

$f(2) = \dfrac{\binom{4}{2}\binom{48}{0}}{\binom{52}{2}} = \dfrac{(6)(1)}{1326} = .0045$

c. $r = 16, x = 2$

$f(2) = \dfrac{\binom{16}{2}\binom{36}{0}}{\binom{52}{2}} = \dfrac{(120)(1)}{1326} = .0905$

d.   Part (a) provides the probability of blackjack plus the probability of 2 aces plus the probability of two 10s. To find the probability of blackjack we subtract the probabilities in (b) and (c) from the probability in (a).

$$P \text{ (blackjack)} = .1433 - .0045 - .0905 = .0483$$

50. $\quad N = 60 \quad n = 10$

a. $\quad r = 20 \quad x = 0$

$$f(0) \; = \; \frac{\binom{20}{0}\binom{40}{10}}{\binom{60}{10}} = \frac{(1)\left(\frac{40!}{10!30!}\right)}{\frac{60!}{10!50!}} = \left(\frac{40!}{10!30!}\right)\left(\frac{10!50!}{60!}\right)$$

$$= \; \frac{40 \cdot 39 \cdot 38 \cdot 37 \cdot 36 \cdot 35 \cdot 34 \cdot 33 \cdot 32 \cdot 31}{60 \cdot 59 \cdot 58 \cdot 57 \cdot 56 \cdot 55 \cdot 54 \cdot 53 \cdot 52 \cdot 51}$$

$$\approx .01$$

b. $\quad r = 20 \quad x = 1$

$$f(0) \; = \; \frac{\binom{20}{1}\binom{40}{9}}{\binom{60}{10}} = 20\left(\frac{40!}{9!31!}\right)\left(\frac{10!50!}{60!}\right)$$

$$\approx .07$$

c. $\quad 1 - f(0) - f(1) = 1 - .08 = .92$

d. Same as the probability one will be from Hawaii. In part b that was found to equal approximately .07.

51. a. $\quad f(2) = \dfrac{\binom{11}{2}\binom{14}{3}}{\binom{25}{5}} = \dfrac{(55)(364)}{53,130} = .3768$

b. $\quad f(2) = \dfrac{\binom{14}{2}\binom{11}{3}}{\binom{25}{5}} = \dfrac{(91)(165)}{53,130} = .2826$

c. $\quad f(5) = \dfrac{\binom{14}{5}\binom{11}{0}}{\binom{25}{5}} = \dfrac{(2002)(1)}{53,130} = .0377$

d. $f(0) = \dfrac{\dbinom{14}{0}\dbinom{11}{5}}{\dbinom{25}{5}} = \dfrac{(1)(462)}{53,130} = .0087$

52. Hypergeometric with $N = 10$ and $r = 2$.

Focus on the probability of 0 defectives, then the probability of rejecting the shipment is $1 - f(0)$.

a. $n = 3, x = 0$

$f(0) = \dfrac{\dbinom{2}{0}\dbinom{8}{3}}{\dbinom{10}{3}} = \dfrac{56}{120} = .4667$

$P\text{ (Reject)} = 1 - .4667 = .5333$

b. $n = 4, x = 0$

$f(0) = \dfrac{\dbinom{2}{0}\dbinom{8}{4}}{\dbinom{10}{4}} = \dfrac{70}{210} = .3333$

$P\text{ (Reject)} = 1 - .3333 = .6667$

c. $n = 5, x = 0$

$f(0) = \dfrac{\dbinom{2}{0}\dbinom{8}{5}}{\dbinom{10}{5}} = \dfrac{56}{252} = .2222$

$P\text{ (Reject)} = 1 - .2222 = .7778$

d. Continue the process. $n = 7$ would be required with the probability of rejecting $= .9333$

53. a., b. and c.

x	$f(x)$	$xf(x)$	$x - \mu$	$(x - \mu)^2$	$(x - \mu)^2 f(x)$
1	0.18	0.18	-2.30	5.29	0.9522
2	0.18	0.36	-1.30	1.69	0.6084
3	0.03	0.09	-0.30	0.09	0.0081
4	0.38	1.52	0.70	0.49	0.7448
5	0.23	1.15	1.70	2.89	3.3235
	1.00	3.30			5.6370

$$E(x) = \mu = 3.30 \qquad \sigma^2 = 5.6370$$

$$\sigma = \sqrt{5.6370} = 2.3742$$

54. a. and b.

x	$f(x)$	$xf(x)$	$x - \mu$	$(x - \mu)^2$	$(x - \mu)^2 f(x)$
1	0.02	0.02	-2.64	6.9696	0.139392
2	0.06	0.12	-1.64	2.6896	0.161376
3	0.28	0.84	-0.64	0.4096	0.114688
4	0.54	2.16	0.36	0.1296	0.069984
5	0.10	0.50	1.36	1.8496	0.184960
	1.00	3.64			0.670400

$f(x) \geq 0$ and $\Sigma f(x) = 1$

$E(x) = \mu = 3.64$

$\text{Var}(x) = \sigma^2 = 0.6704$

c. People do appear to believe the stock market is overvalued. The average response is slightly over halfway between " fairly valued" and " somewhat over valued."

55. a.

x	$f(x)$
9	.30
10	.20
11	.25
12	.05
13	.20

b. $E(x) = \Sigma x f(x)$

$= 9(.30) + 10(.20) + 11(.25) + 12(.05) + 13(.20) = 10.65$

Expected value of expenses: $10.65 million

c. $\text{Var}(x) = \Sigma(x - \mu)^2 f(x)$

$= (9 - 10.65)^2(.30) + (10 - 10.65)^2(.20) + (11 - 10.65)^2(.25)$
$\quad + (12 - 10.65)^2(.05) + (13 - 10.65)^2(.20)$

$= 2.1275$

d. Looks Good: $E(\text{Profit}) = 12 - 10.65 = 1.35$ million

However, there is a .20 probability that expenses will equal $13 million and the college will run a deficit.

56. a. $n = 20$ and $x = 3$

$$f(3) = \binom{20}{3}(0.04)^3(0.04)^{17} = 0.0364$$

b. $n = 20$ and $x = 0$

$$f(0) = \binom{20}{0}(0.04)^0 (0.96)^{20} = 0.4420$$

c. $E(x) = np = 1200\,(0.04) = 48$

The expected number of appeals is 48.

d. $\sigma^2 = np(1 - p) = 1200\,(0.04)(0.96) = 46.08$

$\sigma = \sqrt{46.08} = 6.7882$

57. a. We must have $E(x) = np \geq 10$

With $p = .4$, this leads to:
$n(.4) \geq 10$
$n \geq 25$

b. With $p = .12$, this leads to:
$n(.12) \geq 10$
$n \geq 83.33$

So, we must contact 84 people in this age group to have an expected number of internet users of at least 10.

c. $\sigma = \sqrt{25(.4)(.6)} = 2.45$

d. $\sigma = \sqrt{25(.12)(.88)} = 1.62$

58. Since the shipment is large we can assume that the probabilities do not change from trial to trial and use the binomial probability distribution.

a. $n = 5$

$$f(0) = \binom{5}{0}(0.01)^0 (0.99)^5 = 0.9510$$

b. $f(1) = \binom{5}{1}(0.01)^1 (0.99)^4 = 0.0480$

c. $1 - f(0) = 1 - .9510 = .0490$

d. No, the probability of finding one or more items in the sample defective when only 1% of the items in the population are defective is small (only .0490). I would consider it likely that more than 1% of the items are defective.

59. a. $E(x) = np = 100(.041) = 4.1$

b. $Var(x) = np(1 - p) = 100(.041)(.959) = 3.9319$

$\sigma = \sqrt{3.9319} = 1.9829$

60. a. $E(x) = 800(.41) = 328$

b. $\sigma = \sqrt{np(1-p)} = \sqrt{800(.41)(.59)} = 13.91$

c. For this one $p = .59$ and $(1-p) = .41$, but the answer is the same as in part (b). For a binomial probability distribution, the variance for the number of successes is the same as the variance for the number of failures. Of course, this also holds true for the standard deviation.

61. $\mu = 15$

prob of 20 or more arrivals $= f(20) + f(21) + \cdots$

$$= .0418 + .0299 + .0204 + .0133 + .0083 + .0050 + .0029$$
$$+ .0016 + .0009 + .0004 + .0002 + .0001 + .0001 = .1249$$

62. $\mu = 1.5$

prob of 3 or more breakdowns is $1 - [f(0) + f(1) + f(2)]$.

$1 - [f(0) + f(1) + f(2)]$

$= 1 - [.2231 + .3347 + .2510]$

$= 1 - .8088$

$= .1912$

63. $\mu = 10 \quad f(4) = .0189$

64. a. $f(3) = \dfrac{3^3 e^{-3}}{3!} = 0.2240$

b. $f(3) + f(4) + \cdots = 1 - [f(0) + f(1) + f(2)]$

$f(0) = \dfrac{3^0 e^{-3}}{0!} = e^{-3} = .0498$

Similarly, $f(1) = .1494, f(2) = .2240$

$\therefore 1 - [.0498 + .1494 + .2241] = .5767$

65. Hypergeometric $N = 52, n = 5$ and $r = 4$.

a. $\dfrac{\binom{4}{2}\binom{48}{3}}{\binom{52}{5}} = \dfrac{6(17296)}{2,598,960} = .0399$

b. $\dfrac{\binom{4}{1}\binom{48}{4}}{\binom{52}{5}} = \dfrac{4(194580)}{2,598,960} = .2995$

c. $\dfrac{\dbinom{4}{0}\dbinom{48}{5}}{\dbinom{52}{5}} = \dfrac{1,712,304}{2,598,960} = .6588$

d. $1 - f(0) = 1 - .6588 = .3412$

66. Use the Hypergeometric probability distribution with $N = 10$, $n = 2$, and $r = 4$.

a. $f(1)\dfrac{\dbinom{4}{1}\dbinom{6}{1}}{\dbinom{10}{2}} = \dfrac{(4)(6)}{45} = .5333$

b. $f(2)\dfrac{\dbinom{4}{2}\dbinom{6}{0}}{\dbinom{10}{2}} = \dfrac{(6)(1)}{45} = .1333$

c. $f(0)\dfrac{\dbinom{4}{0}\dbinom{6}{2}}{\dbinom{10}{2}} = \dfrac{(1)(15)}{45} = .3333$

Chapter 6
Continuous Probability Distributions

Learning Objectives

1. Understand the difference between how probabilities are computed for discrete and continuous random variables.

2. Know how to compute probability values for a continuous uniform probability distribution and be able to compute the expected value and variance for such a distribution.

3. Be able to compute probabilities using a normal probability distribution. Understand the role of the standard normal distribution in this process.

4. Be able to compute probabilities using an exponential probability distribution.

5. Understand the relationship between the Poisson and exponential probability distributions.

Solutions:

1. a.

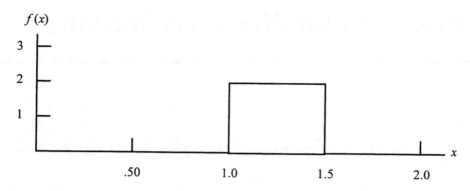

b. $P(x = 1.25) = 0$. The probability of any single point is zero since the area under the curve above any single point is zero.

c. $P(1.0 \leq x \leq 1.25) = 2(.25) = .50$

d. $P(1.20 < x < 1.5) = 2(.30) = .60$

2. a.

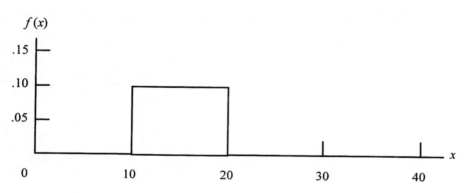

b. $P(x < 15) = .10(5) = .50$

c. $P(12 \leq x \leq 18) = .10(6) = .60$

d. $E(x) = \dfrac{10 + 20}{2} = 15$

e. $\text{Var}(x) = \dfrac{(20 - 10)^2}{12} = 8.33$

3. a.

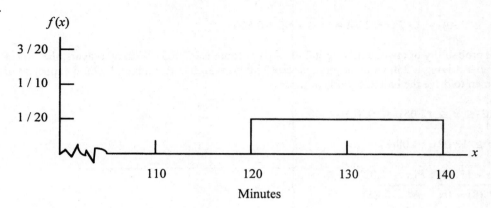

Minutes

b. $P(x \leq 130) = (1/20)(130 - 120) = 0.50$

c. $P(x > 135) = (1/20)(140 - 135) = 0.25$

d. $E(x) = \dfrac{120+140}{2} = 130$ minutes

4. a.

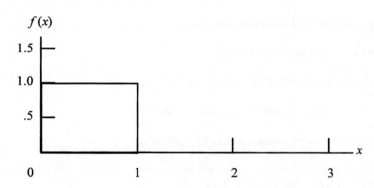

b. $P(.25 < x < .75) = 1(.50) = .50$

c. $P(x \leq .30) = 1(.30) = .30$

d. $P(x > .60) = 1(.40) = .40$

5. a. Length of Interval $= 261.2 - 238.9 = 22.3$

$$f(x) = \begin{cases} \dfrac{1}{22.3} & \text{for } 238.9 \leq x \leq 261.2 \\ 0 & \text{elsewhere} \end{cases}$$

b. Note: $1 / 22.3 = 0.045$

$P(x < 250) = (0.045)(250 - 238.9) = 0.4995$

Almost half drive the ball less than 250 yards.

c. $P(x \geq 255) = (0.045)(261.2 - 255) = 0.279$

d. $P(245 \leq x \leq 260) = (0.045)(260 - 245) = 0.675$

e. $P(x \geq 250) = 1 - P(x < 250) = 1 - 0.4995 = 0.5005$

The probability of anyone driving it 250 yards or more is 0.5005. With 60 players, the expected number driving it 250 yards or more is $(60)(0.5005) = 30.03$. Rounding, I would expect 30 of these women to drive the ball 250 yards or more.

6. a. $P(12 \leq x \leq 12.05) = .05(8) = .40$

b. $P(x \geq 12.02) = .08(8) = .64$

c. $\underbrace{P(x < 11.98)}_{.005(8) = .04} + \underbrace{P(x > 12.02)}_{.64 = .08(8)}$

Therefore, the probability is $.04 + .64 = .68$

7. a. $P(10,000 \leq x < 12,000) = 2000 (1 / 5000) = .40$

The probability your competitor will bid lower than you, and you get the bid, is .40.

b. $P(10,000 \leq x < 14,000) = 4000 (1 / 5000) = .80$

c. A bid of $15,000 gives a probability of 1 of getting the property.

d. Yes, the bid that maximizes expected profit is $13,000.

The probability of getting the property with a bid of $13,000 is

$$P(10,000 \leq x < 13,000) = 3000 (1 / 5000) = .60.$$

The probability of not getting the property with a bid of $13,000 is .40.

The profit you will make if you get the property with a bid of $13,000 is $3000 = $16,000 - 13,000. So your expected profit with a bid of $13,000 is

$$EP (\$13,000) = .6 (\$3000) + .4 (0) = \$1800.$$

If you bid $15,000 the probability of getting the bid is 1, but the profit if you do get the bid is only $1000 = $16,000 - 15,000. So your expected profit with a bid of $15,000 is

$$EP (\$15,000) = 1 (\$1000) + 0 (0) = \$1,000.$$

8.

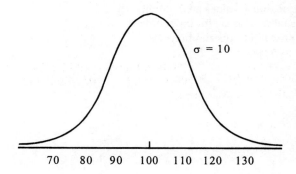

9.   a.

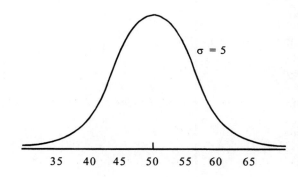

   b.   .6826 since 45 and 55 are within plus or minus 1 standard deviation from the mean of 50.

   c.   .9544 since 40 and 60 are within plus or minus 2 standard deviations from the mean of 50.

10.

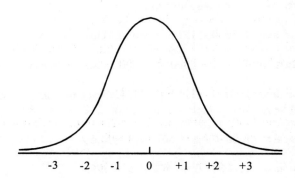

   a.   .3413

   b.   .4332

   c.   .4772

   d.   .4938

11. a. .3413   These probability values are read directly
from the table of areas for the standard

    b. .4332   normal probability distribution. See
Table 1 in Appendix B.

    c. .4772

    d. .4938

    e. .4986

12. a. .2967

    b. .4418

    c. .5000 - .1700 = .3300

    d. .0910 + .5000 = .5910

    e. .3849 + .5000 = .8849

    f. .5000 - .2612 = .2388

13. a. .6879 - .0239 = .6640

    b. .8888 - .6985 = .1903

    c. .9599 - .8508 = .1091

14. a. Using the table of areas for the standard normal probability distribution, the area of .4750 corresponds to $z = 1.96$.

    b. Using the table, the area of .2291 corresponds to $z = .61$.

    c. Look in the table for an area of .5000 - .1314 = .3686. This provides $z = 1.12$.

    d. Look in the table for an area of .6700 - .5000 = .1700. This provides $z = .44$.

15. a. Look in the table for an area of .5000 - .2119 = .2881. Since the value we are seeking is below the mean, the z value must be negative. Thus, for an area of .2881, $z = -.80$.

    b. Look in the table for an area of .9030 / 2 = .4515; $z = 1.66$.

    c. Look in the table for an area of .2052 / 2 = .1026; $z = .26$.

    d. Look in the table for an area of .4948; $z = 2.56$.

    e. Look in the table for an area of .1915. Since the value we are seeking is below the mean, the z value must be negative. Thus, $z = -.50$.

16. a. Look in the table for an area of .5000 - .0100 = .4900. The area value in the table closest to .4900 provides the value $z = 2.33$.

    b. Look in the table for an area of .5000 - .0250 = .4750. This corresponds to $z = 1.96$.

c. Look in the table for an area of .5000 - .0500 = .4500. Since .4500 is exactly halfway between .4495 (z = 1.64) and .4505 (z = 1.65), we select z = 1.645. However, z = 1.64 or z = 1.65 are also acceptable answers.

d. Look in the table for an area of .5000 - .1000 = .4000. The area value in the table closest to .4000 provides the value z = 1.28.

17. Convert mean to inches: $\mu = 69$

   a. At x = 72

$$z = \frac{72 - 69}{3} = 1$$

$$P(x \leq 72) = 0.5000 + 0.3413 = 0.8413$$

$$P(x > 72) = 1 - 0.8413 = 0.1587$$

   b. At x = 60

$$z = \frac{60 - 69}{3} = -3$$

$$P(x \geq 60) = 0.5000 + 0.4986 = 0.9986$$

$$P(x < 60) = 1 - 0.9986 = 0.0014$$

   c. At x = 70

$$z = \frac{70 - 69}{3} = 0.33$$

$$P(x \leq 70) = 0.5000 + 0.1293 = 0.6293$$

   At x = 66

$$z = \frac{66 - 69}{3} = -1$$

$$P(x \leq 66) = 0.5000 - 0.3413 = 0.1587$$

$P(66 \leq x \leq 70) = P(x \leq 70) - P(x \leq 66) = 0.6293 - 0.1587 = 0.4706$

   d. $P(x \leq 72) = 1 - P(x > 72) = 1 - 0.1587 = 0.8413$

18. a. Find $P(x \geq 60)$

   At x = 60

$$z = \frac{60 - 49}{16} = 0.69$$

$$P(x < 60) = 0.5000 + 0.2549 = 0.7549$$
$$P(x \geq 60) = 1 - P(x < 60) = 0.2451$$

   b. Find $P(x \leq 30)$

   At x = 30

$$z = \frac{30 - 49}{16} = -1.19$$

$$P(x \leq 30) = 0.5000 - 0.3830 = 0.1170$$

   c. Find z-score so that $P(z \geq z\text{-score}) = 0.10$

   z-score = 1.28 cuts off 10% in upper tail

   Now, solve for corresponding value of x.

$$1.28 = \frac{x - 49}{16}$$

$x = 49 + (16)(1.28) = 69.48$

So, 10% of subscribers spend 69.48 minutes or more reading *The Wall Street Journal*.

19.   We have $\mu = 3.5$ and $\sigma = .8$.

a. $z = \dfrac{5.0 - 3.5}{.8} \approx 1.88$

$P(x > 5.0) = P(z > 1.88) = 1 - P(z < 1.88) = 1 - .9699 = .0301$

The rainfall exceeds 5 inches in 3.01% of the Aprils.

b. $z = \dfrac{3 - 3.5}{.8} \approx -.63$

$P(x < 3.0) = P(z < -.63) = P(z > .63) = 1 - P(z < .63) = 1 - .7357 = .2643$

The rainfall is less than 3 inches in 26.43% of the Aprils.

c. $z = 1.28$ cuts off approximately .10 in the upper tail of a normal distribution.

$x = 3.5 + 1.28(.8) = 4.524$

If it rains 4.524 inches or more, April will be classified as extremely wet.

20.   We use $\mu = 27$ and $\sigma = 8$

a. $z = \dfrac{11 - 27}{8} = -2$

$P(x \leq 11) = P(z \leq -2) = .5000 - .4772 = .0228$

The probability a randomly selected subscriber spends less than 11 hours on the computer is .025.

b. $z = \dfrac{40 - 27}{8} \approx 1.63$

$P(x > 40) = P(z > 1.63) = 1 - P(z \leq 1.63) = 1 - .9484 = .0516$

5.16% of subscribers spend over 40 hours per week using the computer.

c.   A z-value of .84 cuts off an area of .20 in the upper tail.

$x = 27 + .84(8) = 33.72$

A subscriber who uses the computer 33.72 hours or more would be classified as a heavy user.

21.   From the normal probability tables, a z-value of 2.05 cuts off an area of approximately .02 in the upper tail of the distribution.

$$x = \mu + z\sigma = 100 + 2.05(15) = 130.75$$

A score of 131 or better should qualify a person for membership in Mensa.

22.   Use $\mu = 441.84$ and $\sigma = 90$

   a.   At 400

$$z = \frac{400 - 441.84}{90} \approx -.46$$

At 500

$$z = \frac{500 - 441.84}{90} \approx .65$$

$$P(0 \leq z < .65) = .2422$$
$$P(-.46 \leq z < 0) = .1772$$
$$P(400 \leq z \leq 500) = .1772 + .2422 = .4194$$

The probability a worker earns between $400 and $500 is .4194.

   b.   Must find the z-value that cuts off an area of .20 in the upper tail. Using the normal tables, we find $z = .84$ cuts off approximately .20 in the upper tail.

So, $x = \mu + z\sigma = 441.84 + .84(90) = 517.44$

Weekly earnings of $517.44 or above will put a production worker in the top 20%.

   c.   At 250, $z = \dfrac{250 - 441.84}{90} \approx -2.13$

$$P(x \leq 250) = P(z \leq -2.13) = .5000 - .4834 = .0166$$

The probability a randomly selected production worker earns less than $250 per week is .0166.

23. a. $z = \dfrac{60 - 80}{10} = -2$ Area to left is .5000 - .4772 = .0228

   b.   At $x = 60$

$$z = \frac{60 - 80}{10} = -2 \quad \text{Area to left is .0228}$$

At $x = 75$

$$z = \frac{75 - 80}{10} = -.5 \quad \text{Area to left is .3085}$$

$$P(60 \leq x \leq 75) = .3085 - .0228 = .2857$$

   c. $z = \dfrac{90 - 80}{10} = 1$ Area = .5000 - .3413 = .1587

Therefore 15.87% of students will not complete on time.

$$(60)\,(.1587)\ =\ 9.522$$

We would expect 9.522 students to be unable to complete the exam in time.

24. a. $\bar{x} = \sum \dfrac{x_i}{n} = 902.75$

$$s = \sqrt{\dfrac{\sum (x_i - \bar{x})^2}{n-1}} = 114.185$$

We will use $\bar{x}$ as an estimate of μ and s as an estimate of σ in parts (b) - (d) below.

 b.   Remember the data are in thousands of shares.

At 800

$$z = \dfrac{800 - 902.75}{114.185} \approx -.90$$

$$P(x \le 800) = P(z \le -.90) = 1 - P(z \le .90) = 1 - .8159 = .1841$$

The probability trading volume will be less than 800 million shares is .1841

 c.   At 1000

$$z = \dfrac{1000 - 902.75}{114.185} \approx .85$$

$$P(x \ge 1000) = P(z \ge .85) = 1 - P(z \le .85) = 1 - .8023 = .1977$$

The probability trading volume will exceed 1 billion shares is .1977

 d.   A z-value of 1.645 cuts off an area of .05 in the upper tail

$x = \mu + z\sigma = 902.75 + 1.645(114.185) = 1{,}090.584$

They should issue a press release any time share volume exceeds 1,091 million.

25. a.   Find $P(x > 100)$

At $x = 100$

$$z = \dfrac{100 - 110}{20} = -0.5$$

$$P(x > 100) = P(z \le .5) = 0.6915$$

 b.   Find $P(x \le 90)$

At $x = 90$

$$z = \dfrac{90 - 110}{20} = -1$$

$$P(x \le 90) = .5000 - .3413 = 0.1587$$

c. Find $P(80 \leq x \leq 130)$

At $x = 130$

$$z = \frac{130 - 110}{20} = 1$$

$P(x \leq 130) = 0.8413$

At $x = 80$

$$z = \frac{80 - 110}{20} = -1.5 \quad \text{Area to left is } .0668$$

$P(80 \leq x \leq 130) = .8413 - .0668 = .7745$

26. a. $P(x \leq 6) = 1 - e^{-6/8} = 1 - .4724 = .5276$

b. $P(x \leq 4) = 1 - e^{-4/8} = 1 - .6065 = .3935$

c. $P(x \geq 6) = 1 - P(x \leq 6) = 1 - .5276 = .4724$

d. $P(4 \leq x \leq 6) = P(x \leq 6) - P(x \leq 4) = .5276 - .3935 = .1341$

27. a. $P(x \leq x_0) = 1 - e^{-x_0/3}$

b. $P(x \leq 2) = 1 - e^{-2/3} = 1 - .5134 = .4866$

c. $P(x \geq 3) = 1 - P(x \leq 3) = 1 - (1 - e^{-3/3}) = e^{-1} = .3679$

d. $P(x \leq 5) = 1 - e^{-5/3} = 1 - .1889 = .8111$

e. $P(2 \leq x \leq 5) = P(x \leq 5) - P(x \leq 2) \quad = .8111 - .4866 = .3245$

28. a. $P(x < 10) = 1 - e^{-10/20} = .3935$

b. $P(x > 30) = 1 - P(x \leq 30) = 1 - (1 - e^{-30/20}) = e^{-30/20} = .2231$

c. $P(10 \leq x \leq 30) = P(x \leq 30) - P(x \leq 10)$
$= (1 - e^{-30/20}) - (1 - e^{-10/20})$
$= e^{-10/20} - e^{-30/20}$
$= .6065 - .2231 = .3834$

29. a.

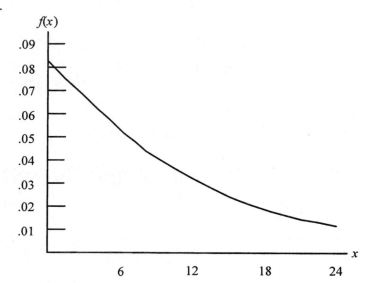

b. $P(x \leq 12) = 1 - e^{-12/12} = 1 - .3679 = .6321$

c. $P(x \leq 6) = 1 - e^{-6/12} = 1 - .6065 = .3935$

d. $P(x \geq 30) = 1 - P(x < 30)$

$$= 1 - (1 - e^{-30/12})$$

$$= .0821$$

30. a. 50 hours

b. $P(x \leq 25) = 1 - e^{-25/50} = 1 - .6065 = .3935$

c. $P(x \geq 100) = 1 - (1 - e^{-100/50})$

$$= .1353$$

31. a. $P(x < 2) = 1 - e^{-2/2.78} = .5130$

b. $P(x > 5) = 1 - P(x \leq 5) = 1 - (1 - e^{-5/2.78}) = e^{-5/2.78} = .1655$

c. $P(x > 2.78) = 1 - P(x \leq 2.78) = 1 - (1 - e^{-2.78/2.78}) = e^{-1} = .3679$

This may seem surprising since the mean is 2.78 minutes. But, for the exponential distribution, the probability of a value greater than the mean is significantly less than the probability of a value less than the mean.

32. a. If the average number of transactions per year follows the Poisson distribution, the time between transactions follows the exponential distribution. So,

$$\mu = \frac{1}{30} \text{ of a year}$$

and $\dfrac{1}{\mu} = \dfrac{1}{1/30} = 30$

then f(x) = 30 e^{-30x}

    b.   A month is 1/12 of a year so,

$$P\left(x > \frac{1}{12}\right) = 1 - P\left(x \le \frac{1}{12}\right) = 1 - (1 - e^{-30/12}) = e^{-30/12} = .0821$$

The probability of no transaction during January is the same as the probability of no transaction during any month: .0821

    c.   Since 1/2 month is 1/24 of a year, we compute,

$$P\left(x \le \frac{1}{24}\right) = 1 - e^{-30/24} = 1 - .2865 = .7135$$

33. a.   Let x = sales price ($1000s)

$$f(x) = \begin{cases} \dfrac{1}{25} & \text{for } 200 \le x \le 225 \\ 0 & \text{elsewhere} \end{cases}$$

    b. $P(x \ge 215) = (1/25)(225 - 215) = 0.40$

    c. $P(x < 210) = (1/25)(210 - 200) = 0.40$

    d. $E(x) = (200 + 225)/2 = 212,500$

If she waits, her expected sale price will be $2,500 higher than if she sells it back to her company now. However, there is a 0.40 probability that she will get less. It's a close call. But, the expected value approach to decision making would suggest she should wait.

34. a.   For a normal distribution, the mean and the median are equal.

$$\mu = 63,000$$

    b.   Find the z-score that cuts off 10% in the lower tail.

$$z\text{-score} = -1.28$$

Solving for x,

$$-1.28 = \frac{x - 63,000}{15,000}$$
$$x = 63,000 - 1.28 (15000)$$
$$= 43,800$$

The lower 10% of mortgage debt is $43,800 or less.

c. Find $P(x > 80,000)$

   At $x = 80,000$

$$z = \frac{80,000 - 63,000}{15,000} = 1.13$$

   $P(x > 80,000) = 1.0000 - .8708 = 0.1292$

d. Find the z-score that cuts off 5% in the upper tail.

   z-score $= 1.645$. Solve for x.

$$1.645 = \frac{x - 63,000}{15,000}$$

$$x = 63,000 + 1.645 \,(15,000)$$

$$= 87,675$$

   The upper 5% of mortgage debt is in excess of $87,675.

35. a. $P(defect)$ $= 1 - P(9.85 \leq x \leq 10.15)$

$$= 1 - P(-1 \leq z \leq 1)$$

$$= 1 - .6826$$

$$= .3174$$

   Expected number of defects $= 1000(.3174) = 317.4$

   b. $P(defect) = 1 - P(9.85 \leq x \leq 10.15)$

$$= 1 - P(-3 \leq z \leq 3)$$

$$= 1 - .9972$$

$$= .0028$$

   Expected number of defects $= 1000(.0028) = 2.8$

   c. Reducing the process standard deviation causes a substantial reduction in the number of defects.

36. a. At 11%, $z = -1.23$

$$-1.23 = \frac{x - \mu}{\sigma} = \frac{1800 - 2071}{\sigma}$$

   Therefore, $\sigma = \frac{1800 - 2071}{-1.23} = \$220.33$

   b. $z = \frac{2000 - 2071}{220.33} = -.32$ Area to left is $.5000 - .3255 = .3745$

$$z = \frac{2500 - 2071}{220.33} = 1.95 \quad \text{Area to left is .9744}$$

$P(2000 \le x \le 2500) = .9744 - .3745 = .5999$

c. $z = -1.88$

$x = 2071 - 1.88\,(220.33) = \$1656.78$

37. $\mu = 10,000 \quad \sigma = 1500$

a. At $x = 12,000$

$$z = \frac{12,000 - 10,000}{1500} = 1.33 \quad \text{Area to left is .9082}$$

$P(x > 12,000) = 1.0000 - .9082 = .0918$

b. At .95

$$z = 1.645 = \frac{x - 10,000}{1500}$$

Therefore, $x = 10,000 + 1.645(1500) = 12,468.$

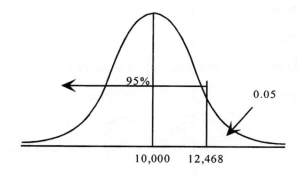

12,468 tubes should be produced.

38. a. At $x = 200$

$$z = \frac{200 - 150}{25} = 2 \quad \text{Area} = .4772$$

$P(x > 200) = .5 - .4772 = .0228$

b. Expected Profit = Expected Revenue - Expected Cost

$= 200 - 150 = \$50$

39. a. Find $P(80,000 \le x \le 150,000)$

At $x = 150,000$

$$z = \frac{150,000 - 126,681}{30,000} = 0.78$$

$P(x \le 150,000) = 0.7823$

At $x = 80,000$

$$z = \frac{80,000 - 126,681}{30,000} = -1.56$$

$P(x \le 80,000) = .5000 - .4406 = 0.0594$

$P(80,000 \le x \le 150,000) = 0.7823 - 0.0594 = 0.7229$

b. Find $P(x < 50,000)$

At $x = 50,000$

$$z = \frac{50,000 - 126,681}{30,000} = -2.56$$

$P(x < 50,000) = .5000 - .4948 = 0.0052$

c. Find the z-score cutting off 95% in the left tail.

z-score $= 1.645$. Solve for x.

$$1.645 = \frac{x - 126,681}{30,000}$$

$$x = 126,681 + 1.645 (30,000)$$

$$= 176,031$$

The probability is 0.95 that the number of lost jobs will not exceed 176,031.

40. a. At 400,

$$z = \frac{400 - 450}{100} = -.500$$

Area to left is .3085

At 500,

$$z = \frac{500 - 450}{100} = +.500$$

Area to left is .6915

$P(400 \le x \le 500) = .6915 - .3085 = .3830$

38.3% will score between 400 and 500.

b. At 630,

$$z = \frac{630 - 450}{100} = 1.80$$

96.41% do worse and 3.59% do better .

c. At 480,

$$z = \frac{480 - 450}{100} = .30$$

Area to left is .6179

38.21% are acceptable.

41. a. At 75,000

$$z = \frac{75,000 - 67,000}{7,000} \approx 1.14$$

$$P(x > 75,000) = P(z > 1.14) = 1 - P(z \leq 1.14) = 1 - .8729 = .1271$$

The probability of a woman receiving a salary in excess of $75,000 is .1271

b. At 75,000

$$z = \frac{75,000 - 65,500}{7,000} \approx 1.36$$

$$P(x > 75,000) = P(z > 1.36) = 1 - P(z \leq 1.36) = 1 - .9131 = .0869$$

The probability of a man receiving a salary in excess of $75,000 is .0869

c. At $x = 50,000$

$$z = \frac{50,000 - 67,000}{7,000} \approx -2.43$$

$$P(x < 50,000) = P(z < -2.43) = 1 - P(z < 2.43) = 1 - .9925 = .0075$$

The probability of a woman receiving a salary below $50,000 is very small: .0075

d. The answer to this is the male copywriter salary that cuts off an area of .01 in the upper tail of the distribution for male copywriters.

Use $z = 2.33$

$x = 65,500 + 2.33(7,000) = 81,810$

A woman who makes $81,810 or more will earn more than 99% of her male counterparts.

42. $\sigma = .6$

At 2%

$$z = -2.05 \quad x = 18$$

$$z = \frac{x - \mu}{\sigma} \qquad \therefore -2.05 = \frac{18 - \mu}{.6}$$

$$\mu = 18 + 2.05\,(.6) = 19.23 \text{ oz.}$$

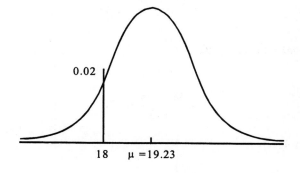

The mean filling weight must be 19.23 oz.

43. a. $P(x \leq 15) = 1 - e^{-15/36} = 1 - .6592 = .3408$

    b. $P(x \leq 45) = 1 - e^{-45/36} = 1 - .2865 = .7135$

    Therefore $P(15 \leq x \leq 45) = .7135 - .3408 = .3727$

    c. $P(x \geq 60) = 1 - P(x < 60)$

    $$= 1 - (1 - e^{-60/36}) = .1889$$

44. a. 4 hours

    b. $f(x) = (1/4) e^{-x/4}$ for $x \geq 0$

    c. $P(x \geq 1) = 1 - P(x < 1) = 1 - (1 - e^{-1/4}) = .7788$

    d. $P(x > 8) = 1 - P(x \leq 8) = e^{-8/4} = .1353$

45. a. $f(x) = \dfrac{1}{1.2} e^{-x/1.2}$ for $x \geq 0$

    b. $P(.5 \leq x \leq 1.0) = P(x \leq 1.0) - P(x \leq .5) = (1 - e^{-1/1.2}) - (1 - e^{-.5/1.2})$

    $$= .5654 - .3408 = .2246$$

    c. $P(x > 1) = 1 - P(x \leq 1) = 1 - .5654 = .4346$

46. a. $\dfrac{1}{\mu} = 0.5$ therefore $\mu = 2$ minutes = mean time between telephone calls

    b. Note: 30 seconds = .5 minutes

    $P(x \leq .5) = 1 - e^{-.5/2} = 1 - .7788 = .2212$

    c. $P(x \leq 1) = 1 - e^{-1/2} = 1 - .6065 = .3935$

    d. $P(x \geq 5) = 1 - P(x < 5) = 1 - (1 - e^{-5/2}) = .0821$

Chapter 7
Sampling and Sampling Distributions

Learning Objectives

1.   Understand the importance of sampling and how results from samples can be used to provide estimates of population characteristics such as the population mean, the population standard deviation and / or the population proportion.

2.   Know what simple random sampling is and how simple random samples are selected.

3.   Understand the concept of a sampling distribution.

4.   Know the central limit theorem and the important role it plays in sampling.

5.   Specifically know the characteristics of the sampling distribution of the sample mean ($\bar{x}$) and the sampling distribution of the sample proportion ($\bar{p}$).

6.   Become aware of the properties of point estimators including unbiasedness, consistency, and efficiency.

7.   Learn about a variety of sampling methods including stratified random sampling, cluster sampling, systematic sampling, convenience sampling and judgment sampling.

8.   Know the definition of the following terms:

simple random sampling	finite population correction factor
sampling with replacement	standard error
sampling without replacement	unbiasedness
sampling distribution	consistency
point estimator	efficiency

Solutions:

1. a.   AB, AC, AD, AE, BC, BD, BE, CD, CE, DE

    b.   With 10 samples, each has a 1/10 probability.

    c.   E and C because 8 and 0 do not apply.; 5 identifies E; 7 does not apply; 5 is skipped since E is already in the sample; 3 identifies C; 2 is not needed since the sample of size 2 is complete.

2.   Using the last 3-digits of each 5-digit grouping provides the random numbers:

         601, 022, 448, 147, 229, 553, 147, 289, 209

         Numbers greater than 350 do not apply and the 147 can only be used once. Thus, the simple random sample of four includes 22, 147, 229, and 289.

3.   459, 147, 385, 113, 340, 401, 215, 2, 33, 348

4. a.   6,8,5,4,1

         IBM, Microsoft, Intel, General Electric, AT&T

    b. $\dfrac{N!}{n!(N-n)!} = \dfrac{10!}{5!(10-5)!} = \dfrac{3,628,500}{(120)(120)} = 252$

5.   283, 610, 39, 254, 568, 353, 602, 421, 638, 164

6.   2782, 493, 825, 1807, 289

7.   108, 290, 201, 292, 322, 9, 244, 249, 226, 125, (continuing at the top of column 9) 147, and 113.

8.   13, 8, 23, 25, 18, 5

         The second occurrences of random numbers 13 and 25 are ignored.

         Washington, Clemson, Oklahoma, Colorado, USC and Wisconsin

9.   511, 791, 99, 671, 152, 584, 45, 783, 301, 568, 754, 750

10.   finite, infinite, infinite, infinite, finite

11. a. $\bar{x} = \Sigma x_i / n = \dfrac{54}{6} = 9$

    b. $s = \sqrt{\dfrac{\Sigma(x_i - \bar{x})^2}{n-1}}$

         $\Sigma(x_i - \bar{x})^2 = (-4)^2 + (-1)^2 + 1^2 (-2)^2 + 1^2 + 5^2 = 48$

         $s = \sqrt{\dfrac{48}{6-1}} = 3.1$

12. a. $\bar{p} = 75/150 = .50$

    b. $\bar{p} = 55/150 = .3667$

13. a. $\bar{x} = \Sigma x_i / n = \dfrac{465}{5} = 93$

    b.

	x_i	$(x_i - \bar{x})$	$(x_i - \bar{x})^2$
	94	+1	1
	100	+7	49
	85	-8	64
	94	+1	1
	92	-1	1
Totals	465	0	116

$$s = \sqrt{\frac{\Sigma(x_i - \bar{x})^2}{n-1}} = \sqrt{\frac{116}{4}} = 5.39$$

14. a. $149/784 = .19$

    b. $251/784 = .32$

    c. Total receiving cash $= 149 + 219 + 251 = 619$

       $619/784 = .79$

15. a. $\bar{x} = \Sigma x_i / n = \dfrac{700}{10} = 7$ years

    b. $s = \sqrt{\dfrac{\Sigma(x_i - \bar{x})^2}{n-1}} = \sqrt{\dfrac{20.2}{10-1}} = 1.5$ years

16. $\bar{p} = 1117/1400 = .80$

17. a. $595/1008 = .59$

    b. $332/1008 = .33$

    c. $81/1008 = .08$

18. a. $E(\bar{x}) = \mu = 200$

    b. $\sigma_{\bar{x}} = \sigma / \sqrt{n} = 50 / \sqrt{100} = 5$

    c. Normal with $E(\bar{x}) = 200$ and $\sigma_{\bar{x}} = 5$

    d. It shows the probability distribution of all possible sample means that can be observed with random samples of size 100. This distribution can be used to compute the probability that $\bar{x}$ is within a specified $\pm$ from μ.

19. a. The sampling distribution is normal with

$$E(\bar{x}) = \mu = 200$$

$$\sigma_{\bar{x}} = \sigma / \sqrt{n} = 50 / \sqrt{100} = 5$$

For ±5, $(\bar{x} - \mu) = 5$

$$z = \frac{\bar{x} - \mu}{\sigma_{\bar{x}}} = \frac{5}{5} = 1$$

Area = .3413
x2
.6826

b. For ± 10, $(\bar{x} - \mu) = 10$

$$z = \frac{\bar{x} - \mu}{\sigma_{\bar{x}}} = \frac{10}{5} = 2$$

Area = .4772
x2
.9544

20. $\sigma_{\bar{x}} = \sigma / \sqrt{n}$

$$\sigma_{\bar{x}} = 25 / \sqrt{50} = 3.54$$

$$\sigma_{\bar{x}} = 25 / \sqrt{100} = 2.50$$

$$\sigma_{\bar{x}} = 25 / \sqrt{150} = 2.04$$

$$\sigma_{\bar{x}} = 25 / \sqrt{200} = 1.77$$

The standard error of the mean decreases as the sample size increases.

21. a. $\sigma_{\bar{x}} = \sigma / \sqrt{n} = 10 / \sqrt{50} = 1.41$

b. $n / N = 50 / 50,000 = .001$

$$\text{Use } \sigma_{\bar{x}} = \sigma / \sqrt{n} = 10 / \sqrt{50} = 1.41$$

c. $n / N = 50 / 5000 = .01$

$$\text{Use } \sigma_{\bar{x}} = \sigma / \sqrt{n} = 10 / \sqrt{50} = 1.41$$

d. $n / N = 50 / 500 = .10$

$$\text{Use } \sigma_{\bar{x}} = \sqrt{\frac{N-n}{N-1}} \frac{\sigma}{\sqrt{n}} = \sqrt{\frac{500-50}{500-1}} \frac{10}{\sqrt{50}} = 1.34 \text{ Use}$$

Note: Only case (d) where $n / N = .10$ requires the use of the finite population correction factor. Note that $\sigma_{\bar{x}}$ is approximately the same even though the population size varies from infinite to 500.

22. a. Using the central limit theorem, we can approximate the sampling distribution of $\bar{x}$ with a normal probability distribution provided $n \geq 30$.

b. $n = 30$

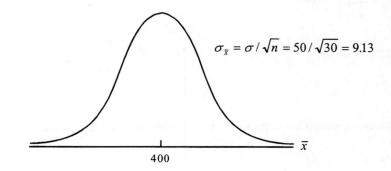

$$\sigma_{\bar{x}} = \sigma / \sqrt{n} = 50 / \sqrt{30} = 9.13$$

$n = 40$

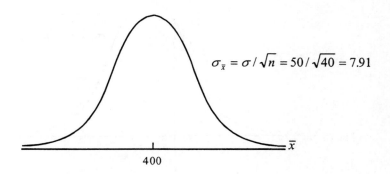

$$\sigma_{\bar{x}} = \sigma / \sqrt{n} = 50 / \sqrt{40} = 7.91$$

23. a. $\sigma_{\bar{x}} = \sigma / \sqrt{n} = 16 / \sqrt{50} = 2.26$

For ± 2, $(\bar{x} - \mu) = 2$

$$z = \frac{\bar{x} - \mu}{\sigma_{\bar{x}}} = \frac{2}{2.26} = 0.88$$

Area = .3106
x2
.6212

b. $\sigma_{\bar{x}} = \frac{16}{\sqrt{100}} = 1.60$

$$z = \frac{\bar{x} - \mu}{\sigma_{\bar{x}}} = \frac{2}{1.60} = 1.25$$

Area = .3944
x2
.7888

c. $\sigma_{\bar{x}} = \frac{16}{\sqrt{200}} = 1.13$

$$z = \frac{\bar{x} - \mu}{\sigma_{\bar{x}}} = \frac{2}{1.13} = 1.77$$

Area = .4616
x2
.9232

d. $\quad \sigma_{\bar{x}} = \dfrac{16}{\sqrt{400}} = 0.80$

$$z = \frac{\bar{x} - \mu}{\sigma_{\bar{x}}} = \frac{2}{0.80} = 2.50$$

Area = .4938
x2
.9876

e. The larger sample provides a higher probability that the sample mean will be within ± 2 of μ.

24. a.

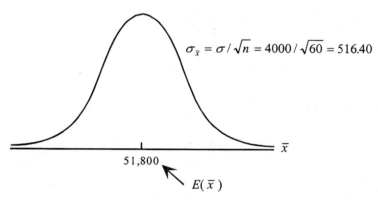

$\sigma_{\bar{x}} = \sigma / \sqrt{n} = 4000 / \sqrt{60} = 516.40$

51,800

$E(\bar{x})$

The normal distribution is based on the Central Limit Theorem.

b. For $n = 120$, $E(\bar{x})$ remains \$51,800 and the sampling distribution of $\bar{x}$ can still be approximated by a normal distribution. However, $\sigma_{\bar{x}}$ is reduced to $4000 / \sqrt{120} = 365.15$.

c. As the sample size is increased, the standard error of the mean, $\sigma_{\bar{x}}$, is reduced. This appears logical from the point of view that larger samples should tend to provide sample means that are closer to the population mean. Thus, the variability in the sample mean, measured in terms of $\sigma_{\bar{x}}$, should decrease as the sample size is increased.

25. a.

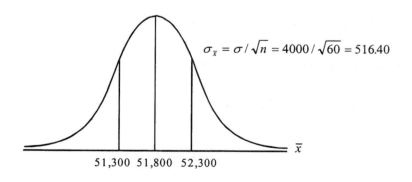

$\sigma_{\bar{x}} = \sigma / \sqrt{n} = 4000 / \sqrt{60} = 516.40$

51,300 51,800 52,300

$$z = \frac{52,300 - 51,800}{516.40} = +.97$$

Area = .3340
x2
.6680

b. $\sigma_{\bar{x}} = \sigma / \sqrt{n} = 4000 / \sqrt{120} = 365.15$

$$z = \frac{52,300 - 51,800}{365.15} = +1.37$$

Area
.4147
x2
.8294

26. a. A normal distribution

$$E(\bar{x}) = 1.20$$

$$\sigma_{\bar{x}} = \sigma / \sqrt{n} = 0.10 / \sqrt{50} = 0.014$$

b. $z = \dfrac{1.22 - 1.20}{0.014} = 1.41$ Area = 0.4207

$z = \dfrac{1.18 - 1.20}{0.014} = -1.41$ Area = 0.4207

probability = 0.4207 + 0.4207 = 0.8414

c. $z = \dfrac{1.21 - 1.20}{0.014} = +0.71$ Area = 0.2612

$z = \dfrac{1.19 - 1.20}{0.014} = -0.71$ Area = 0.2612

probability = 0.2612 + 0.2612 = 0.5224

27. a. $E(\bar{x}) = 1017$

$\sigma_{\bar{x}} = \sigma / \sqrt{n} = 100 / \sqrt{75} = 11.55$

b. $z = \dfrac{1027 - 1017}{11.55} = 0.87$ Area = 0.3078

$z = \dfrac{1007 - 1017}{11.55} = -0.87$ Area = 0.3078

probability = 0.3078 + 0.3078 = 0.6156

c. $z = \dfrac{1037 - 1017}{11.55} = 1.73$ Area = 0.4582

$z = \dfrac{997 - 1017}{11.55} = -1.73$ Area = 0.4582

probability = 0.4582 + 0.4582 = 0.9164

28. a. $z = \dfrac{\bar{x} - 34,000}{\sigma / \sqrt{n}}$

Error = $\bar{x}$ - 34,000 = 250

$n = 30$ $z = \dfrac{250}{2000 / \sqrt{30}} = .68$ $.2518 \, x2 = .5036$

$n = 50$ $z = \dfrac{250}{2000 / \sqrt{50}} = .88$ $.3106 \, x2 = .6212$

$n = 100$ $z = \dfrac{250}{2000 / \sqrt{100}} = 1.25$ $.3944 \, x2 = .7888$

$n = 200$ $z = \dfrac{250}{2000 / \sqrt{200}} = 1.77$ $.4616 \, x2 = .9232$

$n = 400$ $z = \dfrac{250}{2000 / \sqrt{400}} = 2.50$ $.4938 \, x2 = .9876$

b. A larger sample increases the probability that the sample mean will be within a specified distance from the population mean. In the salary example, the probability of being within ±250 of μ ranges from .5036 for a sample of size 30 to .9876 for a sample of size 400.

29. a. $E(\bar{x}) = 982$

$\sigma_{\bar{x}} = \sigma / \sqrt{n} = 210 / \sqrt{40} = 33.2$

$z = \dfrac{\bar{x} - \mu}{\sigma / \sqrt{n}} = \dfrac{100}{210 / \sqrt{40}} = 3.01$

$.4987 \times 2 = .9974$

b. $z = \dfrac{\bar{x} - \mu}{\sigma / \sqrt{n}} = \dfrac{25}{210 / \sqrt{40}} = .75$

$.2734 \times 2 = .5468$

c. The sample with $n = 40$ has a very high probability (.9974) of providing a sample mean within ± $100. However, the sample with $n = 40$ only has a .5468 of providing a sample mean within ± $25. A larger sample size is desirable if the ± $25 is needed.

30. a.   Normal distribution,

$E(\bar{x}) = 166,500$

$\sigma_{\bar{x}} = \sigma / \sqrt{n} = 42,000 / \sqrt{100} = 4200$

b. $z = \dfrac{\bar{x} - \mu}{\sigma / \sqrt{n}} = \dfrac{10,000}{4,200} = 2.38$ $(.4913 \times 2) = .9826$

c. $5000 $z = 5000/4200 = 1.19$ $(.3830 \times 2) = .7660$

$2500 $z = 2500/4200 = .60$ $(.2257 \times 2) = .4514$

$1000 $z = 1000/4200 = .24$ $(.0948 \times 2) = .1896$

d. Increase sample size to improve precision of the estimate. Sample size of 100 only has a .4514 probability of being within ± $2,500.

31. a. $\sigma_{\bar{x}} = \sigma/\sqrt{n} = 5200/\sqrt{30} = 949.39$

   $z = \dfrac{1000}{949.39} = 1.05 \qquad \text{Area} = 0.3531$

   Probability = 0.3531 x 2 = 0.7062

   b. $\sigma_{\bar{x}} = \sigma/\sqrt{n} = 5200/\sqrt{50} = 735.39$

   $z = \dfrac{1000}{735.39} = 1.36 \qquad \text{Area} = 0.4131$

   Probability = 0.4131 x 2 = 0.8262

   c. $\sigma_{\bar{x}} = \sigma/\sqrt{n} = 5200/\sqrt{100} = 520$

   $z = \dfrac{1000}{520} = 1.92 \quad \text{Area} = 0.4726$

   Probability = 0.4726 x 2 = 0.9452

   d. Recommend $n = 100$

32. a. $n/N = 40/4000 = .01 < .05$; therefore, the finite population correction factor is not necessary.

   b. With the finite population correction factor

   $$\sigma_{\bar{x}} = \sqrt{\frac{N-n}{N-1}}\frac{\sigma}{\sqrt{n}} = \sqrt{\frac{4000-40}{4000-1}}\frac{8.2}{\sqrt{40}} = 1.29$$

   Without the finite population correction factor

   $$\sigma_{\bar{x}} = \sigma/\sqrt{n} = 1.30$$

   Including the finite population correction factor provides only a slightly different value for $\sigma_{\bar{x}}$ than when the correction factor is not used.

   c.

   $$z = \frac{\bar{x} - \mu}{1.30} = \frac{2}{1.30} = 1.54$$

Area
.4382
x2
.8764

33. a. $E(\bar{p}) = p = .40$

   b. $\sigma_{\bar{p}} = \sqrt{\dfrac{p(1-p)}{n}} = \sqrt{\dfrac{0.40(0.60)}{100}} = 0.0490$

   c. Normal distribution with $E(\bar{p}) = .40$ and $\sigma_{\bar{p}} = .0490$

d. It shows the probability distribution for the sample proportion $\bar{p}$.

34. a. $E(\bar{p}) = .40$

$$\sigma_{\bar{p}} = \sqrt{\frac{p(1-p)}{n}} = \sqrt{\frac{0.40(0.60)}{200}} = 0.0346$$

$$z = \frac{\bar{p} - p}{\sigma_{\bar{p}}} = \frac{0.03}{0.0346} = 0.87$$

Area
.3078
x2
.6156

b.

$$z = \frac{\bar{p} - p}{\sigma_{\bar{p}}} = \frac{0.05}{0.0346} = 1.45$$

Area
.4265
x2
.8530

35. $$\sigma_{\bar{p}} = \sqrt{\frac{p(1-p)}{n}}$$

$$\sigma_{\bar{p}} = \sqrt{\frac{(0.55)(0.45)}{100}} = 0.0497$$

$$\sigma_{\bar{p}} = \sqrt{\frac{(0.55)(0.45)}{200}} = 0.0352$$

$$\sigma_{\bar{p}} = \sqrt{\frac{(0.55)(0.45)}{500}} = 0.0222$$

$$\sigma_{\bar{p}} = \sqrt{\frac{(0.55)(0.45)}{1000}} = 0.0157$$

$\sigma_{\bar{p}}$ decreases as n increases

36. a. $$\sigma_{\bar{p}} = \sqrt{\frac{(0.30)(0.70)}{100}} = 0.0458$$

$$z = \frac{\bar{p} - p}{\sigma_{\bar{p}}} = \frac{0.04}{0.0458} = 0.87$$

Area = 0.3078 x 2 = 0.6156

b.　$\sigma_{\bar{p}} = \sqrt{\dfrac{(0.30)(0.70)}{200}} = 0.0324$

$z = \dfrac{\bar{p} - p}{\sigma_{\bar{p}}} = \dfrac{0.04}{0.0324} = 1.23$

Area = 0.3907 x 2 = 0.7814

c.　$\sigma_{\bar{p}} = \sqrt{\dfrac{(0.30)(0.70)}{500}} = 0.0205$

$z = \dfrac{\bar{p} - p}{\sigma_{\bar{p}}} = \dfrac{0.04}{0.0205} = 1.95$

Area = 0.4744 x 2 = 0.9488

d.　$\sigma_{\bar{p}} = \sqrt{\dfrac{(0.30)(0.70)}{1000}} = 0.0145$

$z = \dfrac{\bar{p} - p}{\sigma_{\bar{p}}} = \dfrac{0.04}{0.0145} = 2.76$

Area = 0.4971 x 2 = 0.9942

e.　With a larger sample, there is a higher probability $\bar{p}$ will be within $\pm$ .04 of the population proportion p.

37.　a.

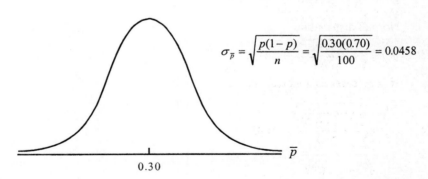

$\sigma_{\bar{p}} = \sqrt{\dfrac{p(1-p)}{n}} = \sqrt{\dfrac{0.30(0.70)}{100}} = 0.0458$

The normal distribution is appropriate because $n\,p = 100\,(.30) = 30$ and $n\,(1 - p) = 100\,(.70) = 70$ are both greater than 5.

b.　$P\,(.20 \le \bar{p} \le .40) = ?$

$$z = \dfrac{.40 - .30}{.0458} = 2.18$$

Area
.4854
x2
.9708

c. $P(.25 \le \bar{p} \le .35) = ?$

$$z = \frac{.35 - .30}{.0458} = 1.09$$

Area
.3621
x2
.7242

38. a. $E(\bar{p}) = .76$

$$\sigma_{\bar{p}} = \sqrt{\frac{p(1-p)}{n}} = \sqrt{\frac{0.76(1-0.76)}{400}} = 0.0214$$

b. $z = \dfrac{0.79 - 0.76}{0.0214} = 1.40$ Area = 0.4192

$z = \dfrac{0.73 - 0.76}{0.0214} = -1.40$ Area = 0.4192

probability = 0.4192 + 0.4192 = 0.8384

c. $\sigma_{\bar{p}} = \sqrt{\dfrac{p(1-p)}{n}} = \sqrt{\dfrac{0.76(1-0.76)}{750}} = 0.0156$

$z = \dfrac{0.79 - 0.76}{0.0156} = 1.92$ Area = 0.4726

$z = \dfrac{0.73 - 0.76}{0.0156} = -1.92$ Area = 0.4726

probability = 0.4726 + 0.4726 = 0.9452

39. a.   Normal distribution

$E(\bar{p}) = .50$

$$\sigma_{\bar{p}} = \sqrt{\frac{p(1-p)}{n}} = \sqrt{\frac{(.50)(1-.50)}{589}} = .0206$$

b. $z = \dfrac{\bar{p} - p}{\sigma_{\bar{p}}} = \dfrac{.04}{.0206} = 1.94$

.4738 x 2 = .9476

c. $z = \dfrac{\bar{p} - p}{\sigma_{\bar{p}}} = \dfrac{.03}{.0206} = 1.46$

.4279 x 2 = .8558

d. $z = \dfrac{\overline{p} - p}{\sigma_{\overline{p}}} = \dfrac{.02}{.0206} = .97$

   .3340 x 2 = .6680

40. a. Normal distribution

   $E(\overline{p}) = 0.25$

   $\sigma_{\overline{p}} = \sqrt{\dfrac{p(1-p)}{n}} = \sqrt{\dfrac{(0.25)(0.75)}{200}} = 0.0306$

   b. $z = \dfrac{0.03}{0.0306} = 0.98$ Area = 0.3365

   probability = 0.3365 x 2 = 0.6730

   c. $z = \dfrac{0.05}{0.0306} = 1.63$ Area = 0.4484

   probability = 0.4484 x 2 = 0.8968

41. a. $E(\overline{p}) = 0.37$

   $\sigma_{\overline{p}} = \sqrt{\dfrac{p(1-p)}{n}} = \sqrt{\dfrac{(0.37)(1-0.37)}{1000}} = 0.0153$

   b. $z = \dfrac{0.40 - 0.37}{0.0153} = 1.96$ Area = 0.4750

   $z = \dfrac{0.34 - 0.37}{0.0153} = -1.96$ Area = 0.4750

   probability = 0.4750 + 0.4750 = 0.9500

   c. $\sigma_{\overline{p}} = \sqrt{\dfrac{p(1-p)}{n}} = \sqrt{\dfrac{(0.37)(1-0.37)}{500}} = 0.0216$

   $z = \dfrac{0.40 - 0.37}{0.0216} = 1.39$ Area = 0.4177

   $z = \dfrac{0.34 - 0.37}{0.0216} = -1.39$ Area = 0.4177

   probability = 0.4177 + 0.4177 = 0.8354

42. a.

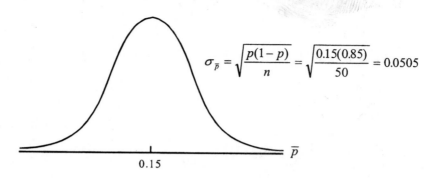

$$\sigma_{\bar{p}} = \sqrt{\frac{p(1-p)}{n}} = \sqrt{\frac{0.15(0.85)}{50}} = 0.0505$$

0.15

b. $P(.12 \le \bar{p} \le .18) = ?$

$$z = \frac{.18 - .15}{.0505} = .59$$

Area
.2224
x2
.4448

c. $P(\bar{p} \ge .10) = ?$

$$z = \frac{.10 - .15}{.0505} = -.99$$

Area
.3389
+.5000
.8389

43. a. $E(\bar{p}) = 0.17$

$$\sigma_{\bar{p}} = \sqrt{\frac{p(1-p)}{n}} = \sqrt{\frac{(0.17)(1-0.17)}{800}} = 0.01328$$

b. $z = \frac{0.19 - 0.17}{0.01328} = 1.51 \quad \text{Area} = 0.4345$

$z = \frac{0.34 - 0.37}{0.01328} = -1.51 \quad \text{Area} = 0.4345$

probability $= 0.4345 + 0.4345 = 0.8690$

c. $\sigma_{\bar{p}} = \sqrt{\frac{p(1-p)}{n}} = \sqrt{\frac{(0.17)(1-0.17)}{1600}} = 0.0094$

$z = \frac{0.19 - 0.17}{0.0094} = 2.13 \quad \text{Area} = 0.4834$

$z = \frac{0.15 - 0.17}{0.0094} = -2.13 \quad \text{Area} = 0.4834$

probability $= 0.4834 + 0.4834 = 0.9668$

44.   112, 145, 73, 324, 293, 875, 318, 618

45. a.   Normal distribution

$E(\bar{x}) = 3$

$\sigma_{\bar{x}} = \dfrac{\sigma}{\sqrt{n}} = \dfrac{1.2}{\sqrt{50}} = .17$

b. $z = \dfrac{\bar{x} - \mu}{\sigma/\sqrt{n}} = \dfrac{.25}{1.2/\sqrt{50}} = 1.47$

$.4292 \times 2 = .8584$

46. a.   Normal distribution

$E(\bar{x}) = 31.5$

$\sigma_{\bar{x}} = \dfrac{\sigma}{\sqrt{n}} = \dfrac{12}{\sqrt{50}} = 1.70$

b. $z = \dfrac{1}{1.70} = 0.59$ Area = 0.2224

probability = 0.2224 x 2 = 0.4448

c. $z = \dfrac{3}{1.70} = 1.77$ Area = 0.4616

probability = 0.4616 x 2 = 0.9232

47. a. $E(\bar{x}) = \$24.07$

$\sigma_{\bar{x}} = \dfrac{\sigma}{\sqrt{n}} = \dfrac{4.80}{\sqrt{120}} = 0.44$

$z = \dfrac{0.50}{0.44} = 1.14$ Area = 0.3729

probability = 0.3729 x 2 = 0.7458

b. $z = \dfrac{1.00}{0.44} = 2.28$ Area = 0.4887

probability = 0.4887 x 2 = 0.9774

48. a. $\sigma_{\bar{x}} = \dfrac{\sigma}{\sqrt{n}} = \dfrac{60}{\sqrt{50}} = 8.49$

b. $z = (115 - 115) / 8.49 = 0$ Area = .5000

   c. $z = 5 / 8.49 = .59$ Area = .2224

       $z = -5 / 8.49 = -.59$ Area = .2224

       probability = .2224 + .2224 = .4448

   d. $\sigma_{\bar{x}} = \dfrac{\sigma}{\sqrt{n}} = \dfrac{60}{\sqrt{100}} = 6$

       $z = 5 / 6 = .83$ Area = .2967

       $z = -5 / 6 = -.83$ Area = .2967

       probability = .2967 + .2967 = .5934

49. a. $\sigma_{\bar{x}} = \sqrt{\dfrac{N-n}{N-1}}\,\dfrac{\sigma}{\sqrt{n}}$

      $N = 2000$

$$\sigma_{\bar{x}} = \sqrt{\frac{2000-50}{2000-1}}\,\frac{144}{\sqrt{50}} = 20.11$$

      $N = 5000$

$$\sigma_{\bar{x}} = \sqrt{\frac{5000-50}{5000-1}}\,\frac{144}{\sqrt{50}} = 20.26$$

      $N = 10{,}000$

$$\sigma_{\bar{x}} = \sqrt{\frac{10{,}000-50}{10{,}000-1}}\,\frac{144}{\sqrt{50}} = 20.31$$

      Note: With $n / N \le .05$ for all three cases, common statistical practice would be to ignore the finite population correction factor and use $\sigma_{\bar{x}} = \dfrac{144}{\sqrt{50}} = 20.36$ for each case.

   b. $N = 2000$

$$z = \frac{25}{20.11} = 1.24$$

$$
\begin{array}{c}
\underline{\text{Area}} \\
.3925 \\
\underline{\text{x2}} \\
.7850
\end{array}
$$

      $N = 5000$

$$z = \frac{25}{20.26} = 1.23$$

$$
\begin{array}{c}
\underline{\text{Area}} \\
.3907 \\
\underline{\text{x2}} \\
.7814
\end{array}
$$

$N = 10,000$

$$z = \frac{25}{20.31} = 1.23$$

Area
.3907
x2
.7814

All probabilities are approximately .78

50. a. $\sigma_{\bar{x}} = \dfrac{\sigma}{\sqrt{n}} = \dfrac{500}{\sqrt{n}} = 20$

$\sqrt{n} \; 500/20 = 25$ and $n = (25)^2 = 625$

b. For ± 25,

$$z = \frac{25}{20} = 1.25$$

Area
.3944
x2
.7888

51. Sampling distribution of $\bar{x}$

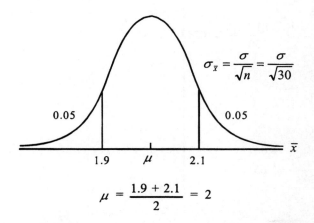

$$\sigma_{\bar{x}} = \frac{\sigma}{\sqrt{n}} = \frac{\sigma}{\sqrt{30}}$$

$$\mu = \frac{1.9 + 2.1}{2} = 2$$

The area between $\mu = 2$ and 2.1 must be .45. An area of .45 in the standard normal table shows $z = 1.645$.

Thus,

$$\mu = \frac{2.1 + 2.0}{\sigma/\sqrt{30}} = 1.645$$

Solve for σ.

$$\sigma = \frac{(0.1)\sqrt{30}}{1.645} = 0.33$$

52. a. $E(\bar{p}) = 0.74$

$$\sigma_{\bar{p}} = \sqrt{\frac{p(1-p)}{n}} = \sqrt{\frac{(0.74)(1-0.74)}{200}} = 0.031$$

b. $z = .04 / .031 = 1.29$ Area $= .4015$

    $z = -.04 / .031 = -1.29$ Area $= .4015$

    probability $= .4015 + .4015 = .8030$

c. $z = .02 / .031 = .64$ Area $= .2389$

    $z = -.02 / .031 = -.64$ Area $= .2389$

    probability $= .2389 + .2389 = .4778$

53. $\sigma_{\bar{p}} = \sqrt{\dfrac{p(1-p)}{n}} = \sqrt{\dfrac{(0.40)(0.60)}{400}} = 0.0245$

    $P(\bar{p} \geq .375) = ?$

$$z = \frac{.375 - .40}{.0245} = -1.02$$

Area
.3461

    $P(\bar{p} \geq .375) = .3461 + .5000 = .8461$

54. a. $\sigma_{\bar{p}} = \sqrt{\dfrac{p(1-p)}{n}} = \sqrt{\dfrac{(.71)(1-.71)}{350}} = .0243$

    $z = \dfrac{\bar{p} - p}{\sigma_{\bar{p}}} = \dfrac{.05}{.0243} = 2.06$

    $.4803 \times 2 = .9606$

b. $z = \dfrac{\bar{p} - p}{\sigma_{\bar{p}}} = \dfrac{.75 - .71}{.0243} = 1.65$

    Area $= .4505$

    $P(\bar{p} \geq .75) = .5000 - .4505 = .0495$

55. a.   Normal distribution with $E(\bar{p}) = .15$ and

$$\sigma_{\bar{p}} = \sqrt{\frac{p(1-p)}{n}} = \sqrt{\frac{(0.15)(0.85)}{150}} = 0.0292$$

b. $P(.12 \leq \bar{p} \leq .18) = ?$

$$z = \frac{.18 - .15}{.0292} = 1.03$$

Area
.3485
x2
.6970

56. a. $\sigma_{\bar{p}} = \sqrt{\dfrac{p(1-p)}{n}} = \sqrt{\dfrac{.25(.75)}{n}} = .0625$

    Solve for n

    $$n = \frac{.25(.75)}{(.0625)^2} = 48$$

    b. Normal distribution with $E(\bar{p}) = .25$ and $\sigma_{\bar{x}} = .0625$

    c. $P(\bar{p} \geq .30) = ?$

    $$z = \frac{.30 - .25}{.0625} = .80$$

    <u>Area</u>
    .2881

    Thus $P(.25 \leq \bar{p} \leq .30) = .2881$ and $P(\bar{p} \geq .30) = .5000 - .2881 = .2119$

Chapter 8
Interval Estimation

Learning Objectives

1. Know how to construct and interpret an interval estimate of a population mean and / or a population proportion.

2. Understand the concept of a sampling error.

3. Be able to use knowledge of a sampling distribution to make probability statements about the sampling error.

4. Understand and be able to compute the margin of error.

5. Learn about the t distribution and its use in constructing an interval estimate for a population mean.

6. Be able to determine the size of a simple random sample necessary to estimate a population mean and/or a population proportion with a specified level of precision.

7. Know the definition of the following terms:

    confidence interval   precision
    confidence coefficient   sampling error
    confidence level   margin of error
                                         degrees of freedom

Solutions:

1. a. $\sigma_{\bar{x}} = \sigma / \sqrt{n} = 5 / \sqrt{40} = 0.79$

    b.   At 95%, $z\sigma / \sqrt{n} = 1.96(5 / \sqrt{40}) = 1.55$

2. a. $32 \pm 1.645 \ (6 / \sqrt{50})$

        32 ± 1.4 (30.6 to 33.4)

    b. $32 \pm 1.96 \ (6 / \sqrt{50})$

        32 ± 1.66 (30.34 to 33.66)

    c. $32 \pm 2.576 \ (6 / \sqrt{50})$

        32 ± 2.19 (29.81 to 34.19)

3. a. $80 \pm 1.96 \ (15 / \sqrt{60})$

        80 ± 3.8 (76.2 to 83.8)

    b. $80 \pm 1.96 \ (15 / \sqrt{120})$

        80 ± 2.68 (77.32 to 82.68)

    c.   Larger sample provides a smaller margin of error.

4. $126 \pm 1.96 \ (s / \sqrt{n})$

        $$1.96 \frac{16.07}{\sqrt{n}} = 4$$

        $$\sqrt{n} = \frac{1.96(16.07)}{4} = 7.874$$

        $$n = 62$$

5. a. $1.96\sigma / \sqrt{n} = 1.96(5.00 / \sqrt{49}) = 1.40$

    b. 24.80 ± 1.40 or (23.40 to 26.20)

6. $\bar{x} \pm 1.96 \ (s / \sqrt{n})$

        $369 \pm 1.96 \ (50 / \sqrt{250})$

        369 ± 6.20 (362.80 to 375.20)

7. $\bar{x} \pm z_{.025}(\sigma/\sqrt{n})$

   $3.37 \pm 1.96\,(.28/\sqrt{120})$

   $3.37 \pm .05$ (3.32 to 3.42)

8. a. $\bar{x} \pm z_{\alpha/2}\dfrac{\sigma}{\sqrt{n}}$

   $12,000 \pm 1.645\,(2,200/\sqrt{245})$

   $12,000 \pm 231$ (11,769 to 12,231)

   b. $12,000 \pm 1.96\,(2,200/\sqrt{245})$

   $12,000 \pm 275$ (11,725 to 12,275)

   c. $12,000 \pm 2.576\,(2,200/\sqrt{245})$

   $12,000 \pm 362$ (11,638 to 12,362)

   d. Interval width must increase since we want to make a statement about μ with greater confidence.

9. a. Using a computer, $\bar{x} = \$12.41$

   b. Using a computer, $s = 3.64$

   c. $\bar{x} \pm 1.96\,(s/\sqrt{n})$

   $12.41 \pm 1.96\,(3.64/\sqrt{60})$

   12.41 ± 0.92 (11.49 to 13.33)

10. $\bar{x} \pm z_{.025}\dfrac{s}{\sqrt{n}}$

    $7.75 \pm 1.96\dfrac{3.45}{\sqrt{180}}$

    $7.75 \pm .50$ (7.25 to 8.25)

11. Using Minitab we obtained a sample standard deviation of 2.163. The confidence interval output is shown below:

    ```
    THE ASSUMED SIGMA =2.16

               N     MEAN   STDEV   SE MEAN   95.0 PERCENT C.I.
    Miami      50    6.340  2.163   0.306     (5.740, 6.940)
    ```

    The 95% confidence interval estimate is 5.74 to 6.94.

12. a. $\bar{x} = \dfrac{\Sigma x_i}{n} = \dfrac{114}{30} = 3.8$ minutes

    b. $s = \sqrt{\dfrac{\Sigma(x_i - \bar{x})^2}{n-1}} = 2.26$ minutes

       Margin of Error $= z_{.025}\dfrac{s}{\sqrt{n}} = 1.96\dfrac{2.26}{\sqrt{30}} = .81$ minutes

    c. $\bar{x} \pm z_{.025}\dfrac{s}{\sqrt{n}}$

       $3.8 \pm .81$ (2.99 to 4.61)

13. a. .95

    b. .90

    c. .01

    d. .05

    e. .95

    f. .85

14. a. 1.734

    b. -1.321

    c. 3.365

    d. -1.761 and +1.761

    e. -2.048 and +2.048

15. a. $\bar{x} = \Sigma x_i / n = \dfrac{80}{8} = 10$

    b. $s = \sqrt{\dfrac{\Sigma(x_i - \bar{x})^2}{n-1}} = \sqrt{\dfrac{84}{8-1}} = 3.464$

    c. With 7 degrees of freedom, $t_{.025} = 2.365$

       $\bar{x} \pm t_{.025}(s/\sqrt{n})$

       $10 \pm 2.365 \, (3.464/\sqrt{8})$

       10 ± 2.90 (7.10 to 12.90)

16. a. $17.25 \pm 1.729 \, (3.3/\sqrt{20})$

       17.25 ± 1.28 (15.97 to 18.53)

   b. $17.25 \pm 2.09 \, (3.3/\sqrt{20})$

       17.25 ± 1.54 (15.71 to 18.79)

   c. $17.25 \pm 2.861 \, (3.3/\sqrt{20})$

       17.25 ± 2.11 (15.14 to 19.36)

17.   At 90% , $80 \pm t_{.05}(s/\sqrt{n})$ with df = 17 $t_{.05} = 1.740$

     $80 \pm 1.740 \, (10/\sqrt{18})$

     80 ± 4.10 (75.90 to 84.10)

     At 95%, $80 \pm 2.11 \, (10/\sqrt{18})$ with df = 17 $t_{.05} = 2.110$

     80 ± 4.97 (75.03 to 84.97)

18. a. $\bar{x} = \dfrac{\Sigma x_i}{n} = \dfrac{18.96}{12} = \$1.58$

   b. $s = \sqrt{\dfrac{\Sigma(x_i - \bar{x})^2}{n-1}} = \sqrt{\dfrac{.239}{12-1}} = .1474$

   c. $t_{.025} = 2.201$

      $\bar{x} \pm t_{.025}(s/\sqrt{n})$

      $1.58 \pm 2.201 \, (.1474/\sqrt{12})$

      $1.58 \pm .09$ (1.49 to 1.67)

19. $\bar{x} = \Sigma x_i / n = 6.53$ minutes

     $s = \sqrt{\dfrac{\Sigma(x_i - \bar{x})^2}{n-1}} = 0.54$ minutes

     $\bar{x} \pm t_{.025}(s/\sqrt{n})$

     $6.53 \pm 2.093 \, (0.54/\sqrt{20})$

     $6.53 \pm .25$ (6.28 to 6.78)

20. a. $22.4 \pm 1.96\,(5/\sqrt{61})$

    22.4 ± 1.25 $\qquad\qquad$ (21.15 to 23.65)

 b. With df $=$ 60, $\quad t_{.025} = 2.000$

    $22.4 \pm 2\,(5/\sqrt{61})$

    22.4 ± 1.28 $\qquad\qquad$ (21.12 to 23.68)

 c. $\bar{x} \pm t_{.025}\,(s/\sqrt{n})$

    Confidence intervals are essentially the same regardless of whether z or t is used.

21. $\qquad \bar{x} = \dfrac{\Sigma x_i}{n} = \dfrac{864}{8} = \$108$

    $s = \sqrt{\dfrac{\Sigma(x_i - \bar{x})^2}{n-1}} = \sqrt{\dfrac{654}{8-1}} = 9.6658$

    $t_{.025} = 2.365$

    $\bar{x} \pm t_{.025}\,(s/\sqrt{n})$

    $108 \pm 2.365\,(9.6658/\sqrt{8})$

    108 ± 8.08 $\qquad\qquad$ (99.92 to 116.08)

22. a. Using a computer, $\bar{x} = 6.86 \quad s = 0.78$

 b. $\bar{x} \pm t_{.025}\,(s/\sqrt{n}) \quad t_{.025} = 2.064 \quad df = 24$

    $6.86 \pm 2.064\,(0.78/\sqrt{25})$

    6.86 ± 0.32 $\qquad\qquad$ (6.54 to 7.18)

23. $\qquad n = \dfrac{z_{.025}^2 \sigma^2}{E^2} = \dfrac{(1.96)^2 (25)^2}{5^2} = 96.04 \quad$ Use $n = 97$

24. a. Planning value of $\sigma = $ Range/4 $= 36/4 = 9$

 b. $n = \dfrac{z_{.025}^2 \sigma^2}{E^2} = \dfrac{(1.96)^2 (9)^2}{3^2} = 34.57 \quad$ Use $n = 35$

 c. $n = \dfrac{(1.96)^2 (9)^2}{2^2} = 77.79 \quad$ Use $n = 78$

25. $\quad n = \dfrac{(1.96)^2 (6.82)^2}{(1.5)^2} = 79.41 \quad$ Use $n = 80$

$\quad\quad n = \dfrac{(1.645)^2 (6.82)^2}{2^2} = 31.47 \quad$ Use $n = 32$

26. a. $\quad n = \dfrac{z^2 \sigma^2}{E^2} = \dfrac{(1.96)^2 (9400)^2}{(1000)^2} = 339.44 \quad$ Use 340

   b. $\quad n = \dfrac{(1.96)^2 (9400)^2}{(500)^2} = 1357.78 \quad$ Use 1358

   c. $\quad n = \dfrac{(1.96)^2 (9400)^2}{200} = 8486.09 \quad$ Use 8487

27. a. $\quad n = \dfrac{(1.96)^2 (2,000)^2}{(500)^2} = 61.47 \quad$ Use $n = 62$

   b. $\quad n = \dfrac{(1.96)^2 (2,000)^2}{(200)^2} = 384.16 \quad$ Use $n = 385$

   c. $\quad n = \dfrac{(1.96)^2 (2,000)^2}{(100)^2} = 1536.64 \quad$ Use $n = 1537$

28. a. $\quad n = \dfrac{z^2 \sigma^2}{E^2} = \dfrac{(1.645)^2 (220)^2}{(50)^2} = 52.39 \quad$ Use 53

   b. $\quad n = \dfrac{(1.96)^2 (220)^2}{(50)^2} = 74.37 \quad$ Use 75

   c. $\quad n = \dfrac{(2.576)^2 (220)^2}{(50)^2} = 128.47 \quad$ Use 129

   d. Must increase sample size to increase confidence.

29. a. $\quad n = \dfrac{(1.96)^2 (6.25)^2}{2^2} = 37.52 \quad$ Use $n = 38$

   b. $\quad n = \dfrac{(1.96)^2 (6.25)^2}{1^2} = 150.06 \quad$ Use $n = 151$

30. $\quad n = \dfrac{(1.96)^2 (7.8)^2}{2^2} = 58.43 \quad$ Use $n = 59$

31 . a. $\overline{p} = 100/400 = 0.25$

b. $\sqrt{\dfrac{\overline{p}(1-\overline{p})}{n}} = \sqrt{\dfrac{0.25(0.75)}{400}} = 0.0217$

c. $\overline{p} \pm z_{.025}\sqrt{\dfrac{\overline{p}(1-\overline{p})}{n}}$

$.25 \pm 1.96\,(.0217)$

$.25 \pm .0424$ (.2076 to .2924)

32. a. $.70 \pm 1.645\sqrt{\dfrac{0.70(0.30)}{800}}$

$.70 \pm .0267$ (.6733 to .7267)

b. $.70 \pm 1.96\sqrt{\dfrac{0.70(0.30)}{800}}$

$.70 \pm .0318$ (.6682 to .7318)

33. $n = \dfrac{z_{.025}^2\,p(1-p)}{E^2} = \dfrac{(1.96)^2(0.35)(0.65)}{(0.05)^2} = 349.59$ Use $n = 350$

34.   Use planning value $p = .50$

$n = \dfrac{(1.96)^2(0.50)(0.50)}{(0.03)^2} = 1067.11$ Use $n = 1068$

35. a. $\overline{p} = 562/814 = 0.6904$

b. $1.645\sqrt{\dfrac{\overline{p}(1-\overline{p})}{n}} = 1.645\sqrt{\dfrac{0.6904(1-0.6904)}{814}} = 0.0267$

c. 0.6904 ± 0.0267 (0.6637 to 0.7171)

36. a. $\overline{p} = 152/346 = .4393$

b. $\sigma_{\overline{p}} = \sqrt{\dfrac{\overline{p}(1-\overline{p})}{n}} = \sqrt{\dfrac{.4393(1-.4393)}{346}} = .0267$

$\overline{p} \pm z_{.025}\sigma_{\overline{p}}$

$.4393 \pm 1.96(.0267)$

$.4393 \pm .0523$ (.3870 to .4916)

37. $$\overline{p} \pm 1.96\sqrt{\frac{\overline{p}(1-\overline{p})}{n}}$$

$$\overline{p} = \frac{182}{650} = .28$$

$$.28 \pm 1.96\sqrt{\frac{(0.28)(0.72)}{650}}$$

$$0.28 \pm 0.0345 \qquad\qquad (0.2455 \text{ to } 0.3145)$$

38. a. $$1.96\sqrt{\frac{\overline{p}(1-\overline{p})}{n}} = 1.96\sqrt{\frac{(0.26)(0.74)}{400}} = 0.0430$$

   b. $0.26 \pm 0.0430 \qquad\qquad (0.2170 \text{ to } 0.3030)$

   c. $$n = \frac{1.96^2(0.26)(0.74)}{(0.03)^2} = 821.25 \quad \text{Use } n = 822$$

39. a. $$n = \frac{z_{.025}^2 p(1-p)}{E^2} = \frac{(1.96)^2(.33)(1-.33)}{(.03)^2} = 943.75 \quad \text{Use } 944$$

   b. $$n = \frac{z_{.005}^2 p(1-p)}{E^2} = \frac{(2.576)^2(.33)(1-.33)}{(.03)^2} = 1630.19 \quad \text{Use } 1631$$

40. a. $\overline{p} = 255/1018 = 0.2505$

   b. $$1.96\sqrt{\frac{(0.2505)(1-0.2505)}{1018}} = 0.0266$$

41. $$\sigma_{\overline{p}} = \sqrt{\frac{\overline{p}(1-\overline{p})}{n}} = \sqrt{\frac{.16(1-.16)}{1285}} = .0102$$

Margin of Error $= 1.96\,\sigma_{\overline{p}} = 1.96(.0102) = .02$

$.16 \pm 1.96\,\sigma_{\overline{p}}$

$.16 \pm .02 \qquad\qquad (.14 \text{ to } .18)$

42. a. $$\sigma_{\overline{p}} = \sqrt{\frac{p(1-p)}{n}} = \sqrt{\frac{.50(1-.50)}{491}} = .0226$$

$z_{.025}\sigma_{\overline{p}} = 1.96(.0226) = .0442$

   b. $$n = \frac{z_{.025}^2 p(1-p)}{E^2}$$

September $\quad n = \dfrac{1.96^2(.50)(1-.50)}{.04^2} = 600.25 \quad$ Use 601

October $\quad n = \dfrac{1.96^2(.50)(1-.50)}{.03^2} = 1067.11 \quad$ Use 1068

November $\quad n = \dfrac{1.96^2(.50)(1-.50)}{.02^2} = 2401$

Pre-Election $\quad n = \dfrac{1.96^2(.50)(1-.50)}{.01^2} = 9604$

43. a. $\quad n = \dfrac{1.96^2(0.5)(1-0.5)}{(0.04)^2} = 600.25 \quad$ Use $n = 601$

   b. $\quad \bar{p} = 445/601 = 0.7404$

   c. $\quad 0.7404 \pm 1.96 \sqrt{\dfrac{(0.7404)(0.2596)}{601}}$

   $\quad 0.7404 \pm 0.0350 \qquad\qquad$ (0.7054 to 0.7755)

44. a. $\quad z_{.025} \dfrac{s}{\sqrt{n}} = 1.96 \dfrac{20,500}{\sqrt{400}} = 2009$

   b. $\quad \bar{x} \pm z_{.025}(s/\sqrt{n})$

   $\quad 50,000 \pm 2009 \qquad\qquad$ (47,991 to 52,009)

45. a. $\quad \bar{x} \pm z_{.025}(s/\sqrt{n})$

   $\quad 252.45 \pm 1.96(74.50/\sqrt{64})$

   $\quad 252.45 \pm 18.25$ or $234.20 to $270.70

   b. Yes. the lower limit for the population mean at Niagara Falls is $234.20 which is greater than $215.60.

46. a. Using a computer, $\bar{x} = 49.8$ minutes

   b. Using a computer, $s = 15.99$ minutes

   c. $\quad \bar{x} \pm 1.96(s/\sqrt{n})$

   $\quad 49.8 \pm 1.96(15.99/\sqrt{200})$

   $\quad 49.8 \pm 2.22 \qquad\qquad$ (47.58 to 52.02)

47. a. Using a computer, $\bar{x} = 16.8$ and $s = 4.25$

   With 19 degrees of freedom, $t_{.025} = 2.093$

   $\bar{x} \pm 2.093\,(s/\sqrt{n})$

   $16.8 \pm 2.093\,(4.25/\sqrt{20})$

   16.8 ± 1.99 (14.81 to 18.79)

   b. Using a computer, $\bar{x} = 24.1$ and $s = 6.21$

   $24.1 \pm 2.093\,(6.21/\sqrt{20})$

   24.1 ± 2.90 (21.2 to 27.0)

   c. $16.8 / 24.1 = 0.697$ or 69.7% or approximately 70%

48. a. $\bar{x} = \Sigma x_i / n = \dfrac{132}{10} = 13.2$

   b. $s = \sqrt{\dfrac{\Sigma(x_i - \bar{x})^2}{n-1}} = \sqrt{\dfrac{547.6}{9}} = 7.8$

   c. With $df = 9$, $t_{.025} = 2.262$

   $\bar{x} \pm t_{.025}\,(s/\sqrt{n})$

   $13.2 \pm 2.262\,(7.8/\sqrt{10})$

   13.2 ± 5.58 (7.62 to 18.78)

   d. The $\pm$ 5.58 shows poor precision. A larger sample size is desired.

49. $n = \dfrac{1.96^2(0.45)}{10^2} = 77.79$ Use $n = 78$

50. $n = \dfrac{(2.33)^2(2.6)^2}{1^2} = 36.7$ Use $n = 37$

51. $n = \dfrac{(1.96)^2(8)^2}{2^2} = 61.47$ Use $n = 62$

   $n = \dfrac{(2.576)^2(8)^2}{2^2} = 106.17$ Use $n = 107$

52. $n = \dfrac{(1.96)^2(675)^2}{100^2} = 175.03$ Use $n = 176$

53. a. $\bar{p} \pm 1.96 \sqrt{\dfrac{\bar{p}(1-\bar{p})}{n}}$

$0.47 \pm 1.96 \sqrt{\dfrac{(0.47)(0.53)}{450}}$

0.47 ± 0.0461 $\quad\quad\quad\quad$ (0.4239 to 0.5161)

b. $0.47 \pm 2.576 \sqrt{\dfrac{(0.47)(0.53)}{450}}$

0.47 ± 0.0606 $\quad\quad\quad\quad$ (0.4094 to 0.5306)

c. The margin of error becomes larger.

54. a. $\bar{p} = 200/369 = 0.5420$

b. $1.96 \sqrt{\dfrac{\bar{p}(1-\bar{p})}{n}} = 1.96 \sqrt{\dfrac{(0.5420)(0.4580)}{369}} = 0.0508$

c. 0.5420 ± 0.0508 $\quad\quad\quad$ (0.4912 to 0.5928)

55. a. $\bar{p} = 504 / 1400 = .36$

b. $1.96 \sqrt{\dfrac{(0.36)(0.64)}{1400}} = 0.0251$

56. a. $n = \dfrac{(2.33)^2 (0.70)(0.30)}{(0.03)^2} = 1266.74$ $\quad$ Use $n = 1267$

b. $n = \dfrac{(2.33)^2 (0.50)(0.50)}{(0.03)^2} = 1508.03$ $\quad$ Use $n = 1509$

57. a. $\bar{p} = 110 / 200 = 0.55$

$0.55 \pm 1.96 \sqrt{\dfrac{(0.55)(0.45)}{200}}$

$.55 \pm .0689$ $\quad\quad\quad\quad$ (.4811 to .6189)

b. $n = \dfrac{(1.96)^2 (0.55)(0.45)}{(0.05)^2} = 380.32$ $\quad$ Use $n = 381$

58. a. $\bar{p} = 340/500 = .68$

b. $\sigma_{\bar{p}} = \sqrt{\dfrac{\bar{p}(1-\bar{p})}{n}} = \sqrt{\dfrac{.68(1-.68)}{500}} = .0209$

$$\overline{p} \pm z_{.025}\sigma_{\overline{p}}$$

$.68 \pm 1.96(.0209)$

$.68 \pm .0409$ $\qquad$ (.6391 to .7209)

59. a. $\quad n = \dfrac{(1.96)^2(0.3)(0.7)}{(0.02)^2} = 2016.84$ $\quad$ Use $n = 2017$

b. $\quad \overline{p} = 520/2017 = 0.2578$

c. $\quad \overline{p} \pm 1.96\sqrt{\dfrac{\overline{p}(1-\overline{p})}{n}}$

$0.2578 \pm 1.96\sqrt{\dfrac{(0.2578)(0.7422)}{2017}}$

0.2578 ± 0.0191 $\qquad$ (0.2387 to 0.2769)

60. a. $\quad \overline{p} = 618 / 1993 = .3101$

b. $\quad \overline{p} \pm 1.96\sqrt{\dfrac{\overline{p}(1-\overline{p})}{1993}}$

$0.3101 \pm 1.96\sqrt{\dfrac{(0.3101)(0.6899)}{1993}}$

$.3101 \pm .0203$ $\quad$ (.2898 to .3304)

c. $\quad n = \dfrac{z^2 p(1-p)}{E^2}$

$z = \dfrac{(1.96)^2(0.3101)(0.6899)}{(0.01)^2} = 8218.64$ $\quad$ Use $n = 8219$

No; the sample appears unnecessarily large. The .02 margin of error reported in part (b) should provide adequate precision.

Chapter 9
Hypothesis Testing

Learning Objectives

1. Learn how to formulate and test hypotheses about a population mean and/or a population proportion.

2. Understand the types of errors possible when conducting a hypothesis test.

3. Be able to determine the probability of making various errors in hypothesis tests.

4. Know how to compute and interpret p-values.

5. Be able to determine the size of a simple random sample necessary to keep the probability of hypothesis testing errors within acceptable limits.

6. Know the definition of the following terms:

    null hypothesis   one-tailed test
    alternative hypothesis   two-tailed test
    type I error p-value
    type II error   operating characteristic curve
    critical value   power curve
    level of significance

Solutions:

1. a. H_0: $\mu \leq 600$ Manager's claim.

    H_a: $\mu > 600$

    b. We are not able to conclude that the manager's claim is wrong.

    c. The manager's claim can be rejected. We can conclude that $\mu > 400$.

2. a. H_0: $\mu \leq 14$

    H_a: $\mu > 14$ Research hypothesis

    b. There is no statistical evidence that the new bonus plan increases sales volume.

    c. The research hypothesis that $\mu > 14$ is supported. We can conclude that the new bonus plan increases the mean sales volume.

3. a. H_0: $\mu = 32$ Specified filling weight

    H_a: $\mu \neq 32$ Overfilling or underfilling exists

    b. There is no evidence that the production line is not operating properly. Allow the production process to continue.

    c. Conclude $\mu \neq 32$ and that overfilling or underfilling exists. Shut down and adjust the production line.

4. a. H_0: $\mu \geq 220$

    H_a: $\mu < 220$ Research hypothesis to see if mean cost is less than $220.

    b. We are unable to conclude that the new method reduces costs.

    c. Conclude $\mu < 220$. Consider implementing the new method based on the conclusion that it lowers the mean cost per hour.

5. a. The Type I error is rejecting H_0 when it is true. In this case, this error occurs if the researcher concludes that the mean newspaper-reading time for individuals in management positions is greater than the national average of 8.6 minutes when in fact it is not.

    b. The Type II error is accepting H_0 when it is false. In this case, this error occurs if the researcher concludes that the mean newspaper-reading time for individuals in management positions is less than or equal to the national average of 8.6 minutes when in fact it is greater than 8.6 minutes.

6. a. H_0: $\mu \leq 1$ The label claim or assumption.

    H_a: $\mu > 1$

    b. Claiming $\mu > 1$ when it is not. This is the error of rejecting the product's claim when the claim is true.

    c. Concluding $\mu \leq 1$ when it is not. In this case, we miss the fact that the product is not meeting its label specification.

7. a. H_0: $\mu \leq 8000$

    H_a: $\mu > 8000$ Research hypothesis to see if the plan increases average sales.

    b. Claiming $\mu > 8000$ when the plan does not increase sales. A mistake could be implementing the plan when it does not help.

    c. Concluding $\mu \leq 8000$ when the plan really would increase sales. This could lead to not implementing a plan that would increase sales.

8. a. H_0: $\mu \geq 220$

    H_a: $\mu < 220$

    b. Claiming $\mu < 220$ when the new method does not lower costs. A mistake could be implementing the method when it does not help.

    c. Concluding $\mu \geq 220$ when the method really would lower costs. This could lead to not implementing a method that would lower costs.

9. a. $z = -1.645$

    Reject H_0 if $z < -1.645$

    b. $z = \dfrac{\overline{x} - \mu}{s/\sqrt{n}} = \dfrac{9.46 - 10}{2/\sqrt{50}} = -1.91$

    Reject H_0; conclude H_a is true.

10. a. $z = 2.05$

    Reject H_0 if $z > 2.05$

    b. $z = \dfrac{\overline{x} - \mu}{s/\sqrt{n}} = \dfrac{16.5 - 15}{7/\sqrt{40}} = 1.36$

    c. Area from $z = 0$ to $z = 1.36$ is .4131
        p-value $= .5000 - .4131 = .0869$

    d. Do not reject H_0

11.   Reject H_0 if $z < -1.645$

    a. $z = \dfrac{\overline{x} - \mu}{\sigma/\sqrt{n}} = \dfrac{22 - 25}{12/\sqrt{100}} = -2.50$ Reject H_0

    b. $z = \dfrac{24 - 25}{12/\sqrt{100}} = -.83$ Do not reject H_0

    c. $z = \dfrac{23.5 - 25}{12/\sqrt{100}} = -1.25$ Do not reject H_0

d. $z = \dfrac{22.8 - 25}{12 / \sqrt{100}} = -1.83$ Reject H_0

12. a. p-value = .5000 - .4656 = .0344   Reject H_0

    b. p-value = .5000 - .1736 = .3264   Do not reject H_0

    c. p-value = .5000 - .4332 = .0668   Do not reject H_0

    d. $z = 3.09$ is the largest table value with .5000 - .4990 = .001 area in tail. For $z = 3.30$, the p-value is less than .001 or approximately 0.   Reject H_0.

    e. Since z is to the left of the mean and the rejection region is in the upper tail, p-value = .5000 + .3413 = .8413.   Do not reject H_0.

13. a. H_0: $\mu \geq 1056$

       H_a: $\mu < 1056$

    b. Reject H_0 if $z < -1.645$

    c. $z = \dfrac{\bar{x} - \mu_0}{s / \sqrt{n}} = \dfrac{910 - 1056}{1600 / \sqrt{400}} = -1.83$

    d. Reject H_0 and conclude that the mean refund of "last minute" filers is less than \$1056.

    e. p-value = .5000 - .4664 = .0336

14. a. $z_{.01} = 2.33$

       Reject H_0 if $z > 2.33$

    b. $z = \dfrac{\bar{x} - \mu}{s / \sqrt{n}} = \dfrac{7.25 - 6.70}{2.5 / \sqrt{200}} = 3.11$

    c. Reject H_0; conclude the mean television viewing time per day is greater than 6.70.

15. a. $z_{.05} = 1.645$

       Reject H_0 if $z < -1.645$

    b. $z = \dfrac{\bar{x} - \mu}{s / \sqrt{n}} = \dfrac{9300 - 10,192}{4500 / \sqrt{100}} = -1.98$

    c. Reject H_0; conclude that the mean sales price of used cars is less than the national average.

16. a. H_0: $\mu \geq 13$

       H_a: $\mu < 13$

    b. $z_{.01} = 2.33$

       Reject H_0 if $z < -2.33$

c. $z = \dfrac{\bar{x} - \mu}{s/\sqrt{n}} = \dfrac{10.8 - 13}{9.2/\sqrt{145}} = -2.88$

d.   Reject H_0; conclude Canadian mean internet usage is less than 13 hours per month.

      Note: p-value = .002

17. a. H_0: $\mu \leq 15$

     H_a: $\mu > 15$

    b. $z = \dfrac{\bar{x} - \mu}{s/\sqrt{n}} = \dfrac{17 - 15}{4/\sqrt{35}} = 2.96$

    c. p-value = .5000 - .4985 = .0015

    d.   Reject H_0; the premium rate should be charged.

18. a. H_0: $\mu \leq 5.72$

     H_a: $\mu > 5.72$

    b. $z = \dfrac{\bar{x} - \mu}{s/\sqrt{n}} = \dfrac{5.98 - 5.72}{1.24/\sqrt{102}} = 2.12$

    c. p-value = .5000 - .4830 = .0170

    d. p-value $< \alpha$; reject H_0. Conclude teens in Chicago have a mean expenditure greater than 5.72.

19. a. H_0: $\mu \geq 181,900$

     H_a: $\mu < 181,900$

    b. $z = \dfrac{\bar{x} - \mu}{s/\sqrt{n}} = \dfrac{166,400 - 181,900}{33,500/\sqrt{40}} = -2.93$

    c. p-value = .5000 - .4983 = .0017

    d. p-value $< \alpha$; reject H_0. Conclude mean selling price in South is less than the national mean selling price.

20. a. H_0: $\mu \leq 37,000$

     H_a: $\mu > 37,000$

    b. $z = \dfrac{\bar{x} - \mu}{s/\sqrt{n}} = \dfrac{38,100 - 37,000}{5200/\sqrt{48}} = 1.47$

    c. p-value = .5000 - .4292 = .0708

    d. p-value $> \alpha$; do not reject H_0. Cannot conclude population mean salary has increased in June 2001.

21. a. Reject H_0 if $z < -1.96$ or $z > 1.96$

    b. $z = \dfrac{\bar{x} - \mu}{s/\sqrt{n}} = \dfrac{10.8 - 10}{2.5/\sqrt{36}} = 2.40$

    Reject H_0; conclude H_a is true.

22. a. Reject H_0 if $z < -2.33$ or $z > 2.33$

    b. $z = \dfrac{\bar{x} - \mu}{s/\sqrt{n}} = \dfrac{14.2 - 15}{5/\sqrt{50}} = -1.13$

    c. p-value $= (2)(.5000 - .3708) = .2584$

    d. Do not reject H_0

23. Reject H_0 if $z < -1.96$ or $z > 1.96$

    a. $z = \dfrac{22 - 25}{10/\sqrt{80}} = -2.68$ Reject H_0

    b. $z = \dfrac{27 - 25}{10/\sqrt{80}} = 1.79$ Do not reject H_0

    c. $z = \dfrac{23.5 - 25}{10/\sqrt{80}} = -1.34$ Do not reject H_0

    d. $z = \dfrac{28 - 25}{10/\sqrt{80}} = 2.68$ Reject H_0

24. a. p-value $= 2(.5000 - .4641) = .0718$ Do not reject H_0

    b. p-value $= 2(.5000 - .1736) = .6528$ Do not reject H_0

    c. p-value $= 2(.5000 - .4798) = .0404$ Reject H_0

    d. approximately 0   Reject H_0

    e. p-value $= 2(.5000 - .3413) = .3174$ Do not reject H_0

25. a. $z_{.025} = 1.96$

    Reject H_0 if $z < -1.96$ or $z > 1.96$

    b. $z = \dfrac{\bar{x} - \mu}{s/\sqrt{n}} = \dfrac{38.5 - 39.2}{4.8/\sqrt{112}} = -1.54$

    c. Do not reject H_0. Cannot conclude a change in the population mean has occurred.

    d. p-value $= 2(.5000 - .4382) = .1236$

26. a. $H_0: \mu = 8$

    $H_a: \mu \ne 8$

    Reject H_0 if $z < -1.96$ or if $z > 1.96$

b. $z = \dfrac{\bar{x} - \mu_0}{s / \sqrt{n}} = \dfrac{7.5 - 8}{3.2 / \sqrt{120}} = -1.71$

c. Do not reject H_0; cannot conclude the mean waiting time differs from eight minutes.

27. a. H_0: $\mu = 16$ Continue production

    H_a: $\mu \neq 16$ Shut down

    Reject H_0 if $z < -1.96$ or if $z > 1.96$

    b. $z = \dfrac{\bar{x} - \mu_0}{\sigma / \sqrt{n}} = \dfrac{16.32 - 16}{.8 / \sqrt{30}} = 2.19$

    Reject H_0 and shut down for adjustment.

    c. $z = \dfrac{\bar{x} - \mu_0}{\sigma / \sqrt{n}} = \dfrac{15.82 - 16}{.8 / \sqrt{30}} = -1.23$

    Do not reject H_0; continue to run.

    d. For $\bar{x} = 16.32$, p-value $= 2 (.5000 - .4857) = .0286$

    For $\bar{x} = 15.82$, p-value $= 2 (.5000 - .3907) = .2186$

28. a. H_0: $\mu = 1075$

    H_a: $\mu \neq 1075$

    b. $z = \dfrac{\bar{x} - \mu}{s / \sqrt{n}} = \dfrac{1160 - 1075}{840 / \sqrt{200}} = 1.43$

    c. p-value $= 2(.5000 - .4236) = .1528$

    d. Do not reject H_0. Cannot conclude a change in mean amount of charitable giving.

29. a. H_0: $\mu = 15.20$

    H_a: $\mu \neq 15.20$

    $z = \dfrac{\bar{x} - \mu_0}{s / \sqrt{n}} = \dfrac{14.30 - 15.20}{5 / \sqrt{35}} = -1.06$

    b. p-value $= 2(.5000 - .3554) = .2892$

    c. Do not reject H_0; the sample does not provide evidence to conclude that there has been a change.

30. a. H_0: $\mu = 26,133$

    H_a: $\mu \neq 26,133$

    b. $z = \dfrac{\bar{x} - \mu}{s / \sqrt{n}} = \dfrac{25,457 - 26,133}{7600 / \sqrt{410}} = -2.09$

c. p-value = $2(.5000 - .4817) = .0366$

d. p-value < α; reject H_0. Conclude population mean wage in Collier County differs from the state mean wage.

31. a. $\bar{x} \pm z_{.025} \dfrac{\sigma}{\sqrt{n}}$

$935 \pm 1.96 \left(\dfrac{180}{\sqrt{200}} \right)$

935 ± 25 or 910 to 960

Since 900 is not in the interval, reject H_0 and conclude $\mu \neq 900$.

b. Reject H_0 if z < -1.96 or if z > 1.96

$z = \dfrac{\bar{x} - \mu_0}{\sigma / \sqrt{n}} = \dfrac{935 - 900}{180 / \sqrt{200}} = 2.75$

Reject H_0

c. p-value = $2(.5000 - .4970) = .0060$

32. a. The upper 95% confidence limit is computed as follows:

$\bar{x} + z_{.05} \left(\dfrac{s}{\sqrt{n}} \right)$

$14.50 + 1.645 \left(\dfrac{.60}{\sqrt{36}} \right) = 14.66$

Thus, we are 95% confident that μ is $14.66 per hour or less.

b. Since $15.00 is not in the interval $14.66 per hour or less, we reject H_0.

Conclude that the mean wage rate is less than $15.00.

33. a. With 15 degrees of freedom, $t_{.05}$ = 1.753

Reject H_0 if t > 1.753

b. $t = \dfrac{\bar{x} - \mu_0}{s / \sqrt{n}} = \dfrac{11 - 10}{3 / \sqrt{16}} = 1.33$ Do not reject H_0

34. a. $\bar{x} = \sum x_i / n = 108 / 6 = 18$

b. $s = \sqrt{\dfrac{\sum (x_i - \bar{x})}{n - 1}} = \sqrt{\dfrac{10}{6 - 1}} = 1.414$

c. Reject H_0 if t < -2.571 or t > 2.571

d. $t = \dfrac{\bar{x} - \mu_0}{s/\sqrt{n}} = \dfrac{18 - 20}{1.414/\sqrt{6}} = -3.46$

e. Reject H_0; conclude H_a is true.

35. Reject H_0 if $t < -1.721$

a. $t = \dfrac{13 - 15}{8/\sqrt{22}} = -1.17$ Do not reject H_0

b. $t = \dfrac{11.5 - 15}{8/\sqrt{22}} = -2.05$ Reject H_0

c. $t = \dfrac{15 - 15}{8/\sqrt{22}} = 0$ Do not reject H_0

d. $t = \dfrac{19 - 15}{8/\sqrt{22}} = 2.35$ Do not reject H_0

36. Use the t distribution with 15 degrees of freedom

a. p-value $= .01$ Reject H_0

b. p-value $= .10$ Do not reject H_0

c. p-value is between .025 and .05   Reject H_0

d. p-value is greater than .10   Do not reject H_0

e. p-value is approximately 0   Reject H_0

37. a. H_0: $\mu = 3.00$

H_a: $\mu \neq 3.00$

b. $t_{.025} = 2.262$

Reject H_0 if $t < -2.262$ or if $t > 2.262$

c. $\bar{x} = \dfrac{\Sigma x_i}{n} = \dfrac{28}{10} = 2.80$

d. $s = \sqrt{\dfrac{\Sigma(x_i - \bar{x})^2}{n-1}} = \sqrt{\dfrac{.44}{10-1}} = .70$

e. $t = \dfrac{\bar{x} - \mu}{s/\sqrt{n}} = \dfrac{2.80 - 3.00}{.70/\sqrt{10}} = -.90$

f. Do not reject H_0; cannot conclude the population means earning per share has changed.

g. $t_{.10} = 1.383$

   p-value is greater than $.10 \times 2 = .20$

   Actual p-value $= .3916$

38. a. $t_{.025} = 2.064$ 24 degrees of freedom

    Reject H_0 if $t < -2.064$ or if $t > 2.064$

    b. $t = \dfrac{\bar{x} - \mu}{s/\sqrt{n}} = \dfrac{84.50 - 90}{14.50/\sqrt{25}} = -1.90$

    c. Do not reject H_0; cannot conclude the mean expenditure in Corning differs from the U.S. mean expenditure.

39. a. $t_{.05} = 1.895$ 7 degrees of freedom

    b. $\bar{x} = \dfrac{\Sigma x_i}{n} = \dfrac{475}{8} = 59.375$

    c. $s = \sqrt{\dfrac{\Sigma(x_i - \bar{x})^2}{n-1}} = \sqrt{\dfrac{123.87}{8-1}} = 4.21$

    d. $t = \dfrac{\bar{x} - \mu}{s/\sqrt{n}} = \dfrac{59.38 - 55}{4.21/\sqrt{8}} = 2.94$

    c. Reject H_0; conclude that the mean number of hours worked exceeds 55.

40. a. H_0: $\mu = 4000$

    H_a: $\mu \neq 4000$

    b. $t_{.05} = 2.160$ 13 degrees of freedom

    Reject H_0 if $t < -2.160$ or if $t > 2.160$

    c. $t = \dfrac{\bar{x} - \mu}{s/\sqrt{n}} = \dfrac{4120 - 4000}{275/\sqrt{14}} = +1.63$

    d. Do not reject H_0; Cannot conclude that the mean cost in New City differs from $4000.

    e. With 13 degrees of freedom

    $t_{.05} = 1.771$

    $t_{.10} = 1.350$

    1.63 is between 1.350 and 1.771. Therefore the p-value is between .10 and .20.

41. a. H_0: $\mu \le 280$

   H_a: $\mu > 280$

   b.   286.9 - 280 = 6.9 yards

   c. $t_{.05} = 1.860$ with 8 degrees of freedom

   d. $t = \dfrac{\bar{x} - \mu}{s/\sqrt{n}} = \dfrac{286.9 - 280}{10/\sqrt{9}} = 2.07$

   e.   Reject H_0; The population mean distance of the new driver is greater than the USGA approved driver..

   f. $t_{.05} = 1.860$

   $t_{.025} = 2.306$

   p-value is between .025 and .05

   Actual p-value = .0361

42. a. H_0: $\mu \le 2$

   H_a: $\mu > 2$

   b.   With 9 degrees of freedom, reject H_0 if $t > 1.833$

   c. $\bar{x} = \sum x_i / n = 24 / 10 = 2.4$

   d. $s = \sqrt{\dfrac{\sum(x_i - \bar{x})^2}{n-1}} = \sqrt{\dfrac{2.40}{9}} = .516$

   e. $t = \dfrac{\bar{x} - \mu_0}{s/\sqrt{n}} = \dfrac{2.4 - 2}{.516/\sqrt{10}} = 2.45$

   f.   Reject H_0 and claim μ is greater than 2 hours. For cost estimating purposes, consider using more than 2 hours of labor time.

   g. $t_{.025} = 2.262$, $t_{.01} = 2.821$

   p-value is between .025 and .01.

43. a.   Reject H_0 if $z > 1.645$

   b. $\sigma_{\bar{p}} = \sqrt{\dfrac{.50(.50)}{200}} = .0354$

   $z = \dfrac{\bar{p} - p}{\sigma_{\bar{p}}} = \dfrac{.57 - .50}{.0354} = 1.98$ Reject H_0

44. a. Reject H_0 if $z < -1.96$ or $z > 1.96$

    b. $\sigma_{\bar{p}} = \sqrt{\dfrac{.20(.80)}{400}} = .02$

    $z = \dfrac{\bar{p} - p}{\sigma_{\bar{p}}} = \dfrac{.175 - .20}{.02} = -1.25$

    c. p-value $= 2(.5000 - .3944) = .2122$

    d. Do not reject H_0.

45. Reject H_0 if $z < -1.645$

    a. $\sigma_{\bar{p}} = \sqrt{\dfrac{.75(.25)}{300}} = .0250$

    $z = \dfrac{\bar{p} - p}{\sigma_{\bar{p}}} = \dfrac{.68 - .75}{.025} = -2.80$

    p-value $= .5000 - .4974 = .0026$

    Reject H_0.

    b. $z = \dfrac{\bar{p} - p}{\sigma_{\bar{p}}} = \dfrac{.72 - .75}{.025} = -1.20$

    p-value $= .5000 - .3849 = .1151$

    Do not reject H_0.

    c. $z = \dfrac{\bar{p} - p}{\sigma_{\bar{p}}} = \dfrac{.70 - .75}{.025} = -2.00$

    p-value $= .5000 - .4772 = .0228$

    Reject H_0.

    d. $z = \dfrac{\bar{p} - p}{\sigma_{\bar{p}}} = \dfrac{.77 - .75}{.025} = .80$

    p-value $= .5000 + .2881 = .7881$

    Do not reject H_0.

46. a. H_0: $p \leq .40$

    H_a: $p > .40$

    b. Reject H_0 if $z > 1.645$

    c. $\bar{p} = 188/420 = .4476$

$$\sigma_{\overline{p}} = \sqrt{\frac{p(1-p)}{n}} = \sqrt{\frac{.40(1-.40)}{420}} = .0239$$

$$z = \frac{\overline{p} - p}{\sigma_{\overline{p}}} = \frac{.4476 - .40}{.0239} = 1.99$$

d. Reject H_0. Conclude that there has been an increase in the proportion of users receiving more than ten e-mails per day.

47. a. $z_{.05} = 1.645$

    Reject H_0 if $z < -1.645$

  b. $\overline{p} = 52/100 = .52$

$$\sigma_{\overline{p}} = \sqrt{\frac{p(1-p)}{n}} = \sqrt{\frac{.64(1-.64)}{100}} = .0480$$

$$z = \frac{\overline{p} - p}{\sigma_{\overline{p}}} = \frac{.52 - .64}{.0480} = -2.50$$

  c. Reject H_0. Conclude less than 64% of shoppers believe supermarket ketchup is as good as the national brand.

  d. p-value $= .5000 - .4938 = .0062$

48. a. $\overline{p} = 285/500 = .57$

  b. $\sigma_{\overline{p}} = \sqrt{\frac{p(1-p)}{n}} = \sqrt{\frac{.50(1-.50)}{500}} = .0224$

$$z = \frac{\overline{p} - p}{\sigma_{\overline{p}}} = \frac{.57 - .50}{.0224} = 3.13$$

  c. $z = 3.13$ is not in the table. Closest value is $z = 3.09$. Thus, p-value is approximately .5000 - .4990 = .001

  d. p-value $< .01$, Reject H_0. Over 50% prefer Burger King fries.

  e. Yes; the statistical evidence shows Burger King fries are preferred. The give-away was a good way to get potential customers to try the new fries.

49. a. H_0: $p = .48$

    H_a: $p \neq .48$

  b. $z_{.025} = 1.96$

    Reject H_0 if $z < -1.96$ or if $z > 1.96$

  c. $\overline{p} = 368/800 = .45$

d. $\quad \sigma_{\bar{p}} = \sqrt{\dfrac{p(1-p)}{n}} = \sqrt{\dfrac{.48(1-.48)}{800}} = .0177$

$z = \dfrac{\bar{p}-p}{\sigma_{\bar{p}}} = \dfrac{.45-.48}{.0177} = -1.70$

d.   Do not reject H_0. Cannot conclude the proportion of drivers who do not stop has changed.

50. a. $\bar{p} = 67/105 = .6381$ (about 64%)

     b. $\sigma_{\bar{p}} = \sqrt{\dfrac{p(1-p)}{n}} = \sqrt{\dfrac{.50(1-.50)}{105}} = .0488$

$z = \dfrac{\bar{p}-p}{\sigma_{\bar{p}}} = \dfrac{.6381-.50}{.0488} = 2.83$

     c. p-value = $2(.5000 - .4977) = .0046$

     d. p-value $< .01$, reject H_0. Conclude preference is for the four ten-hour day schedule.

51. a. H_0: $p = .44$

        H_a: $p \neq .44$

     b. $\bar{p} = 205/500 = .41$

$\sigma_{\bar{p}} = \sqrt{\dfrac{p(1-p)}{n}} = \sqrt{\dfrac{.44(1-.44)}{500}} = .0222$

$z = \dfrac{\bar{p}-p}{\sigma_{\bar{p}}} = \dfrac{.41-.44}{.0222} = -1.35$

p-value = $2(.5 - .4115) = .1770$

Do not reject H_0. Cannot conclude that there has been a change in the proportion of repeat customers.

     c. $\bar{p} = 245/500 = .49$

$z = \dfrac{\bar{p}-p}{\sigma_{\bar{p}}} = \dfrac{.49-.44}{.0222} = 2.25$

p-value = $2(.5 - .4878) = .0244$

Reject H_0. conclude that the proportion of repeat customers has changed. The point estimate of the percentage of repeat customers is now 49%.

52. a. $\sigma_{\bar{p}} = \sqrt{\dfrac{p(1-p)}{n}} = \sqrt{\dfrac{.75(1-.75)}{300}} = .025$

    $z = \dfrac{\bar{p} - p}{\sigma_{\bar{p}}} = \dfrac{.72 - .75}{.025} = -1.20$

    b. p-value = .5000 - .3849 = .1151

    c. Do not reject H_0. Cannot conclude the manager's claim is wrong based on this sample evidence.

53. $H_0: p \leq .15$

    $H_a: p > .15$

    Reject H_0 if $z > 2.33$

    $\sigma_{\bar{p}} = \sqrt{\dfrac{p(1-p)}{n}} = \sqrt{\dfrac{.15(.85)}{500}} = .0160$

    $\bar{p} = 88/500 = .176$

    $z = \dfrac{\bar{p} - p_0}{\sigma_{\bar{p}}} = \dfrac{.176 - .15}{.0160} = 1.63$

    Do not reject H_0; $p \leq .15$ cannot be rejected. Thus the special offer should not be initiated.

    p-value = .5000 - .4484 = .0516

54. a. $H_0: p \geq .047$

    $H_a: p < .047$

    b. $\bar{p} = 35/1182 = .0296$

    c. $\sigma_{\bar{p}} = \sqrt{\dfrac{.047(1-.047)}{1182}} = .0062$

    $z = \dfrac{\bar{p} - p}{\sigma_{\bar{p}}} = \dfrac{.0296 - .047}{.0062} = -2.82$

    d. p-value = .5000 - .4976 = .0024

    e. p-value $< \alpha$, reject H_0. The error rate for Brooks Robinson is less than the overall error rate.

55. $H_0: p \geq .20$

    $H_a: p < .20$

    Reject H_0 if $z < -1.645$

    $\bar{p} = 83/596 = .1393$

$$\sigma_{\bar{p}} = \sqrt{\frac{p(1-p)}{n}} = \sqrt{\frac{.20(1-.20)}{596}} = .0164$$

$$z = \frac{\bar{p} - p}{\sigma_{\bar{p}}} = \frac{.1393 - .20}{.0164} = -3.71$$

p-value ≈ 0

Reject H_0; conclude that less than 20% of workers would work for less pay in order to have more personal and leisure time.

56.　　$\sigma_{\bar{x}} = \dfrac{\sigma}{\sqrt{n}} = \dfrac{5}{\sqrt{120}} = .46$

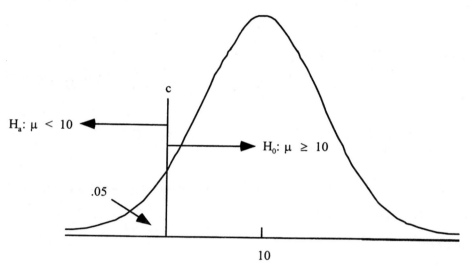

$c = 10 - 1.645 (5 / \sqrt{120}) = 9.25$

Reject H_0 if $\bar{x} < 9.25$

a. When $\mu = 9$,

$$z = \frac{9.25 - 9}{5 / \sqrt{120}} = .55$$

Prob $(H_0) = (.5000 - .2088) = .2912$

b. Type II error

c. When $\mu = 8$,

$$z = \frac{9.25 - 8}{5 / \sqrt{120}} = 2.74$$

$\beta = (.5000 - .4969) = .0031$

57.   Reject H_0 if $z < -1.96$ or if $z > 1.96$

$$\sigma_{\bar{x}} = \frac{\sigma}{\sqrt{n}} = \frac{10}{\sqrt{200}} = .71$$

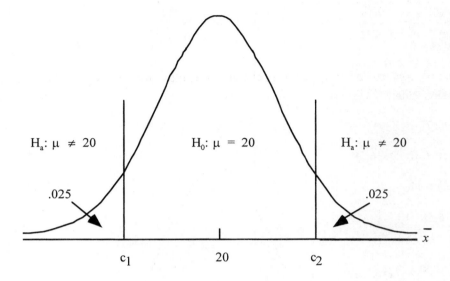

$c_1 = 20 - 1.96 \, (10 / \sqrt{200} \,) = 18.61$

$c_2 = 20 + 1.96 \, (10 / \sqrt{200} \,) = 21.39$

a. $\mu = 18$

$$z = \frac{18.61 - 18}{10 / \sqrt{200}} = .86$$

$\beta = .5000 - .3051 = .1949$

b. $\mu = 22.5$

$$z = \frac{21.39 - 22.5}{10 / \sqrt{200}} = -1.57$$

$\beta = .5000 - .4418 = .0582$

c. $\mu = 21$

$$z = \frac{21.39 - 21}{10 / \sqrt{200}} = .55$$

$\beta = .5000 + .2088 = .7088$

58. a. H_0: $\mu \leq 15$

H_a: $\mu > 15$

Concluding $\mu \leq 15$ when this is not true. Fowle would not charge the premium rate even though the rate should be charged.

b. Reject H_0 if $z > 2.33$

$$z = \frac{\bar{x} - \mu_0}{\sigma/\sqrt{n}} = \frac{\bar{x} - 15}{4/\sqrt{35}} = 2.33$$

Solve for $\bar{x} = 16.58$

Decision Rule:

Accept H_0 if $\bar{x} \leq 16.58$

Reject H_0 if $\bar{x} > 16.58$

For $\mu = 17$,

$$z = \frac{16.58 - 17}{4/\sqrt{35}} = -.62$$

$\beta = .5000 - .2324 = .2676$

c. For $\mu = 18$,

$$z = \frac{16.58 - 18}{4/\sqrt{35}} = -2.10$$

$\beta = .5000 - .4821 = .0179$

59. a. H_0: $\mu \geq 25$

   H_a: $\mu < 25$

   Reject H_0 if $z < -2.05$

   $$z = \frac{\bar{x} - \mu_0}{\sigma/\sqrt{n}} = \frac{\bar{x} - 25}{3/\sqrt{30}} = -2.05$$

   Solve for $\bar{x} = 23.88$

   Decision Rule:

   Accept H_0 if $\bar{x} \geq 23.88$

   Reject H_0 if $\bar{x} < 23.88$

b. For $\mu = 23$,

$$z = \frac{23.88 - 23}{3/\sqrt{30}} = 1.61$$

$\beta = .5000 - .4463 = .0537$

c. For $\mu = 24$,

$$z = \frac{23.88 - 24}{3/\sqrt{30}} = -.22$$

$\beta = .5000 + .0871 = .5871$

d. The Type II error cannot be made in this case. Note that when $\mu = 25.5$, H_0 is true. The Type II error can only be made when H_0 is false.

60. a. Accepting H_0 and concluding the mean average age was 28 years when it was not.

b. Reject H_0 if $z < -1.96$ or if $z > 1.96$

$$z = \frac{\bar{x} - \mu_0}{\sigma/\sqrt{n}} = \frac{\bar{x} - 28}{6/\sqrt{100}}$$

Solving for $\bar{x}$, we find

at $z = -1.96$, $\bar{x} = 26.82$
at $z = +1.96$, $\bar{x} = 29.18$

Decision Rule:

Accept H_0 if $26.82 \leq \bar{x} \leq 29.18$

Reject H_0 if $\bar{x} < 26.82$ or if $\bar{x} > 29.18$

At $\mu = 26$,

$$z = \frac{26.82 - 26}{6/\sqrt{100}} = 1.37$$

$\beta = .5000 + .4147 = .0853$

At $\mu = 27$,

$$z = \frac{26.82 - 27}{6/\sqrt{100}} = -.30$$

$\beta = .5000 + .1179 = .6179$

At $\mu = 29$,

$$z = \frac{29.18 - 29}{6/\sqrt{100}} = .30$$

$\beta = .5000 + .1179 = .6179$

At $\mu = 30$,

$$z = \frac{29.18 - 30}{6/\sqrt{100}} = -1.37$$

$\beta = .5000 - .4147 = .0853$

c.   Power $= 1 - \beta$

at $\mu = 26$,   Power $= 1 - .0853 = .9147$

When $\mu = 26$, there is a .9147 probability that the test will correctly reject the null hypothesis that $\mu = 28$.

61. a.   Accepting H_0 and letting the process continue to run when actually over - filling or under - filling exists.

b.   Decision Rule: Reject H_0 if $z < -1.96$ or if $z > 1.96$ indicates

Accept H_0 if $15.71 \leq \bar{x} \leq 16.29$

Reject H_0 if $\bar{x} < 15.71$ or if $\bar{x} > 16.29$

For $\mu = 16.5$

$$z = \frac{16.29 - 16.5}{.8/\sqrt{30}} = -1.44$$

$\beta = .5000 - .4251 = .0749$

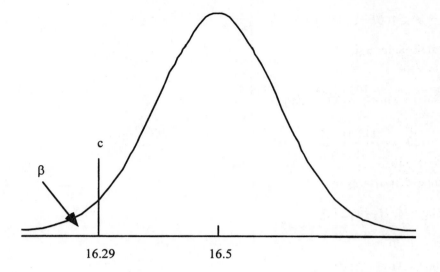

16.29   16.5

c.   Power = 1 - .0749 = .9251

d.   The power curve shows the probability of rejecting H_0 for various possible values of μ. In particular, it shows the probability of stopping and adjusting the machine under a variety of underfilling and overfilling situations. The general shape of the power curve for this case is

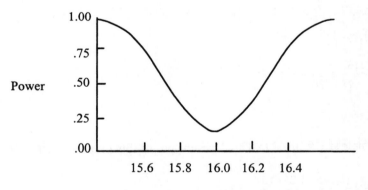

Possible Values of u

62. $c = \mu_0 + z_{.01} \dfrac{\sigma}{\sqrt{n}} = 15 + 2.33 \dfrac{4}{\sqrt{50}} = 16.32$

At $\mu = 17$ $z = \dfrac{16.32 - 17}{4/\sqrt{50}} = -1.20$

$\beta = .5000 - .3849 = .1151$

At $\mu = 18$ $z = \dfrac{16.32 - 18}{4/\sqrt{50}} = -2.97$

$\beta = .5000 - .4985 = .0015$

Increasing the sample size reduces the probability of making a Type II error.

63. a.   Accept $\mu \le 100$ when it is false.

   b.   Critical value for test:

$$c = \mu_0 + z_{.05}\frac{\sigma}{\sqrt{n}} = 100 + 1.645\frac{75}{\sqrt{40}} = 119.51$$

At $\mu = 120$ $z = \dfrac{119.51-120}{75/\sqrt{40}} = -.04$

$\beta = .5000 - .0160 = .4840$

   c.   At $\mu = 13$ $z = \dfrac{119.51-130}{75/\sqrt{40}} = -.88$

$\beta = .5000 - .3106 = .1894$

   d.   Critical value for test:

$$c = \mu_0 + z_{.05}\frac{\sigma}{\sqrt{n}} = 100 + 1.645\frac{75}{\sqrt{80}} = 113.79$$

At $\mu = 120$ $z = \dfrac{113.79-120}{75/\sqrt{80}} = -.74$

$\beta = .5000 - .2704 = .2296$

At $\mu = 130$ $z = \dfrac{113.79-130}{75/\sqrt{80}} = -1.93$

$\beta = .5000 - .4732 = .0268$

Increasing the sample size from 40 to 80 reduces the probability of making a Type II error.

64. $n = \dfrac{(z_\alpha + z_\beta)^2 \sigma^2}{(\mu_0 - \mu_a)^2} = \dfrac{(1.645 + 1.28)^2 (5)^2}{(10-9)^2} = 214$

65. $n = \dfrac{(z_\alpha + z_\beta)^2 \sigma^2}{(\mu_0 - \mu_a)^2} = \dfrac{(1.96 + 1.645)^2 (10)^2}{(20-22)^2} = 325$

66.   At $\mu_0 = 3$, $\alpha = .01$. $z_{.01} = 2.33$

   At $\mu_a = 2.9375$, $\beta = .10$. $z_{.10} = 1.28$

   $\sigma = .18$

$$n = \frac{(z_\alpha + z_\beta)^2 \sigma^2}{(\mu_0 - \mu_a)^2} = \frac{(2.33 + 1.28)^2 (.18)^2}{(3 - 2.9375)^2} = 108.09 \quad \text{Use } 109$$

67. $\quad$ At $\mu_0 = 400,\qquad \alpha = .02.\qquad z_{.02} = 2.05$

$\quad$ At $\mu_a = 385,\qquad \beta = .10.\qquad z_{.10} = 1.28$

$\quad \sigma = 30$

$$n = \frac{(z_\alpha + z_\beta)^2 \sigma^2}{(\mu_0 - \mu_a)^2} = \frac{(2.05 + 1.28)^2 (30)^2}{(400 - 385)^2} = 44.4 \quad \text{Use } 45$$

68. $\quad$ At $\mu_0 = 28,\qquad \alpha = .05.$ Note however for this two - tailed test, $z_{\alpha/2} = z_{.025} = 1.96$

$\quad$ At $\mu_a = 29,\qquad \beta = .15.\qquad z_{.15} = 1.04$

$\quad \sigma = 6$

$$n = \frac{(z_{\alpha/2} + z_\beta)^2 \sigma^2}{(\mu_0 - \mu_a)^2} = \frac{(1.96 + 1.04)^2 (6)^2}{(28 - 29)^2} = 324$$

69. $\quad$ At $\mu_0 = 25,\qquad \alpha = .02.\qquad z_{.02} = 2.05$

$\quad$ At $\mu_a = 24,\qquad \beta = .20.\qquad z_{.20} = .84$

$\quad \sigma = 3$

$$n = \frac{(z_\alpha + z_\beta)^2 \sigma^2}{(\mu_0 - \mu_a)^2} = \frac{(2.05 + .84)^2 (3)^2}{(25 - 24)^2} = 75.2 \quad \text{Use } 76$$

70. a. $\quad H_0: \mu \le 45{,}250$

$\quad\quad H_a: \mu > 45{,}250$

$\quad$ b. $\quad z = \dfrac{\bar{x} - \mu}{s/\sqrt{n}} = \dfrac{47{,}000 - 45{,}250}{6300/\sqrt{95}} = 2.71$

$\quad$ c. $\quad p\text{-value} = .5000 - .4966 = .0034$

$\quad$ d. $\quad p\text{-value} < \alpha$; reject H_0. New York City school teachers must have a higher mean annual salary.

71. $\quad H_0: \mu \ge 30$

$\quad\quad H_a: \mu < 30$

$\quad$ Reject H_0 if $z < -2.33$

$$z = \frac{\bar{x} - \mu_0}{s/\sqrt{n}} = \frac{29.5 - 30}{1.8/\sqrt{50}} = -1.96$$

$\quad p\text{-value} = .5000 - .4750 = .0250$

Do not reject H_0; the sample evidence does not support the conclusion that the Ford Taurus provides less than 30 miles per gallon.

72. H_0: $\mu \le 25,000$

  H_a: $\mu > 25,000$

  Reject H_0 if $z > 1.645$

$$z = \frac{\bar{x} - \mu_0}{s/\sqrt{n}} = \frac{26,000 - 25,000}{2,500/\sqrt{32}} = 2.26$$

  p-value = .5000 - .4881 = .0119

  Reject H_0; the claim should be rejected. The mean cost is greater than $25,000.

73. H_0: $\mu = 120$

  H_a: $\mu \ne 120$

  With $n = 10$, use a t distribution with 9 degrees of freedom.

  Reject H_0 if $t < -2.262$ or of $t > 2.262$

$$\bar{x} = \frac{\Sigma x_i}{n} = 118.9$$

$$s = \sqrt{\frac{\Sigma(x_i - \bar{x})^2}{n-1}} = 4.93$$

$$t = \frac{\bar{x} - \mu_0}{s/\sqrt{n}} = \frac{118.9 - 120}{4.93/\sqrt{10}} = -.71$$

  Do not reject H_0; the results do not permit rejection of the assumption that $\mu = 120$.

74. a. H_0: $\mu = 550$

  H_a: $\mu \ne 550$

  Reject H_0 if $z < -1.96$ or if $z > 1.96$

$$z = \frac{\bar{x} - \mu_0}{s/\sqrt{n}} = \frac{562 - 550}{40/\sqrt{36}} = 1.80$$

  Do not reject H_0; the claim of $550 per month cannot be rejected.

 b. p-value = 2(.5000 - .4641) = .0718

75. a. H_0: $\mu \le 75$

  H_a: $\mu > 75$

  Reject H_0 if $z > 1.645$

b. $z = \dfrac{\bar{x} - \mu_0}{s/\sqrt{n}} = \dfrac{82.50 - 75.00}{30/\sqrt{40}} = 1.58$

Do not reject H_0; there is no evidence to conclude an increase in maintenance cost exists.

c. p-value $= .5000 - .4429 = .0571$

Since $.0571 > .05$, do not reject H_0.

76. a. H_0: $\mu \le 72$

H_a: $\mu > 72$

$z = \dfrac{\bar{x} - 72}{s/\sqrt{n}} = \dfrac{80 - 72}{20/\sqrt{30}} = 2.19$

p-value $= .5000 - .4857 = .0143$

b. Since p-value $< .05$, reject H_0; the mean idle time exceeds 72 minutes per day.

77. a. H_0: $p \le .60$

H_a: $p > .60$

Reject H_0 if $z > 1.645$

$\sigma_{\bar{p}} = \sqrt{\dfrac{p(1-p)}{n}} = \sqrt{\dfrac{.60(.40)}{40}} = .0775$

$\bar{p} = 27/40 = .675$

$z = \dfrac{\bar{p} - p}{\sigma_{\bar{p}}} = \dfrac{.675 - .60}{.0775} = .97$

Do not reject H_0; the sample results do not justify the conclusion that $p > .60$ for Midwesterners.

b. p-value $= .5000 - .3340 = .1660$

78. a. $\bar{p} = 355/546 = .6502$

b. $\sigma_{\bar{p}} = \sqrt{\dfrac{p(1-p)}{n}} = \sqrt{\dfrac{.67(1-.67)}{546}} = .0201$

$z = \dfrac{\bar{p} - p}{\sigma_{\bar{p}}} = \dfrac{.6502 - .67}{.0201} = -.98$

c. p-value $= 2(.5000 - .3365) = .3270$

d. p-value $\ge \alpha$, do not reject H_0. The assumption of two-thirds cannot be rejected.

79. H_0: $p \geq .79$

        H_a: $p < .79$

        Reject H_0 if $z < -1.645$

        $\bar{p} = 360/500 = .72$

$$z = \frac{\bar{p} - p_0}{\sigma_{\bar{p}}} = \frac{.72 - .79}{\sqrt{\frac{(.79)(.21)}{500}}} = -3.84$$

        Reject H_0; conclude that the proportion is less than .79 in 1995.

80. a. The research is attempting to see if it can be concluded that less than 50% of the working population hold jobs that they planned to hold.

      b. $\sigma_{\bar{p}} = \sqrt{\frac{.50(.50)}{1350}} = .0136$

          $z = \frac{.41 - .50}{.0136} = -6.62$

          p-value ≈ 0

          Reject H_0 if $z < -2.33$

          Reject H_0; it can be concluded that less than 50% of the working population hold jobs that they planned to hold. The majority hold jobs due to chance, lack of choice, or some other unplanned reason.

81. $\sigma_{\bar{p}} = \sqrt{\frac{.75(.25)}{356}} = .0229$

        $\bar{p} = 313/356 = .88$

        $z = \frac{.88 - .75}{.0229} = 5.68$

        p-value ≈ 0

        Reject H_0; conclude $p \neq .75$. Data suggest that 88% of women wear shoes that are at least one size too small.

82. a. $\bar{p} = 330/400 = .825$

      b. $\sigma_{\bar{p}} = \sqrt{\frac{p(1-p)}{n}} = \sqrt{\frac{.78(1-.78)}{400}} = .0207$

          $z = \frac{\bar{p} - p}{\sigma_{\bar{p}}} = \frac{.825 - .78}{.0207} = 2.17$

c. p-value $= 2(.5000 - .4850) = .03$

d. p-value $< \alpha$, reject H_0. Arrival rate has changed from 78%. Service appears to be improving.

83. $H_0: \ p \ \geq \ .90$

   $H_a: \ p \ < \ .90$

   Reject H_0 if $z \ < \ -1.645$

   $\sigma_{\bar{p}} = \sqrt{\dfrac{.90(.10)}{58}} = .0394$

   $\bar{p} = 49/58 = .845$

   $z = \dfrac{\bar{p} - p}{\sigma_{\bar{p}}} = \dfrac{.845 - .90}{.0394} = -1.40$

   p-value $= \ .5000 - .4192 \ = \ .0808$

   Do not reject H_0; the station's claim cannot be rejected

84.   a. $\bar{p} = 44/125 = .352$

   b. $\sigma_{\bar{p}} = \sqrt{\dfrac{p(1-p)}{n}} = \sqrt{\dfrac{.47(1-.47)}{125}} = .0446$

      $z = \dfrac{\bar{p} - p}{\sigma_{\bar{p}}} = \dfrac{.352 - .47}{.0446} = -2.64$

   c. p-value $= \ .5000 - .4959 \ = \ .0041$

   d.   Reject H_0; conclude that the proportion of food sample containing pesticide residues has been reduced.

85.   a. $H_0: \ \mu \ \leq \ 72$

   $H_a: \ \mu \ > \ 72$

   Reject H_0 if $z \ > \ 1.645$

   $z = \dfrac{\bar{x} - \mu_0}{\sigma/\sqrt{n}} = \dfrac{\bar{x} - 72}{20/\sqrt{30}} = 1.645$

   Solve for $\bar{x} = 78$

   Decision Rule:

   Accept H_0 if $\bar{x} \leq 78$

   Reject H_0 if $\bar{x} > 78$

For $\mu = 80$

$$z = \frac{78-80}{20/\sqrt{30}} = -.55$$

$\beta = .5000 - .2088 = .2912$

b.   For $\mu = 75$,

$$z = \frac{78-75}{20/\sqrt{30}} = .82$$

$\beta = .5000 + .2939 = .7939$

c.   For $\mu = 70$, H_0 is true. In this case the Type II error cannot be made.

d.   Power $= 1 - \beta$

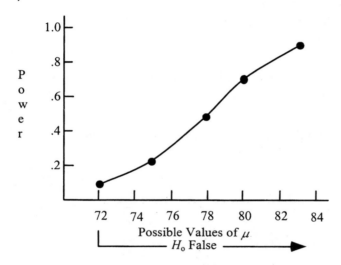

86. H_0: $\mu \geq 15,000$

H_a: $\mu < 15,000$

At $\mu_0 = 15,000, \alpha = .02.$ $z_{.02} = 2.05$

At $\mu_a = 14,000, \beta = .05.$ $z_{.10} = 1.645$

$$n = \frac{(z_\alpha + z_\beta)^2 \sigma^2}{(\mu_0 - \mu_a)^2} = \frac{(2.05 + 1.645)^2 (4,000)^2}{(15,000 - 14,000)^2} = 218.5 \quad \text{Use 219}$$

87. H_0: $\mu = 120$

H_a: $\mu \neq 120$

At $\mu_0 = 120,$ $\alpha = .05.$ With a two - tailed test, $z_{\alpha/2} = z_{.025} = 1.96$

At $\mu_a = 117,$ $\beta = .02.$ $z_{.02} = 2.05$

$$n = \frac{(z_{\alpha/2} + z_{\beta})^2 \sigma^2}{(\mu_0 - \mu_a)^2} = \frac{(1.96 + 2.05)^2 (5)^2}{(120 - 117)^2} = 44.7 \quad \text{Use 45}$$

b. Example calculation for $\mu = 118$.

Reject H_0 if $z < -1.96$ or if $z > 1.96$

$$z = \frac{\bar{x} - \mu_0}{\sigma / \sqrt{n}} = \frac{\bar{x} - 120}{5 / \sqrt{45}}$$

Solve for $\bar{x}$.   At $z = -1.96$, $\bar{x} = 118.54$

At $z = +1.96$, $\bar{x} = 121.46$

Decision Rule:

Accept H_0 if $118.54 \leq \bar{x} \leq 121.46$

Reject H_0 if $\bar{x} < 118.54$ or if $\bar{x} > 121.46$

For $\mu = 118$,

$$z = \frac{118.54 - 118}{5 / \sqrt{45}} = .72$$

$\beta = .5000 + .2642 = .2358$

Other Results:

If μ is	z	β
117	2.07	.0192
118	.72	.2358
119	-.62	.7291
121	+.62	.7291
122	+.72	.2358
123	-2.07	.0192

Chapter 10
Statistical Inference about Means and Proportions with Two Populations

Learning Objectives

1. Be able to develop interval estimates and conduct hypothesis tests about the difference between the means of two populations.

2. Know the properties of the sampling distribution of the difference between two means $(\bar{x}_1 - \bar{x}_2)$.

3. Be able to use the t distribution to conduct statistical inferences about the difference between the means of two normal populations with equal variances.

4. Understand the concept and use of a pooled variance estimate.

5. Learn how to analyze the difference between the means of two populations when the samples are independent and when the samples are matched.

6. Be able to develop interval estimates and conduct hypothesis tests about the difference between the proportions of two populations.

7. Know the properties of the sampling distribution of the difference between two proportions $(\bar{p}_1 - \bar{p}_2)$.

Solutions:

1. a. $\bar{x}_1 - \bar{x}_2 = 13.6 - 11.6 = 2$

    b. $s_{\bar{x}_1 - \bar{x}_2} = \sqrt{\dfrac{s_1^2}{n_1} + \dfrac{s_2^2}{n_2}} = \sqrt{\dfrac{(2.2)^2}{50} + \dfrac{(3)^2}{35}} = 0.595$

    $2 \pm 1.645\,(.595)$

    $2 \pm .98 \qquad (1.02 \text{ to } 2.98)$

    c. $2 \pm 1.96\,(.595)$

    $2 \pm 1.17 \qquad (0.83 \text{ to } 3.17)$

2. a. $\bar{x}_1 - \bar{x}_2 = 22.5 - 20.1 = 2.4$

    b. $s^2 = \dfrac{(n_1 - 1)s_1^2 + (n_2 - 1)s_2^2}{n_1 + n_2 - 2} = \dfrac{9(2.5)^2 + 7(2)^2}{10 + 8 - 2} = 5.27$

    c. $s_{\bar{x}_1 - \bar{x}_2} = \sqrt{s^2\left(\dfrac{1}{n_1} + \dfrac{1}{n_2}\right)} = \sqrt{5.27\left(\dfrac{1}{10} + \dfrac{1}{8}\right)} = 1.09$

    16 degrees of freedom, $t_{.025} = 2.12$

    $2.4 \pm 2.12\,(1.09)$

    $2.4 \pm 2.31 \qquad (.09 \text{ to } 4.71)$

3. a. $\bar{x}_1 = \sum x_i / n = 54 / 6 = 9$

    $\bar{x}_2 = \sum x_i / n = 42 / 6 = 7$

    b. $s_1 = \sqrt{\dfrac{\sum (x_i - \bar{x}_1)^2}{n_1 - 1}} = \sqrt{\dfrac{18}{6 - 1}} = 1.90$

    $s_2 = \sqrt{\dfrac{\sum (x_i - \bar{x}_2)^2}{n_2 - 1}} = \sqrt{\dfrac{16}{6 - 1}} = 1.79$

    c. $\bar{x}_1 - \bar{x}_2 = 9 - 7 = 2$

    d. $s^2 = \dfrac{(n_1 - 1)s_1^2 + (n_2 - 1)s_2^2}{n_1 + n_2 - 2} = \dfrac{5(1.90)^2 + 5(1.79)^2}{6 + 6 - 2} = 3.41$

    e. With 10 degrees of freedom, $t_{.025} = 2.228$

    $s_{\bar{x}_1 - \bar{x}_2} = \sqrt{s^2\left(\dfrac{1}{n_1} + \dfrac{1}{n_2}\right)} = \sqrt{3.41\left(\dfrac{1}{6} + \dfrac{1}{6}\right)} = 1.07$

$2 \pm 2.228 \ (1.07)$

$2 \pm 2.37 \qquad (-0.37 \text{ to } 4.37)$

4. a. $\bar{x}_1 - \bar{x}_2 = 1.58 - 0.98 = \$0.60$

   b. $s_{\bar{x}_1 - \bar{x}_2} = \sqrt{\dfrac{s_1^2}{n_1} + \dfrac{s_2^2}{n_2}} = \sqrt{\dfrac{.12^2}{50} + \dfrac{.08^2}{42}} = .021$

   $\bar{x}_1 - \bar{x}_2 \ \pm \ z_{.025} \ s_{\bar{x}_1 - \bar{x}_2}$

   $.60 \pm 1.96(.021)$

   $.60 \pm .04 \qquad\qquad (.56 \text{ to } .64)$

5. a. $22.5 - 18.6 \ = \ 3.9 \text{ miles per day}$

   b. $\bar{x}_1 - \bar{x}_2 \ \pm \ z_{\alpha/2} \ s_{\bar{x}_1 - \bar{x}_2}$

   $s_{\bar{x}_1 - \bar{x}_2} = \sqrt{\dfrac{s_1^2}{n_1} + \dfrac{s_2^2}{n_2}} = \sqrt{\dfrac{(8.4)^2}{50} + \dfrac{(7.4)^2}{50}} = 1.58$

   $22.5 - 18.6 \ \pm \ 1.96 \ (1.58)$

   $3.9 \ \pm \ 3.1 \ \text{ or } \ 0.6 \text{ to } 7.0$

6.

	LA	Miami
$\bar{x}$	6.72	6.34
s	2.374	2.163

   $\bar{x}_1 - \bar{x}_2 \pm z_{\alpha/2} s_{\bar{x}_1 - \bar{x}_2}$

   $s_{\bar{x}_1 - \bar{x}_2} = \sqrt{\dfrac{s_1^2}{n_1} + \dfrac{s_2^2}{n_2}} = \sqrt{\dfrac{(2.374)^2}{50} + \dfrac{(2.163)^2}{50}} = 0.454$

   $6.72 - 6.34 \pm 1.96 \ (.454)$

   $.38 \pm .89 \ \text{ or } \ -.51 \text{ to } 1.27$

7. a. $\bar{x}_1 - \bar{x}_2 = 14.9 - 10.3 = 4.6 \text{ years}$

   b. $s_{\bar{x}_1 - \bar{x}_2} = \sqrt{\dfrac{s_1^2}{n_1} + \dfrac{s_2^2}{n_2}} = \sqrt{\dfrac{5.2^2}{100} + \dfrac{3.8^2}{85}} = .66$

   $z_{.025} \ s_{\bar{x}_1 - \bar{x}_2} = 1.96(.66) = 1.3$

c. $\bar{x}_1 - \bar{x}_2 \pm z_{.025} \ s_{\bar{x}_1 - \bar{x}_2}$

4.6 ± 1.3 (3.3 to 5.9)

8.   a. $\bar{x}_1 - \bar{x}_2 = 15{,}700 - 14{,}500 = 1{,}200$

b.   Pooled variance

$$s^2 = \frac{7(700)^2 + 11(850)^2}{18} = 632{,}083$$

$$s_{\bar{x}_1 - \bar{x}_2} = \sqrt{632{,}083\left(\frac{1}{8} + \frac{1}{12}\right)} = 362.88$$

With 18 degrees of freedom $t_{.025} = 2.101$

$1200 \pm 2.101 \,(362.88)$

1200 ± 762 (438 to 1962)

c.   Populations are normally distributed with equal variances.

9.   a. $n_1 = 10$ $n_2 = 8$

$\bar{x}_1 = 21.2$ $\bar{x}_2 = 22.8$

$s_1 = 2.70$ $s_2 = 3.55$

$\bar{x}_1 - \bar{x}_2 = 21.2 - 22.8 = -1.6$

Kitchens are less expensive by $1,600.

b. $\bar{x}_1 - \bar{x}_2 \pm z_{\alpha/2} \ s_{\bar{x}_1 - \bar{x}_2}$

Degrees of freedom $= n_1 + n_2 - 2 = 16$

$t_{.05} = 1.746$

$$s^2 = \frac{9(2.70)^2 + 7(3.55)^2}{10 + 8 - 2} = 9.63$$

$$s_{\bar{x}_1 - \bar{x}_2} = \sqrt{9.63\left(\frac{1}{10} + \frac{1}{8}\right)} = 1.47$$

$-1.6 \pm 1.746 \,(1.47)$

-1.6 ± 2.57 (-4.17 to +.97)

10.   a. $\bar{x}_1 = 17.54$ $\bar{x}_2 = 15.36$

$\bar{x}_1 - \bar{x}_2 = 17.54 - 15.36 = \$2.18$ per hour greater for union workers.

b. $s^2 = \dfrac{(n_1 - 1)s_1^2 + (n_2 - 1)s_2^2}{n_1 + n_2 - 2} = \dfrac{14(2.24)^2 + 19(1.99)^2}{15 + 20 - 2} = 4.41$

c. $\bar{x}_1 - \bar{x}_2 \pm t_{\alpha/2} s_{\bar{x}_1 - \bar{x}_2}$

$s_{\bar{x}_1 - \bar{x}_2} = \sqrt{4.41 \left(\dfrac{1}{15} + \dfrac{1}{20} \right)} = 0.72$

$17.54 - 15.36 \pm t_{\alpha/2}(.72)$

$2.18 \pm t_{\alpha/2}(.72)$

Note: Values for $t_{.025}$ are not listed for 33 degrees of freedom; for 30 d.f. $t_{.025}$ = 2.042 and for 40 d.f. $t_{.025}$ = 2.021. We will use the more conservative value of 2.042 as an approximation.

$2.18 \pm 2.042\ (.72)$

2.18 ± 1.47 or 0.71 to 3.65

11. a. $s_{\bar{x}_1 - \bar{x}_2} = \sqrt{\dfrac{s_1^2}{n_1} + \dfrac{s_2^2}{n_2}} = \sqrt{\dfrac{(5.2)^2}{40} + \dfrac{(6)^2}{50}} = 1.18$

$z = \dfrac{(25.2 - 22.8)}{1.18} = 2.03$

Reject H_0 if z > 1.645

Reject H_0; conclude H_a is true and $\mu_1 - \mu_2 > 0$.

b. p - value = .5000 - .4788 = .0212

12. a. $s_{\bar{x}_1 - \bar{x}_2} = \sqrt{\dfrac{s_1^2}{n_1} + \dfrac{s_2^2}{n_2}} = \sqrt{\dfrac{(8.4)^2}{80} + \dfrac{(7.6)^2}{70}} = 1.31$

$z = \dfrac{(\bar{x}_1 - \bar{x}_2) - (\mu_1 - \mu_2)}{s_{\bar{x}_1 - \bar{x}_2}} = \dfrac{(104 - 106) - 0}{1.31} = -1.53$

Reject H_0 if z < -1.96 or z > 1.96

Do not reject H_0

b. p - value = 2(.5000 - .4370) = .1260

13. a. $\bar{x}_1 - \bar{x}_2 = 1.4 - 1.0 = 0.4$

$s^2 = \dfrac{(n_1 - 1)s_1^2 + (n_2 - 1)s_2^2}{n_1 + n_2 - 2} = \dfrac{7(.4)^2 + 6(.6)^2}{8 + 7 - 2} = 0.2523$

$$s_{\bar{x}_1 - \bar{x}_2} = \sqrt{0.2523\left(\frac{1}{8} + \frac{1}{7}\right)} = 0.26$$

With 13 degrees of freedom. $t_{.025} = 2.16$

Reject H_0 if $t < -2.16$ or $t > 2.16$

$$t = \frac{(\bar{x}_1 - \bar{x}_2) - (\mu_1 - \mu_2)}{s_{\bar{x}_1 - \bar{x}_2}} = \frac{0.4}{0.26} = 1.54$$

Do not reject H_0

14. a. $H_0: \mu_1 - \mu_2 = 0$

 $H_a: \mu_1 - \mu_2 \neq 0$

 b. Reject H_0 if $z < -1.96$ or if $z > 1.96$

 c. $s_{\bar{x}_1 - \bar{x}_2} = \sqrt{\frac{s_1^2}{n_1} + \frac{s_2^2}{n_2}} = \sqrt{\frac{16.8^2}{150} + \frac{15.2^2}{175}} = 1.79$

 $$z = \frac{(\bar{x}_1 - \bar{x}_2) - 0}{s_{\bar{x}_1 - \bar{x}_2}} = \frac{(39.3 - 35.4) - 0}{1.79} = 2.18$$

 d. Reject H_0; conclude the population means differ.

 e. p-value = 2(.5000 - .4854) = .0292

15. $H_0: \mu_1 - \mu_2 = 0$

 $H_a: \mu_1 - \mu_2 \neq 0$

 Reject H_0 if $z < -1.96$ or if $z > 1.96$

 $$z = \frac{(\bar{x}_1 - \bar{x}_2) - 0}{\sqrt{\frac{\sigma_1^2}{n_1} + \frac{\sigma_2^2}{n_2}}} = \frac{(40 - 35)}{\sqrt{\frac{(9)^2}{36} + \frac{(10)^2}{49}}} = 2.41$$

 Reject H_0; customers at the two stores differ in terms of mean ages.

 p-value = 2(.5000 - .4920) = .0160

16. $H_0: \mu_1 - \mu_2 \leq 0$

 $H_a: \mu_1 - \mu_2 > 0$

 Reject H_0 if $z > 2.05$

$$z = \frac{(\bar{x}_1 - \bar{x}_2) - (\mu_1 - \mu_2)}{\sqrt{\dfrac{\sigma_1^2}{n_1} + \dfrac{\sigma_2^2}{n_2}}} = \frac{(547 - 525) - 0}{\sqrt{\dfrac{83^2}{562} + \dfrac{78^2}{852}}} = 4.99$$

Reject H_0; conclude that the females have a higher mean verbal score.

p-value ≈ 0

17.   Population 1 is supplier A.

Population 2 is supplier B.

H_0: $\mu_1 - \mu_2 \le 0$ Stay with supplier A

H_a: $\mu_1 - \mu_2 > 0$ Change to supplier B

Reject H_0 if $z > 1.645$

$$z = \frac{(\bar{x}_1 - \bar{x}_2) - (\mu_1 - \mu_2)}{\sqrt{\dfrac{\sigma_1^2}{n_1} + \dfrac{\sigma_2^2}{n_2}}} = \frac{(14 - 12.5) - 0}{\sqrt{\dfrac{(3)^2}{50} + \dfrac{(2)^2}{30}}} = 2.68$$

p-value = .5000 - .4963 = .0037

Reject H_0; change to supplier B.

18. a. H_0: $\mu_1 - \mu_2 = 0$

H_a: $\mu_1 - \mu_2 \ne 0$

$$\sigma_{\bar{x}_1 - \bar{x}_2} = \sqrt{\frac{\sigma_1^2}{n_1} + \frac{\sigma_2^2}{n_2}} = \sqrt{\frac{2.5^2}{112} + \frac{2.5^2}{84}} = .36$$

$$z = \frac{(\bar{x}_1 - \bar{x}_2) - 0}{\sigma_{\bar{x}_1 - \bar{x}_2}} = \frac{69.95 - 69.56}{.36} = 1.08$$

b. p-value = 2(.5000 - .3599) = .2802

c.   Do no reject H_0. Cannot conclude that there is a difference between the population mean scores for the two golfers.

19. a. H_0: $\mu_1 - \mu_2 = 0$

H_a: $\mu_1 - \mu_2 \ne 0$

b. $t_{.025} = 2.021$ $df = n_1 + n_2 - 2 = 22 + 20 - 2 = 40$

Reject H_0 if $t < -2.021$ or if $t > 2.021$

c. $$s^2 = \frac{(n_1 - 1)s_1^2 + (n_2 - 1)s_2^2}{n_1 + n_2 - 2} = \frac{(22 - 1)(.8)^2 + (20 - 1)(1.1)^2}{22 + 20 - 2} = .9108$$

$$s_{\bar{x}_1-\bar{x}_2} = \sqrt{s^2\left(\frac{1}{n_1}+\frac{1}{n_2}\right)} = \sqrt{.9108\left(\frac{1}{22}+\frac{1}{20}\right)} = .2948$$

$$t = \frac{(\bar{x}_1-\bar{x}_2)-0}{s_{\bar{x}_1-\bar{x}_2}} = \frac{2.5-2.1}{.2948} = 1.36$$

d. Do not reject H_0. Cannot conclude that a difference between population mean exists.

e. With $df = 40$, $t_{.05} = 1.684$ and $t_{.10} = 1.303$

With two tails, p-value is between .10 and .20.

20. a. $H_0: \mu_1 - \mu_2 \leq 0$

$H_a: \mu_1 - \mu_2 > 0$

b. $t_{.05} = 1.711$ $df = n_1 + n_2 - 2 = 16 + 10 - 2 = 24$

Reject H_0 if $t > 1.711$

c. $s^2 = \frac{(n_1-1)s_1^2+(n_2-1)s_2^2}{n_1+n_2-2} = \frac{(16-1)(.64)^2+(10-1)(.75)^2}{16+10+2} = .4669$

$$s_{\bar{x}_1-\bar{x}_2} = \sqrt{s^2\left(\frac{1}{n_1}+\frac{1}{n_2}\right)} = \sqrt{.4669\left(\frac{1}{16}+\frac{1}{10}\right)} = .2755$$

$$t = \frac{(\bar{x}_1-\bar{x}_2)-0}{s_{\bar{x}_1-\bar{x}_2}} = \frac{6.82-6.25}{.2755} = 2.07$$

d. Reject H_0. Conclude that the consultant with the more experience has the higher population mean rating.

e. With $24df$, $t_{.025} = 2.064$

p-value is approximately .025

21. a. 1, 2, 0, 0, 2

b. $\bar{d} = \sum d_i / n = 5/5 = 1$

c. $s_d = \sqrt{\frac{\sum(d_i-\bar{d})^2}{n-1}} = \sqrt{\frac{4}{5-1}} = 1$

d. With 4 degrees of freedom, $t_{.05} = 2.132$

Reject H_0 if $t > 2.132$

$$t = \frac{\bar{d}-\mu_d}{s_d/\sqrt{n}} = \frac{1-0}{1/\sqrt{5}} = 2.24$$

p-value is between .025 and .05

Reject H_0; conclude $\mu_d > 0$.

22. a. 3, -1, 3, 5, 3, 0, 1

    b. $\bar{d} = \sum d_i / n = 14/7 = 2$

    c. $s_d = \sqrt{\dfrac{\sum(d_i - \bar{d})^2}{n-1}} = \sqrt{\dfrac{26}{7-1}} = 2.082$

    d. $\bar{d} = 2$

    e. With 6 degrees of freedom $t_{.025} = 2.447$

    $2 \pm 2.447 \left(2.082 / \sqrt{7} \right)$

    2 ± 1.93 \qquad (.07 to 3.93)

23. Difference = rating after - rating before

    H_0: $\mu_d \leq 0$

    H_a: $\mu_d > 0$

    With 7 degrees of freedom, reject H_0 if $t > 1.895$

    $\bar{d} = .625$ and $s_d = 1.3025$

    $t = \dfrac{\bar{d} - \mu_d}{s_d / \sqrt{n}} = \dfrac{.625 - 0}{1.3025 / \sqrt{8}} = 1.36$

    p-value is greater than .10

    Do not reject H_0; we cannot conclude that seeing the commercial improves the mean potential to purchase.

24. Differences: .20, .29, .39, .02, .24, .20, .20, .52, .29, .20

    $\bar{d} = \sum d_i / n = 2.55/10 = .255$

    $s_d = \sqrt{\dfrac{\sum(d_i - \bar{d})^2}{n-1}} = .1327$

    With $df = 9$, $t_{.025} = 2.262$

    $\bar{d} \pm t_{.025} \dfrac{s_d}{\sqrt{n}}$

$$.255 \pm 2.262 \left(\frac{.1327}{\sqrt{10}} \right)$$

$.255 \pm .095$ \qquad\qquad (.16 to .35)

25. \qquad Differences: 8, 9.5, 6, 10.5, 15, 9, 11, 7.5, 12, 5

$\bar{d} = 93.5/10 = 9.35$ and $s_d = 2.954$

$t_{.025} = 2.262$

$9.35 \pm 2.262 \left(2.954 / \sqrt{10} \right) = 9.35 \pm 2.11$

Interval estimate is 7.24 to 11.46

26. \qquad $H_0: \mu_d = 0$

$H_a: \mu_d \neq 0$

Reject H_0 if $t < -2.365$ or if $t > 2.365$ \quad $df = 7$

Differences -.01, .03, -.06, .16, .21, .17, -.09, .11

$\bar{d} = \Sigma d_i / n = .52/8 = .065$

$s_d = \sqrt{\dfrac{\Sigma(d_i - \bar{d})^2}{n-1}} = .1131$

$t = \dfrac{\bar{d} - 0}{\dfrac{s_d}{\sqrt{n}}} = \dfrac{.065}{\dfrac{.1131}{\sqrt{8}}} = 1.63$

Do not reject H_0. Cannot conclude that the population means differ.

27. \qquad Using matched samples, the differences are as follows: 4, -2, 8, 8, 5, 6, -4, -2, -3, 0, 11, -5, 5, 9, 5

$H_0: \mu_d \leq 0$

$H_a: \mu_d > 0$

$\bar{d} = 3$ and $s_d = 5.21$

$t = \dfrac{\bar{d} - \mu_d}{s_d / \sqrt{n}} = \dfrac{3-0}{5.21/\sqrt{15}} = 2.23$

p-value is between .01 and .025

With 14 degrees of freedom, reject H_0 if $t > 1.761$

Reject H_0. Conclude that the population of readers spends more time, on average, watching television than reading.

28. a. $H_0: \mu_1 - \mu_2 = 0$

$H_a: \mu_1 - \mu_2 \neq 0$

With $df = 11$, $t_{.025} = 2.201$

Reject H_0 if $t < -2.201$ or if $t > 2.201$

Calculate the difference, d_i, for each stock.

$\bar{d} = \Sigma d_i / n = 85 / 12 = 7.08$

$s_d = \sqrt{\dfrac{\Sigma(d_i - \bar{d})^2}{n-1}} = 3.34$

$t = \dfrac{\bar{x} - \mu}{s_d / \sqrt{n}} = 7.34$

p-value ≈ 0

Reject H_0; a decrease in P/E ratios is being projected for 1998.

b. $\bar{d} \pm t_{.025} \dfrac{s_d}{\sqrt{n}}$

$7.08 \pm 2.201 \left(\dfrac{3.34}{\sqrt{12}} \right)$

7.08 ± 2.12

(4.96 to 9.21)

29. a. Difference = Price deluxe - Price Standard

$H_0: \mu_d = 10$

$H_a: \mu_d \neq 10$

With 6 degrees of freedom, reject H_0 if $t < -2.447$ or if $t > 2.447$

$\bar{d} = 8.86$ and $s_d = 2.61$

$t = \dfrac{\bar{d} - \mu_d}{s_d / \sqrt{n}} = \dfrac{8.86 - 10}{2.61 / \sqrt{7}} = -1.16$

p-value is greater than .20

Do not reject H_0; we cannot reject the hypothesis that a $10 price differential exists.

b. $\bar{d} \pm t_{\alpha/2} \dfrac{s_d}{\sqrt{n}}$

$8.86 \pm 2.447 \left(\dfrac{2.61}{\sqrt{7}} \right)$

8.86 ± 2.41

$(6.45 \text{ to } 11.27)$

30. a. $(\bar{p}_1 - \bar{p}_2) = .48 - .36 = .12$

b. $s_{\bar{p}_1 - \bar{p}_2} = \sqrt{\dfrac{\bar{p}_1(1 - \bar{p}_1)}{n_1} + \dfrac{\bar{p}_2(1 - \bar{p}_2)}{n_2}} = \sqrt{\dfrac{0.48(0.52)}{400} + \dfrac{0.36(0.64)}{300}} = 0.0373$

$0.12 \pm 1.645 \, (0.0373)$

$0.12 \pm 0.0614 \quad (0.0586 \text{ to } 0.1814)$

c. $0.12 \pm 1.96 \, (0.0373)$

$0.12 \pm 0.0731 \quad (0.0469 \text{ to } 0.1931)$

31. a. $\bar{p} = \dfrac{n_1\bar{p}_1 + n_2\bar{p}_2}{n_1 + n_2} = \dfrac{200(0.22) + 300(0.16)}{200 + 300} = 0.184$

$s_{\bar{p}_1 - \bar{p}_2} = \sqrt{(0.184)(0.816)\left(\dfrac{1}{200} + \dfrac{1}{300} \right)} = 0.0354$

Reject H_0 if $z > 1.645$

$z = \dfrac{(.22 - .16) - 0}{.0354} = 1.69$

Reject H_0

b. p - value $= (.5000 - .4545) = .0455$

32. $\bar{p}_1 = 220/400 = 0.55$

$\bar{p}_2 = 192/400 = 0.48$

$s_{\bar{p}_1 - \bar{p}_2} = \sqrt{\dfrac{0.55(0.45)}{400} + \dfrac{0.48(0.52)}{400}} = 0.0353$

$\bar{p}_1 - \bar{p}_2 \pm 1.96 \, s_{\bar{p}_1 - \bar{p}_2}$

$0.55 - 0.48 \pm 1.96 \, (0.0353)$

$0.07 \pm 0.0691 \quad (0.0009 \text{ to } 0.1391)$

7% more executives are predicting an increase in full-time jobs. The confidence interval shows the difference may be from 0% to 14%.

33. $\bar{p}_1 - \bar{p}_2 \pm z_{\alpha/2} s_{\bar{p}_1 - \bar{p}_2}$

$$s_{\bar{p}_1 - \bar{p}_2} = \sqrt{\frac{\bar{p}_1(1-\bar{p}_1)}{n_1} + \frac{\bar{p}_2(1-\bar{p}_2)}{n_2}} = \sqrt{\frac{(0.25)(0.75)}{496} + \frac{(0.16)(0.84)}{505}} = 0.025$$

0.25 - 0.16 ± 1.96(0.25)

0.09 ± 0.05   or   0.04 to 0.14

34. a. $\bar{p}_1 = 682/1082 = .6303$ (63%)

$\bar{p}_2 = 413/1008 = .4097$ (41%)

$\bar{p}_1 - \bar{p}_2 = .6303 - .4097 = .2206$ (22%)

b. $\sigma_{\bar{p}_1 - \bar{p}_2} = \sqrt{\frac{\bar{p}_1(1-\bar{p}_1)}{n_1} + \frac{\bar{p}_2(1-\bar{p}_2)}{n_2}} = \sqrt{\frac{.6303(1-.6303)}{1082} + \frac{.4097(1-.4097)}{1008}} = .0213$

$\bar{p}_1 - \bar{p}_2 \pm 1.96 \sigma_{\bar{p}_1 - \bar{p}_2}$

.2206 ± 1.96 (.0213)

.2206 ± .0418   (.1788 to .2624)

35. a. $\bar{p}_1 = 279/300 = 0.93$

$\bar{p}_2 = 255/300 = 0.85$

b. H_0: $p_1 - p_2 = 0$

H_a: $p_1 - p_2 \neq 0$

Reject H_0 if $z < -1.96$ or if $z > 1.96$

$$\bar{p} = \frac{279 + 255}{300 + 300} = 0.89$$

$$s_{\bar{p}_1 - \bar{p}_2} = \sqrt{(0.89)(0.11)\left(\frac{1}{300} + \frac{1}{300}\right)} = 0.0255$$

$$z = \frac{\bar{p}_1 - \bar{p}_2 - 0}{s_{\bar{p}_1 - \bar{p}_2}} = \frac{0.93 - 0.85}{0.0255} = 3.13$$

p-value is less than .001

Reject H_0; women and men differ on this question.

c. $\bar{p}_1 - \bar{p}_2 \pm 1.96 s_{\bar{p}_1-\bar{p}_2}$

$$s_{\bar{p}_1-\bar{p}_2} = \sqrt{\frac{(0.93)(0.07)}{300} + \frac{(0.85)(0.15)}{300}} = 0.0253$$

$0.93 - 0.85 \pm 1.96\,(0.0253)$

0.08 ± 0.05 $(0.03 \text{ to } 0.13)$

95% confident, 3% to 13% more women than men agree with this statement.

36. H_0: $p_1 \le p_2$

      H_a: $p_1 > p_2$

$$z = \frac{(\bar{p}_1 - \bar{p}_2) - (p_1 - p_2)}{s_{\bar{p}_1-\bar{p}_2}}$$

$$\bar{p} = \frac{n_1\bar{p}_1 + n_2\bar{p}_2}{n_1 + n_2} = \frac{1545(0.675) + 1691(0.608)}{1545 + 1691} = 0.64$$

$$s_{\bar{p}_1-\bar{p}_2} = \sqrt{\bar{p}(1-\bar{p})\left(\frac{1}{n_1} + \frac{1}{n_2}\right)} = \sqrt{(0.64)(0.36)\left(\frac{1}{1545} + \frac{1}{1691}\right)} = 0.017$$

$$z = \frac{(0.675 - 0.608) - 0}{0.017} = 3.94$$

Since $3.94 > z_{.05} = 1.645$, we reject H_0

p-value ≈ 0

Conclusion: The proportion of men that feel that the division of housework is fair is greater than the proportion of women that feel that the division of housework is fair.

37. H_0: $p_1 - p_2 = 0$

      H_a: $p_1 - p_2 \ne 0$

Reject H_0 if $z < -1.96$ or if $z > 1.96$

$$\bar{p} = \frac{63 + 60}{150 + 200} = 0.3514$$

$$s_{\bar{p}_1-\bar{p}_2} = \sqrt{(0.3514)(0.6486)\left(\frac{1}{150} + \frac{1}{200}\right)} = 0.0516$$

$\bar{p}_1 = 63/150 = 0.42$ $\bar{p}_2 = 60/200 = 0.30$

$$z = \frac{(\bar{p}_1 - \bar{p}_2) - (p_1 - p_2)}{s_{\bar{p}_1-\bar{p}_2}} = \frac{(0.42 - 0.30) - 0}{0.0516} = 2.33$$

p-value $= 2(.5000 - .4901) = .0198$

Reject H_0; there is a difference between the recall rates for the two commercials.

b. $(0.42 - 0.30) \pm 1.96\sqrt{\dfrac{0.42(58)}{150} + \dfrac{0.30(0.70)}{200}}$

.12 $\pm$ .10   (.02 to .22)

38. $\bar{p} = \dfrac{n_1 p_1 + n_2 p_2}{n_1 + n_2} = \dfrac{232(.815) + 210(.724)}{232 + 210} = .7718$

$s_{\bar{p}_1 - \bar{p}_2} = \sqrt{\bar{p}(1-\bar{p})\left(\dfrac{1}{n_1} + \dfrac{1}{n_2}\right)} = \sqrt{(.7718)(1-7718)\left(\dfrac{1}{232} + \dfrac{1}{210}\right)} = .04$

$z = \dfrac{(\bar{p}_1 - \bar{p}_2) - 0}{s_{\bar{p}_1 - \bar{p}_2}} = \dfrac{.815 - .724}{.04} = 2.28$

p-value = 2(.5 - .4887) = .0226

p-value < .05, reject H_0. The population proportions differ. NYSE is showing a greater proportion of stocks below their 1997 highs.

39. H_0: $p_1 - p_2 \leq 0$

H_a: $p_1 - p_2 > 0$

$\bar{p} = \dfrac{n_1 p_1 + n_2 p_2}{n_1 + n_2} = \dfrac{240(.40) + 250(.32)}{240 + 250} = .3592$

$s_{\bar{p}_1 - \bar{p}_2} = \sqrt{\bar{p}(1-\bar{p})\left(\dfrac{1}{n_1} + \dfrac{1}{n_2}\right)} = \sqrt{(.3592)(1-.3592)\left(\dfrac{1}{240} + \dfrac{1}{250}\right)} = .0434$

$z = \dfrac{(\bar{p}_1 - \bar{p}_2) - 0}{s_{\bar{p}_1 - \bar{p}_2}} = \dfrac{.40 - .32}{.0434} = 1.85$

p-value = .5000 - .4678 = .0322

p-value < .05, reject H_0. The proportion of users at work is greater in Washington D.C.

40. $\bar{x}_1 - \bar{x}_2 \pm z_{.05}\sqrt{\dfrac{s_1^2}{n_1} + \dfrac{s_2^2}{n_2}}$

$40,000 - 35,000 \pm 1.645\sqrt{\dfrac{(2500)^2}{60} + \dfrac{(2000)^2}{80}}$

5000 $\pm$ 646

(4354 to 5646)

41. $H_0: \mu_1 - \mu_2 = 0$

       $H_a: \mu_1 - \mu_2 \neq 0$

       Reject H_0 if $z < -1.96$ or if $z > 1.96$

$$z = \frac{(\bar{x}_1 - \bar{x}_2) - (\mu_1 - \mu_2)}{\sqrt{\dfrac{\sigma_1^2}{n_1} + \dfrac{\sigma_2^2}{n_2}}} = \frac{(4.1 - 3.3) - 0}{\sqrt{\dfrac{(2.2)^2}{120} + \dfrac{(1.5)^2}{100}}} = 3.19$$

       Reject H_0; a difference exists with system B having the lower mean checkout time.

42. a. $H_0: \mu_1 - \mu_2 \leq 0$

       $H_a: \mu_1 - \mu_2 > 0$

       Reject H_0 if $z > 1.645$

    b.   Using the computer,

       $n_1 = 30$ $n_2 = 30$

       $\bar{x}_1 = 16.23$ $\bar{x}_2 = 15.70$

       $s_1 = 3.52$ $s_2 = 3.31$

$$s_{\bar{x}_1 - \bar{x}_2} = \sqrt{\frac{(3.52)^2}{30} + \frac{(3.31)^2}{30}} = 0.88$$

$$z = \frac{(\bar{x}_1 - \bar{x}_2) - 0}{s_{\bar{x}_1 - \bar{x}_2}} = \frac{(16.23 - 15.70)}{0.88} = 0.59$$

       Do not reject H_0; cannot conclude that the mutual funds with a load have a greater mean rate of return.

       Load funds 16.23% ; no load funds 15.7%

    c.   At $z = 0.59$, Area $= 0.2224$

       p-value $= 0.5000 - 0.2224 = 0.2776$

43. $H_0: \mu_1 - \mu_2 = 0$

       $H_a: \mu_1 - \mu_2 \neq 0$

       Use 25 degrees of freedom. Reject H_0 if $t < -2.06$ or if $t > 2.06$

$$s^2 = \frac{11(8)^2 + 14(10)^2}{25} = 84.16$$

$$t = \frac{(\bar{x}_1 - \bar{x}_2) - (\mu_1 - \mu_2)}{\sqrt{s^2 \left(\frac{1}{n_1} + \frac{1}{n_2} \right)}} = \frac{(72 - 78) - 0}{\sqrt{84.16 \left(\frac{1}{12} + \frac{1}{15} \right)}} = -1.69$$

p-value is between .10 and .20

Do not reject H_0; cannot conclude a difference exists.

44.   Difference = before - after

H_0: $\mu_d \leq 0$

H_a: $\mu_d > 0$

With 5 degrees of freedom, reject H_0 if $t > 2.015$

$\bar{d} = 6.167$ and $s_d = 6.585$

$$t = \frac{\bar{d} - \mu_d}{s_d / \sqrt{n}} = \frac{6.167 - 0}{6.585 / \sqrt{6}} = 2.29$$

p-value is between .05 and .10

Reject H_0; conclude that the program provides weight loss.

45. a.   Population 1 - 1996

Population 2 - 1997

H_0: $\mu_1 - \mu_2 \leq 0$

H_a: $\mu_1 - \mu_2 > 0$

b. $\bar{d} = \sum d_i / n = 1.74 / 14 = 0.12$

$$s_d = \sqrt{\frac{\sum (d_i - \bar{d})^2}{n - 1}} = 0.33$$

Degrees of freedom = 13; $t_{.05} = 1.771$

Reject H_0 if $t > 1.771$

$$t = \frac{\bar{d} - 0}{s_d / \sqrt{n}} = \frac{0.12}{0.33 / \sqrt{14}} = 1.42$$

p-value is between .05 and .10

Do not reject H_0. The sample of 14 companies shows earnings are down in the fourth quarter by a mean of 0.12 per share. However, data does not support the conclusion that mean earnings for all companies are down in 1997.

46. a. H_0: $p_1 - p_2 \leq 0$

    H_a: $p_1 - p_2 > 0$

    b. $\bar{p}_1 = 704/1035 = .6802$ (68%)

    $\bar{p}_2 = 582/1004 = .5797$ (58%)

    $\bar{p}_1 - \bar{p}_2 = .6802 - .5797 = .1005$

    $$\bar{p} = \frac{n_1\bar{p}_1 + n_2\bar{p}_2}{n_1 + n_2} = \frac{1035(0.6802) + 1004(0.5797)}{1035 + 1004} = .6307$$

    $$s_{\bar{p}_1 - \bar{p}_2} = \sqrt{\bar{p}(1-\bar{p})\left(\frac{1}{n_1} + \frac{1}{n_2}\right)} = \sqrt{(.6307)(1-.6307)\left(\frac{1}{1035} + \frac{1}{1004}\right)} = .0214$$

    $$z = \frac{(\bar{p}_1 - \bar{p}_2) - 0}{s_{\bar{p}_1 - \bar{p}_2}} = \frac{.6802 - .5797}{.0214} = 4.70$$

    p-value ≈ 0

    c. Reject H_0; proportion indicating good/excellent increased.

47. a. H_0: $p_1 - p_2 = 0$

    H_a: $p_1 - p_2 \neq 0$

    Reject H_0 if $z < -1.96$ or if $z > 1.96$

    $$\bar{p} = \frac{76 + 90}{400 + 900} = 0.1277$$

    $$s_{\bar{p}_1 - \bar{p}_2} = \sqrt{(0.1277)(0.8723)\left(\frac{1}{400} + \frac{1}{900}\right)} = 0.02$$

    $\bar{p}_1 = 76/400 = 0.19 \qquad \bar{p}_2 = 90/900 = 0.10$

    $$z = \frac{(\bar{p}_1 - \bar{p}_2) - (p_1 - p_2)}{s_{\bar{p}_1 - \bar{p}_2}} = \frac{(0.19 - 0.10) - 0}{0.02} = 4.50$$

    p-value ≈ 0

    Reject H_0; there is a difference between claim rates.

    b. $0.09 \pm 1.96\sqrt{\dfrac{0.19(0.81)}{400} + \dfrac{0.10(0.90)}{900}}$

    $.09 \pm .0432 \qquad$ (.0468 to .1332)

48. $$\bar{p} = \frac{9+5}{142+268} = \frac{14}{410} = 0.0341$$

$$s_{\bar{p}_1 - \bar{p}_2} = \sqrt{(0.0341)(0.9659)\left(\frac{1}{142} + \frac{1}{268}\right)} = 0.0188$$

$$\bar{p}_1 = 9/142 = 0.0634 \qquad \bar{p}_2 = 5/268 = 0.0187$$

$$\bar{p}_1 - \bar{p}_2 = 0.0634 - 0.0187 = 0.0447$$

$$z = \frac{0.0447 - 0}{0.0188} = 2.38$$

p-value $= 2(0.5000 - 0.4913) = 0.0174$

Reject H_0; There is a significant difference in drug resistance between the two states. New Jersey has the higher drug resistance rate.

Chapter 11
Inferences About Population Variances

Learning Objectives

1. Understand the importance of variance in a decision-making situation.

2   Understand the role of statistical inference in developing conclusions about the variance of a single population.

3. Know the sampling distribution of $(n - 1) s^2/\sigma^2$ has a chi-square distribution and be able to use this result to develop a confidence interval estimate of σ^2.

4. Know how to test hypotheses involving σ^2.

5. Understand the role of statistical inference in developing conclusions about the variances of two populations.

6. Know that the sampling distribution of s_1^2 / s_2^2 has an F distribution and be able to use this result to test hypotheses involving the variances of two populations.

Solutions:

1. a. 11.0705

    b. 27.4884

    c. 9.59083

    d. 23.2093

    e. 9.39046

2. $s^2 = 25$

    a. With 19 degrees of freedom $\chi^2_{.05} = 30.1435$ and $\chi^2_{.95} = 10.1170$

    $$\frac{19(25)}{30.1435} \leq \sigma^2 \leq \frac{19(25)}{10.1170}$$

    $15.76 \leq \sigma^2 \leq 46.95$

    b. With 19 degrees of freedom $\chi^2_{.025} = 32.8523$ and $\chi^2_{.975} = 8.90655$

    $$\frac{19(25)}{32.8523} \leq \sigma^2 \leq \frac{19(25)}{8.90655}$$

    $14.46 \leq \sigma^2 \leq 53.33$

    c. $3.8 \leq \sigma^2 \leq 7.3$

3. With 15 degrees of freedom $\chi^2_{.05} = 24.9958$

    Reject H_0 if $\chi^2 > 24.9958$

    $$\chi^2 = \frac{(n-1)s^2}{\sigma^2} = \frac{(16-1)(8)^2}{50} = 19.2$$

    Do not reject H_0

4. a. $n = 18$

    $s^2 = .36$

    $\chi^2_{.05} = 27.5871$ $\chi^2_{.95} = 8.67176$ (17 degrees of freedom)

    $$\frac{17(.36)}{27.5871} \leq \sigma^2 \leq \frac{17(.36)}{8.67176}$$

    $.22 \leq \sigma^2 \leq .71$

    b. $.47 \leq \sigma \leq .84$

5. a. $s^2 = \dfrac{\Sigma(x_2 - \overline{x})^2}{n-1} = 31.07$

    $s = \sqrt{31.07} = 5.57$

    b. $\chi^2_{.025} = 16.0128 \qquad \chi^2_{.975} = 1.68987$

    $\dfrac{(8-1)(31.07)}{16.0128} \le \sigma^2 \le \dfrac{(8-1)(31.07)}{1.68987}$

    $13.58 \le \sigma^2 \le 128.71$

    c. $3.69 \le \sigma \le 11.34$

6. a. $s^2 = \dfrac{\Sigma(x_i - \overline{x})^2}{n-1} = 176.96$

    $s = \sqrt{176.96} = 13.30$

    b. $\chi^2_{.025} = 11.1433 \qquad \chi^2_{.975} = 0.484419$

    $\dfrac{(5-1)(176.96)}{11.1433} \le \sigma^2 \le \dfrac{(5-1)(176.96)}{0.484419}$

    $63.52 \le \sigma^2 \le 1461.21$

    $7.97 \le \sigma \le 38.23$

7. a. $s^2 = \dfrac{\Sigma(x_i - \overline{x})^2}{n-1} = 2.62$

    $s = \sqrt{2.62} = 1.62$

    b. $\chi^2_{.025} = 16.0128 \qquad \chi^2_{.095} = 1.68987$

    $\dfrac{(8-1)(2.62)}{16.0128} \le \sigma^2 \le \dfrac{(8-1)(2.62)}{1.68987}$

    $1.14 \le \sigma^2 \le 10.85$

    c. $1.07 \le \sigma \le 3.29$

8. a. $s^2 = \sqrt{\dfrac{\Sigma(x_i - \overline{x})^2}{n-1}} = \sqrt{\dfrac{.0929}{12-1}} = .00845$

    b. $s = \sqrt{.00845} = .0919$

c.   11 degrees of freedom

$$\chi^2_{.025} = 21.92 \qquad \chi^2_{.975} = 3.81575$$

$$\frac{(n-1)s^2}{\chi^2_{.025}} \le \sigma^2 \le \frac{(n-1)s^2}{\chi^2_{.975}}$$

$$\frac{(12-1).00845}{21.92} \le \sigma^2 \le \frac{(12-1).00845}{3.81575}$$

$$.0042 \le \sigma^2 \le .0244$$

d. $.0651 \le \sigma \le .1561$

9. $H_0: \sigma^2 \le .0004$

   $H_a: \sigma^2 > .0004$

   $n = 30$

   $\chi^2_{.05} = 42.5569$ (29 degrees of freedom)

   $$\chi^2 = \frac{(29)(.0005)}{.0004} = 36.25$$

   Do not reject H_0; the product specification does not appear to be violated.

10. $H_0: \sigma^2 \le .75$

   $H_a: \sigma^2 > .75$

   $\chi^2_{.05} = 42.5569$ (29 degrees of freedom)

   $$\chi^2 = \frac{(n-1)s^2}{\sigma_0^2} = \frac{(29)(2)^2}{(.75)^2} = 206.22$$

   Since $\chi^2 = 206.22 > 42.5569$, reject H_0

   The standard deviation for television sets is greater than the standard deviation for VCR's.

11.   19 degrees of freedom

   $$\chi^2_{.975} = 8.90655 \qquad \chi^2_{.025} = 32.8523$$

   Reject H_0 if $\chi^2 < 8.90655$ or if $\chi^2 > 32.8523$

   $$\chi^2 = \frac{(n-1)s^2}{\sigma^2} = \frac{(20-1)(.114)^2}{.009216} = 26.79$$

   Do not reject H_0. Cannot conclude the variance in interest rates has changed.

12. $s^2 = \dfrac{\Sigma(x_i - \bar{x})^2}{n-1} = .8106$

     $H_0: \sigma^2 = .94$

     $H_a: \sigma^2 \neq .94$

     $\chi^2 = \dfrac{(n-1)s^2}{\sigma_0^2} = \dfrac{(11)(.8106)}{.94} = 9.49$

     With 11 degrees of freedom, reject if $\chi^2 < \chi_{.975}^2 = 3.81575$ or $\chi^2 > \chi_{.025}^2 = 21.92$.

     Since $\chi^2 = 9.49$ is not in the rejection region, we cannot reject H_0.

13.   a. $F_{.05} = 2.91$

     b. $F_{.025} = 2.76$

     c. $F_{.01} = 4.50$

     d. $F_{.975} = \dfrac{1}{F_{.025,20,10}} = \dfrac{1}{3.42} = .29$

     Remember to reverse the degrees of freedom in the $F_{.025}$ above.

14. $F_{.05,15,19} = 2.23$

     Reject H_0 if $F > 2.23$

     $F = \dfrac{s_1^2}{s_2^2} = \dfrac{5.8}{2.4} = 2.42$

     Reject H_0: conclude $\sigma_1^2 > \sigma_2^2$

15.   We recommend placing the larger sample variance in the numerator. With $\alpha = .05$,

     $F_{.025,20,24} = 2.33$. Reject if $F > 2.33$.

     $F = 8.2/4.0 = 2.05$ Do not reject H_0

     Or if we had the lower tail F value,

     $F_{.025,20,24} = \dfrac{1}{F_{.025,24,20}} = \dfrac{1}{2.41} = .41$

     $F = 4.0/8.2 = .49$ $\therefore F > .41$ Do not reject H_0

16. $H_0: \sigma_1^2 \leq \sigma_2^2$

     $H_a: \sigma_1^2 > \sigma_2^2$

$F_{.01,24,29} = 2.49$ Reject H_0 if $F > 2.49$

$$F = \frac{s_1^2}{s_2^2} = \frac{94^2}{58^2} = 2.63$$

Reject H_0; Conclude adults have a greater variance in online times than teens.

17. a. Let $\sigma_1^2 =$ variance in repair costs (4 year old automobiles)

$\sigma_2^2 =$ variance in repair costs (2 year old automobiles)

$H_0: \sigma_1^2 \le \sigma_2^2$

$H_a: \sigma_1^2 > \sigma_2^2$

   b. $s_1^2 = (170)^2 = 28,900$

$s_2^2 = (100)^2 = 10,000$

$$F = \frac{s_1^2}{s_2^2} = \frac{28,900}{10,000} = 2.89$$

$F_{.01,24,24} = 2.66$

Reject H_0; conclude that 4 year old automobiles have a larger variance in annual repair costs compared to 2 year old automobiles. This is expected due to the fact that older automobiles are more likely to have some very expensive repairs which lead to greater variance in the annual repair costs.

18. $H_0: \sigma_1^2 = \sigma_2^2$

$H_a: \sigma_1^2 \ne \sigma_2^2$

$F_{\alpha/2} = F_{.025,9,6} = 5.52$

$$F = \frac{s_1^2}{s_2^2} = \frac{4.27^2}{2.27^2} = 3.54$$

Do not reject H_0; Cannot conclude any difference between variances of the two industries.

19. $H_0: \sigma_1^2 = \sigma_2^2$

$H_a: \sigma_1^2 \ne \sigma_2^2$

$F_{.025} = 2.37$ (Degrees of freedom are 24 numerator, 21 denominator)

Using Minitab,

Machine 1: $n_1 = 25$ $s_1 = .2211$ $\bar{x}_1 = 3.328$

Machine 1: $n_1 = 22$ $s_1 = .0768$ $\bar{x}_1 = 3.278$

$$F = \frac{s_1^2}{s_2^2} = \frac{(.2211)^2}{(.0768)^2} = 8.29$$

Reject H_0; the process variances are significantly different. Machine 1 offers the best opportunity for process quality improvements.

Note that the sample means are similar with the mean bag weights of approximately 3.3 grams. However, the process variances are significantly different.

20. $H_0 : \sigma_1^2 = \sigma_2^2$

$H_a : \sigma_1^2 \neq \sigma_2^2$

$F_{.025} = 2.37$ (Degrees of freedom are 24 numerator, 24 denominator)

With 11.1 the larger sample variance, we have

$F = 11.1/2.1 = 5.29$

Reject H_0; the variances are not equal for seniors and managers.

21. a. $s^2 = \dfrac{\Sigma(x_i - \bar{x})^2}{n - 1}$

$s_{Nov}^2 = 9663.57$ $s_{Dec}^2 = 19,237.73$

b. $H_0 : \sigma_{Nov}^2 = \sigma_{Dec}^2$

$H_a : \sigma_{Nov}^2 \neq \sigma_{Dec}^2$

$$F = \frac{s_{Dec}^2}{s_{Nov}^2} = \frac{19,237.73}{9663.57} = 1.99$$

$F_{.05,9,9} = 3.18$

Since $F = 1.99 < 3.18$, do not reject H_0

There is no evidence that the population variances differ.

22. $H_0 : \sigma_{wet}^2 \leq \sigma_{dry}^2$

$H_a : \sigma_{wet}^2 > \sigma_{dry}^2$

$s_{wet}^2 = 32^2 = 1024$ $s_{dry}^2 = 16^2 = 256$

$F_{.05} = 2.40$

$$F = \frac{s_{wet}^2}{s_{dry}^2} = \frac{1024}{256} = 4$$

Since $F = 4 > 2.40$, reject H_0 and conclude that there is greater variability in stopping distances on wet pavement.

b.   Drive carefully on wet pavement because of the uncertainty in stopping distances.

23.   a. $s^2 = (30)^2 = 900$

b. $\chi_{.05}^2 = 30.1435$ and $\chi_{.95}^2 = 10.1170$ (19 degrees of freedom)

$$\frac{(19)(900)}{30.1435} \le \sigma^2 \le \frac{(19)(900)}{10.1170}$$

$567.29 \le \sigma^2 \le 1690.22$

c. $23.82 \le \sigma \le 41.11$

24.   With 12 degrees of freedom,

$\chi_{.025}^2 = 23.3367$ $\chi_{.975}^2 = 4.40379$

$$\frac{(12)(14.95)^2}{23.3367} \le \sigma^2 \le \frac{(12)(14.95)^2}{4.40379}$$

$114.93 \le \sigma^2 \le 609.03$

$10.72 \le \sigma \le 24.68$

25.   a. $\bar{x} = \dfrac{\Sigma x_i}{n} = \$260.16$

b. $s^2 = \dfrac{\Sigma (x_i - \bar{x})^2}{n-1} = 4996.79$

$s = \sqrt{4996.79} = 70.69$

c. $\chi_{.025}^2 = 32.8523$ $\chi_{.975}^2 = 8.90655$

$$\frac{(20-1)(4996.78)}{32.8523} \le \sigma^2 \le \frac{(20-1)(4996.78)}{8.90655}$$

$2889.87 \le \sigma^2 \le 10,659.45$

$53.76 \le \sigma \le 103.24$

26. a. $H_0: \sigma^2 \le .0001$

$H_a: \sigma^2 > .0001$

$\chi^2_{.10} = 21.0642$ (14 degrees of freedom)

$\chi^2 = \dfrac{(14)(.014)^2}{.0001} = 27.44$

Reject H_0; σ^2 exceeds maximum variance requirement.

b. $\chi^2_{.05} = 23.6848$ and $\chi^2_{.95} = 6.57063$ (14 degrees of freedom)

$\dfrac{(14)(.014)^2}{23.6848} \le \sigma^2 \le \dfrac{(14)(.014)^2}{6.57063}$

$.00012 \le \sigma^2 \le .00042$

27. $H_0: \sigma^2 \le .02$

$H_a: \sigma^2 > .02$

$\chi^2_{.05} = 55.7585$ (40 degrees of freedom)

$\chi^2 = \dfrac{(40)(.16)^2}{.02} = 51.2$

Do not reject H_0; the variance does not appear to be exceeding the standard.

28. $n = 22$ $s^2 = 1.5$

$H_0: \sigma^2 \le 1$

$H_a: \sigma^2 > 1$

$\chi^2_{.10} = 29.6151$ (21 degrees of freedom)

$\chi^2 = \dfrac{(21)(1.5)}{1} = 31.5$

Reject H_0; conclude that $\sigma^2 > 1$.

29. $s^2 = \dfrac{\Sigma(x_i - \overline{x})^2}{n-1} = \dfrac{101.56}{9-1} = 12.69$

$H_0: \sigma^2 = 10$

$H_a: \sigma^2 \ne 10$

$$\chi^2 = \frac{(n-1)s^2}{\sigma_0^2} = \frac{(8)(12.69)}{10} = 10.16$$

With 8 degrees of freedom, reject if

$$\chi^2 < \chi_{.95}^2 = 2.73264 \text{ or } \chi^2 > \chi_{.05}^2 = 15.5073$$

Since $\chi^2 = 10.16$ is not in the rejection region, we cannot reject H_0.

30. a. Try $n = 15$

$$\chi_{.025}^2 = 26.1190 \qquad \chi_{.975}^2 = 5.62872 \text{ (14 degrees of freedom)}$$

$$\frac{(14)(64)}{26.1190} \leq \sigma^2 \leq \frac{(14)(64)}{5.62872}$$

$$34.30 \leq \sigma^2 \leq 159.18$$

$$5.86 \leq \sigma \leq 12.62$$

∴ A sample size of 15 was used.

b. $n = 25$; expected the width of the interval to be smaller.

$$\chi_{.05}^2 = 39.3641 \qquad \chi_{.975}^2 = 12.4011 \text{ (24 degrees of freedom)}$$

$$\frac{(24)(8)^2}{39.3641} \leq \sigma^2 \leq \frac{(24)(8)^2}{12.4011}$$

$$39.02 \leq \sigma^2 \leq 126.86$$

$$6.25 \leq \sigma \leq 11.13$$

31. $H_0: \sigma_1^2 = \sigma_2^2$

$H_a: \sigma_1^2 \neq \sigma_2^2$

$F_{\alpha/2} = F_{.05,9,9} = 3.18$

$$F = \frac{s_1^2}{s_2^2} = \frac{15.8^2}{7.9^2} = 4$$

Reject H_0. Conclude the variances differ with NASDAQ stocks showing the greater variance.

32. $H_0: \sigma_1^2 = \sigma_2^2$

$H_a: \sigma_1^2 \neq \sigma_2^2$

$F_{.025} = 1.466$

$$F = \frac{s_1^2}{s_2^2} = \frac{.940^2}{.797^2} = 1.39$$

Do not reject H_0; We are not able to conclude students who complete the course and students who drop out have different variances of grade point averages.

33.　　$n_1 = 16$　　　　$s_1^2 = 5.4$

　　　$n_2 = 16$　　　　$s_2^2 = 2.3$

　　　$H_0 : \sigma_1^2 = \sigma_2^2$

　　　$H_a : \sigma_1^2 \neq \sigma_2^2$

　　　$F_{.05} = 2.40$　(Degrees of freedom are 15 numerator, 15 denominator)

$$F = \frac{s_1^2}{s_2^2} = \frac{5.4}{2.3} = 2.35$$

Do not reject H_0; data does not indicate a difference between the population variances.

34.　　$H_0 : \sigma_1^2 = \sigma_2^2$

　　　$H_a : \sigma_1^2 \neq \sigma_2^2$

　　　$F_{.05} = 1.94$　(30 numerator and 24 denominator degrees of freedom)

$$F = \frac{s_1^2}{s_2^2} = \frac{25}{12} = 2.08$$

Reject H_0; conclude that the variances of assembly times are not equal.

Chapter 12
Tests of Goodness of Fit and Independence

Learning Objectives

1. Know how to conduct a goodness of fit test.

2. Know how to use sample data to test for independence of two variables.

3. Understand the role of the chi-square distribution in conducting tests of goodness of fit and independence.

4. Be able to conduct a goodness of fit test for cases where the population is hypothesized to have either a multinomial, a Poisson, or a normal probability distribution.

5. For a test of independence, be able to set up a contingency table, determine the observed and expected frequencies, and determine if the two variables are independent.

Solutions:

1.   Expected frequencies: $e_1 = 200\,(.40) = 80, \; e_2 = 200\,(.40) = 80$

                                    $e_3 = 200\,(.20) = 40$

    Actual frequencies: $f_1 = 60, f_2 = 120, f_3 = 20$

$$\chi^2 = \frac{(60-80)^2}{80} + \frac{(120-80)^2}{80} + \frac{(20-40)^2}{40}$$

$$= \frac{400}{80} + \frac{1600}{80} + \frac{400}{40}$$

$$= 5 + 20 + 10$$

$$= 35$$

$\chi^2_{.01} = 9.21034$ with $k - 1 = 3 - 1 = 2$ degrees of freedom

Since $\chi^2 = 35 > 9.21034$ reject the null hypothesis. The population proportions are not as stated in the null hypothesis.

2.   Expected frequencies: $e_1 = 300\,(.25) = 75, \; e_2 = 300\,(.25) = 75$

                                    $e_3 = 300\,(.25) = 75, \; e_4 = 300\,(.25) = 75$

    Actual frequencies: $f_1 = 85, f_2 = 95, f_3 = 50, f_4 = 70$

$$\chi^2 = \frac{(85-75)^2}{75} + \frac{(95-75)^2}{75} + \frac{(50-75)^2}{75} + \frac{(70-75)^2}{75}$$

$$= \frac{100}{75} + \frac{400}{75} + \frac{625}{75} + \frac{25}{75}$$

$$= \frac{1150}{75}$$

$$= 15.33$$

$\chi^2_{.05} = 7.81473$ with $k - 1 = 4 - 1 = 3$ degrees of freedom

Since $\chi^2 = 15.33 > 7.81473$ reject H_0

We conclude that the proportions are not all equal.

3. $H_0 = p_{ABC} = .29, p_{CBS} = .28, p_{NBC} = .25, p_{IND} = .18$

    $H_a =$ The proportions are not $p_{ABC} = .29, p_{CBS} = .28, p_{NBC} = .25, p_{IND} = .18$

Expected frequencies: $300\,(.29) = 87,\ 300\,(.28) = 84$

$$300\,(.25) = 75,\ 300\,(.18) = 54$$

$$e_1 = 87,\ e_2 = 84,\ e_3 = 75,\ e_4 = 54$$

Actual frequencies: $f_1 = 95, f_2 = 70, f_3 = 89, f_4 = 46$

$\chi^2_{.05} = 7.81$ (3 degrees of freedom)

$$\chi^2 = \frac{(95 - 87)^2}{87} + \frac{(70 - 84)^2}{84} + \frac{(89 - 75)^2}{75} + \frac{(46 - 54)^2}{54}$$

$$= 6.87$$

Do not reject H_0; there is no significant change in the viewing audience proportions.

4.

Category	Hypothesized Proportion	Observed Frequency (f_i)	Expected Frequency (e_i)	$(f_i - e_i)^2 / e_i$
Brown	0.30	177	151.8	4.18
Yellow	0.20	135	101.2	11.29
Red	0.20	79	101.2	4.87
Orange	0.10	41	50.6	1.82
Green	0.10	36	50.6	4.21
Blue	0.10	38	50.6	3.14
Totals:		506		29.51

$\chi^2_{.05} = 11.07$ (5 degrees of freedom)

Since $29.51 > 11.07$, we conclude that the percentage figures reported by the company have changed.

5.

Category	Hypothesized Proportion	Observed Frequency (f_i)	Expected Frequency (e_i)	$(f_i - e_i)^2 / e_i$
Full Service	1/3	264	249.33	0.86
Discount	1/3	255	249.33	0.13
Both	1/3	229	249.33	1.66
Totals:		748		2.65

$\chi^2_{.10} = 4.61$ (2 degrees of freedom)

Since $2.65 < 4.61$, there is no significant difference in preference among the three service choices.

6.

Category	Hypothesized Proportion	Observed Frequency (f_i)	Expected Frequency (e_i)	$(f_i - e_i)^2 / e_i$
News and Opinion	1/6	20	19.17	.04
General Editorial	1/6	15	19.17	.91
Family Oriented	1/6	30	19.17	6.12
Business/Financial	1/6	22	19.17	.42
Female Oriented	1/6	16	19.17	.52
African-American	1/6	12	19.17	2.68
	Totals:	115		10.69

$\chi^2_{.10} = 9.24$ (5 degrees of freedom)

Since $10.69 > 9.24$, we conclude that there is a difference in the proportion of ads with guilt appeals among the six types of magazines.

7.   Expected frequencies: $e_i = (1/3)(135) = 45$

$$\chi^2 = \frac{(43 - 45)^2}{45} + \frac{(53 - 45)^2}{45} + \frac{(39 - 45)^2}{45} = 2.31$$

With 2 degrees of freedom, $\chi^2_{.05} = 5.99$

Do not reject H_0; there is no justification for concluding a difference in preference exists.

8. H_0: $p_1 = .03, p_2 = .28, p_3 = .45, p_4 = .24$

$df = 3$ $\chi^2_{.01} = 11.34$

Reject H_0 if $\chi^2 > 11.34$

Rating	Observed	Expected	$(f_i - e_i)^2 / e_i$
Excellent	24	.03(400) = 12	12.00
Good	124	.28(400) = 112	1.29
Fair	172	.45(400) = 180	.36
Poor	80	.24(400) = 96	2.67
	400	400	$\chi^2 = 16.31$

Reject H_0; conclude that the ratings differ. A comparison of observed and expected frequencies show telephone service is slightly better with more excellent and good ratings.

9. H_0 = The column variable is independent of the row variable

H_a = The column variable is not independent of the row variable

Expected Frequencies:

	A	B	C
P	28.5	39.9	45.6
Q	21.5	30.1	34.4

$$\chi^2 = \frac{(20-28.5)^2}{28.5} + \frac{(44-39.9)^2}{39.9} + \frac{(50-45.6)^2}{45.6} + \frac{(30-21.5)^2}{21.5} + \frac{(26-30.1)^2}{30.1} + \frac{(30-34.4)^2}{34.4}$$

$$= 7.86$$

$\chi^2_{.025} = 7.37776$ with $(2-1)(3-1) = 2$ degrees of freedom

Since $\chi^2 = 7.86 > 7.37776$ Reject H_0

Conclude that the column variable is not independent of the row variable.

10. $H_0 = $ The column variable is independent of the row variable

      $H_a = $ The column variable is not independent of the row variable

      Expected Frequencies:

	A	B	C
P	17.5000	30.6250	21.8750
Q	28.7500	50.3125	35.9375
R	13.7500	24.0625	17.1875

$$\chi^2 = \frac{(20-17.5000)^2}{17.5000} + \frac{(30-30.6250)^2}{30.6250} + \ldots + \frac{(30-17.1875)^2}{17.1875}$$
$$= 19.78$$

$\chi^2_{.05} = 9.48773$ with $(3-1)(3-1) = 4$ degrees of freedom

Since $\chi^2 = 19.78 > 9.48773$ Reject H_0 Conclude that the column variable is not independent of f the row variable.

11. H_0 : Type of ticket purchased is independent of the type of flight

      H_a: Type of ticket purchased is not independent of the type of flight.

      Expected Frequencies:

$e_{11} = 35.59$ $e_{12} = 15.41$
$e_{21} = 150.73$ $e_{22} = 65.27$
$e_{31} = 455.68$ $e_{32} = 197.32$

Ticket	Flight	Observed Frequency (f_i)	Expected Frequency (e_i)	$(f_i - e_i)^2 / e_i$
First	Domestic	29	35.59	1.22
First	International	22	15.41	2.82
Business	Domestic	95	150.73	20.61
Business	International	121	65.27	47.59
Full Fare	Domestic	518	455.68	8.52
Full Fare	International	135	197.32	19.68
	Totals:	920		100.43

$\chi^2_{.05} = 5.99$ with $(3-1)(2-1) = 2$ degrees of freedom

Since 100.43 > 5.99, we conclude that the type of ticket purchased is not independent of the type of flight.

12. a. Observed Frequency (f_{ij})

	Domestic	European	Asian	Total
Same	125	55	68	248
Different	140	105	107	352
Total	265	160	175	600

Expected Frequency (e_{ij})

	Domestic	European	Asian	Total
Same	109.53	66.13	72.33	248
Different	155.47	93.87	102.67	352
Total	265	160	175	600

Chi Square $(f_{ij} - e_{ij})^2 / e_{ij}$

	Domestic	European	Asian	Total
Same	2.18	1.87	0.26	4.32
Different	1.54	1.32	0.18	3.04
				$\chi^2 = 7.36$

Degrees of freedom = 2 $\chi^2_{.05} = 5.99$

Reject H_0; conclude brand loyalty is not independent of manufacturer.

b. Brand Loyalty

Domestic 125/265 = .472 (47.2%) ← Highest
European 55/160 = .344 (34.4%)
Asian   68/175 = .389 (38.9%)

13.

	Industry			
Major	Oil	Chemical	Electrical	Computer
Business	30	22.5	17.5	30
Engineering	30	22.5	17.5	30

Note: Values shown above are the expected frequencies.

$\chi^2_{.01} = 11.3449$ (3 degrees of freedom: 1 x 3 = 3)

$\chi^2 = 12.39$

Reject H_0; conclude that major and industry not independent.

14. Expected Frequencies:

$e_{11} = 31.0$ $e_{12} = 31.0$
$e_{21} = 29.5$ $e_{22} = 29.5$
$e_{31} = 13.0$ $e_{32} = 13.0$
$e_{41} = 5.5$ $e_{42} = 5.5$
$e_{51} = 7.0$ $e_{52} = 7.0$
$e_{61} = 14.0$ $e_{62} = 14.0$

Most Difficult	Gender	Observed Frequency (f_i)	Expected Frequency (e_i)	$(f_i - e_i)^2 / e_i$
Spouse	Men	37	31.0	1.16
Spouse	Women	25	31.0	1.16
Parents	Men	28	29.5	0.08
Parents	Women	31	29.5	0.08
Children	Men	7	13.0	2.77
Children	Women	19	13.0	2.77
Siblings	Men	8	5.5	1.14
Siblings	Women	3	5.5	1.14
In-Laws	Men	4	7.0	1.29
In-Laws	Women	10	7.0	1.29
Other Relatives	Men	16	14.0	0.29
Other Relatives	Women	12	14.0	0.29
	Totals:	200		13.43

$\chi^2_{.05} = 11.0705$ with $(6 - 1)(2 - 1) = 5$ degrees of freedom

Since 13.43 > 11.0705. we conclude that gender is not independent of the most difficult person to buy for.

15. Expected Frequencies:

$e_{11} = 17.16$ $e_{12} = 12.84$
$e_{21} = 14.88$ $e_{22} = 11.12$
$e_{31} = 28.03$ $e_{32} = 20.97$
$e_{41} = 22.31$ $e_{42} = 16.69$
$e_{51} = 17.16$ $e_{52} = 12.84$
$e_{61} = 15.45$ $e_{62} = 11.55$

Magazine	Appeal	Observed Frequency (f_i)	Expected Frequency (e_i)	$(f_i - e_i)^2 / e_i$
News	Guilt	20	17.16	0.47
News	Fear	10	12.84	0.63
General	Guilt	15	14.88	0.00
General	Fear	11	11.12	0.00
Family	Guilt	30	28.03	0.14
Family	Fear	19	20.97	0.18
Business	Guilt	22	22.31	0.00
Business	Fear	17	16.69	0.01
Female	Guilt	16	17.16	0.08
Female	Fear	14	12.84	0.11
African-American	Guilt	12	15.45	0.77
African-American	Fear	15	11.55	1.03
	Totals:	201		3.41

$\chi_{.01}^2 = 15.09$ with $(6 - 1)(2 - 1) = 5$ degrees of freedom

Since $3.41 < 15.09$, the hypothesis of independence cannot be rejected.

34. a.   Observed Frequency (f_{ij})

	Pharm	Consumer	Computer	Telecom	Total
Correct	207	136	151	178	672
Incorrect	3	4	9	12	28
Total	210	140	160	190	700

Expected Frequency (e_{ij})

	Pharm	Consumer	Computer	Telecom	Total
Correct	201.6	134.4	153.6	182.4	672
Incorrect	8.4	5.6	6.4	7.6	28
Total	210	140	160	190	700

Chi Square $(f_{ij} - e_{ij})^2 / e_{ij}$

	Pharm	Consumer	Computer	Telecom	Total
Correct	.14	.02	.04	.11	.31
Incorrect	3.47	.46	1.06	2.55	7.53
					$\chi^2 = 7.85$

Degrees of freedom = 3 $\chi_{.05}^2 = 7.81473$

Do not reject H_0; conclude order fulfillment is not independent of industry.

b.   The pharmaceutical industry is doing the best with 207 of 210 (98.6%) correctly filled orders.

17.   Expected Frequencies:

Supplier	Good	Part Quality Minor Defect	Major Defect
A	88.76	6.07	5.14
B	173.09	11.83	10.08
C	133.15	9.10	7.75

$\chi^2 = 7.96$

$\chi_{.05}^2 = 9.48773$ (4 degrees of freedom: 2 x 2 = 4)

Do not reject H_0; conclude that the assumption of independence cannot be rejected

18.   Expected Frequencies:

Education Level	Democratic	Party Affiliation Republican	Independent
Did not complete high school	28	28	14
High school degree	32	32	16
College degree	40	40	20

$\chi^2 = 13.42$

$\chi_{.01}^2 = 13.2767$ (4 degrees of freedom: 2 x 2 = 4)

Reject H_0; conclude that party affiliation is not independent of education level.

19. Expected Frequencies:

$e_{11} = 11.81$ $e_{12} = 8.44$ $e_{13} = 24.75$
$e_{21} = 8.40$ $e_{22} = 6.00$ $e_{23} = 17.60$
$e_{31} = 21.79$ $e_{32} = 15.56$ $e_{33} = 45.65$

Siskel	Ebert	Observed Frequency (f_i)	Expected Frequency (e_i)	$(f_i - e_i)^2 / e_i$
Con	Con	24	11.81	12.57
Con	Mixed	8	8.44	0.02
Con	Pro	13	24.75	5.58
Mixed	Con	8	8.40	0.02
Mixed	Mixed	13	6.00	8.17
Mixed	Pro	11	17.60	2.48
Pro	Con	10	21.79	6.38
Pro	Mixed	9	15.56	2.77
Pro	Pro	64	45.65	7.38
	Totals:	160		45.36

$\chi^2_{.01} = 13.28$ with $(3-1)(3-1) = 4$ degrees of freedom

Since $45.36 > 13.28$, we conclude that the ratings are not independent.

20. First estimate μ from the sample data. Sample size $= 120$.

$$\mu = \frac{0(39) + 1(30) + 2(30) + 3(18) + 4(3)}{120} = \frac{156}{120} = 1.3$$

Therefore, we use Poisson probabilities with $\mu = 1.3$ to compute expected frequencies.

x	Observed Frequency	Poisson Probability	Expected Frequency	Difference ($f_i - e_i$)
0	39	.2725	32.700	6.300
1	30	.3543	42.516	-12.516
2	30	.2303	27.636	2.364
3	18	.0998	11.976	6.024
4 or more	3	.0430	5.160	-2.160

$$\chi^2 = \frac{(6.300)^2}{32.700} + \frac{(-12.516)^2}{42.516} + \frac{(2.364)^2}{27.636} + \frac{(6.024)^2}{11.976} + \frac{(-2.160)^2}{5.160}$$
$$= 9.0348$$

$\chi^2_{.05} = 7.81473$ with $5 - 1 - 1 = 3$ degrees of freedom

Since $\chi^2 = 9.0348 > 7.81473$ Reject H_0

Conclude that the data do not follow a Poisson probability distribution.

21.   With $n = 30$ we will use six classes with $16\,^2/_3\%$ of the probability associated with each class.

$\overline{x} = 22.80 \quad s = 6.2665$

The z values that create 6 intervals, each with probability .1667 are -.98, -.43, 0, .43, .98

z	Cut off value of x
-.98	22.8 - .98 (6.2665) = 16.66
-.43	22.8 - .43 (6.2665) = 20.11
0	22.8 + 0 (6.2665) = 22.80
.43	22.8 + .43 (6.2665) = 25.49
.98	22.8 + .98 (6.2665) = 28.94

Interval	Observed Frequency	Expected Frequency	Difference
less than 16.66	3	5	-2
16.66 - 20.11	7	5	2
20.11 - 22.80	5	5	0
22.80 - 25.49	7	5	2
25.49 - 28.94	3	5	-2
28.94 and up	5	5	0

$$\chi^2 = \frac{(-2)^2}{5} + \frac{(2)^2}{5} + \frac{(0)^2}{5} + \frac{(2)^2}{5} + \frac{(-2)^2}{5} + \frac{(0)^2}{5} = \frac{16}{5} = 3.20$$

$\chi^2_{.025} = 9.34840$ with 6 - 2 - 1 = 3 degrees of freedom

Since $\chi^2 = 3.20 \leq 9.34840$ Do not reject H_0

The claim that the data comes from a normal distribution cannot be rejected.

22. $\mu = \dfrac{0(34) + 1(25) + 2(11) + 3(7) + 4(3)}{80} = 1$

Use Poisson probabilities with $\mu = 1$.

x	Observed	Poisson Probabilities	Expected	
0	34	.3679	29.432	
1	25	.3679	29.432	
2	11	.1839	14.712	
3	7	.0613	4.904	
4	3	.0153	1.224	combine into 1 category of 3 or more to make $e_i \geq 5$.
5 or more	-	.0037	.296	

$\chi^2 = 4.30$

$\chi^2_{.05} = 5.99147$ (2 degrees of freedom)

Do not reject H_0; the assumption of a Poisson distribution cannot be rejected.

23. $$\mu = \frac{0(15) + 1(31) + 2(20) + 3(15) + 4(13) + 5(4) + 6(2)}{100} = 2$$

x	Observed	Poisson Probabilities	Expected
0	15	.1353	13.53
1	31	.2707	27.07
2	20	.2707	27.07
3	15	.1804	18.04
4	13	.0902	9.02
5 or more	6	.0527	5.27

$\chi^2 = 4.98$

$\chi^2_{.10} = 7.77944$ (4 degrees of freedom)

Do not reject H_0; the assumption of a Poisson distribution cannot be rejected.

24. $\overline{x} = 24.5$ $s = 3$ $n = 30$ Use 6 classes

Interval	Observed Frequency	Expected Frequency
less than 21.56	5	5
21.56 - 23.21	4	5
23.21 - 24.50	3	5
24.50 - 25.79	7	5
25.79 - 27.44	7	5
27.41 up	4	5

$\chi^2 = 2.8$

$\chi^2_{.10} = 6.25139$ (3 degrees of freedom: 6 - 2 - 1 = 3)

Do not reject H_0; the assumption of a normal distribution cannot be rejected.

25. $\overline{x} = 71$ $s = 17$ $n = 25$ Use 5 classes

Interval	Observed Frequency	Expected Frequency
less than 56.7	7	5
56.7 - 66.5	7	5
66.5 - 74.6	1	5
74.6 - 84.5	1	5
84.5 up	9	5

$\chi^2 = 11.2$

$\chi^2_{.01} = 9.21034$ (2 degrees of freedom)

Reject H_0; conclude the distribution is not a normal distribution.

26.

Observed	60	45	59	36
Expected	50	50	50	50

$\chi^2 = 8.04$

$\chi^2_{.05} = 7.81473$ (3 degrees of freedom)

Reject H_0; conclude that the order potentials are not the same in each sales territory.

27.

Observed	48	323	79	16	63
Expected	37.03	306.82	126.96	21.16	37.03

$$\chi^2 = \frac{(48-37.03)^2}{37.03} + \frac{(323-306.82)^2}{306.82} + \cdots + \frac{(63-37.03)^2}{37.03}$$

$= 41.69$

$\chi^2_{.01} = 13.2767$ (4 degrees of freedom)

Since $41.69 > 13.2767$, reject H_0.

Mutual fund investors' attitudes toward corporate bonds differ from their attitudes toward corporate stock.

28.

Observed	20	20	40	60
Expected	35	35	35	35

$$\chi^2 = \frac{(20-35)^2}{35} + \frac{(20-35)^2}{35} + \frac{(40-35)^2}{35} + \frac{(60-35)^2}{35}$$

$= 31.43$

$\chi^2_{.05} = 7.81473$ (3 degrees of freedom)

Since $31.43 > 7.81473$, reject H_0.

The park manager should not plan on the same number attending each day. Plan on a larger staff for Sundays and holidays.

29.

Observed	13	16	28	17	16
Expected	18	18	18	18	18

$\chi^2 = 7.44$

$\chi^2_{.05} = 9.48773$

Do not reject H_0; the assumption that the number of riders is uniformly distributed cannot be rejected.

30.

Category	Hypothesized Proportion	Observed Frequency (f_i)	Expected Frequency (e_i)	$(f_i - e_i)^2 / e_i$
Very Satisfied	0.28	105	140	8.75
Somewhat Satisfied	0.46	235	230	0.11
Neither	0.12	55	60	0.42
Somewhat Dissatisfied	0.10	90	50	32.00
Very Dissatisfied	0.04	15	20	1.25
Totals:		500		42.53

$\chi^2_{.05} = 9.49$ (4 degrees of freedom)

Since $42.53 > 9.49$, we conclude that the job satisfaction for computer programmers is different than the job satisfaction for IS managers.

31.   Expected Frequencies:

	Quality	
Shift	Good	Defective
1st	368.44	31.56
2nd	276.33	23.67
3rd	184.22	15.78

$\chi^2 = 8.11$

$\chi^2_{.05} = 5.99147$ (2 degrees of freedom)

Reject H_0; conclude that shift and quality are not independent.

32.   Expected Frequencies:

$e_{11} = 1046.19 \quad e_{12} = 632.81$
$e_{21} = 28.66 \quad e_{22} = 17.34$
$e_{31} = 258.59 \quad e_{32} = 156.41$
$e_{41} = 516.55 \quad e_{42} = 312.45$

Employment	Region	Observed Frequency (f_i)	Expected Frequency (e_i)	$(f_i - e_i)^2 / e_i$
Full-Time	Eastern	1105	1046.19	3.31
Full-time	Western	574	632.81	5.46
Part-Time	Eastern	31	28.66	0.19
Part-Time	Western	15	17.34	0.32
Self-Employed	Eastern	229	258.59	3.39
Self-Employed	Western	186	156.41	5.60
Not Employed	Eastern	485	516.55	1.93
Not Employed	Western	344	312.45	3.19
Totals:		2969		23.37

$\chi^2_{.05} = 7.81$ with $(4 - 1)(2 - 1) = 3$ degrees of freedom

Since $23.37 > 7.81$, we conclude that employment status is not independent of region.

33.   Expected frequencies:

Loan Offices	Loan Approval Decision	
	Approved	Rejected
Miller	24.86	15.14
McMahon	18.64	11.36
Games	31.07	18.93
Runk	12.43	7.57

$\chi^2 = 2.21$

$\chi^2_{.05} = 7.81473$ (3 degrees of freedom)

Do not reject H_0; the loan decision does not appear to be dependent on the officer.

34. a.   Observed Frequency (f_{ij})

	Never Married	Married	Divorced	Total
Men	234	106	10	350
Women	216	168	16	400
Total	450	274	26	750

Expected Frequency (e_{ij})

	Never Married	Married	Divorced	Total
Men	210	127.87	12.13	350
Women	240	146.13	13.87	400
Total	450	274	26	750

Chi Square $(f_{ij} - e_{ij})^2 / e_{ij}$

	Never Married	Married	Divorced	Total
Men	2.74	3.74	.38	6.86
Women	2.40	3.27	.33	6.00
				$\chi^2 = 12.86$

Degrees of freedom = 2 $\chi^2_{.01} = 9.21$

Reject H_0; conclude martial status is not independent of gender.

b.   Martial Status

	Never Married	Married	Divorced
Men	66.9%	30.3%	2.9%
Women	54.0%	42.0%	4.0%

Men   100 - 66.9 = 33.1% have been married
Women 100 - 54.0 = 46.0% have been married

35.   Expected Frequencies:

$$e_{11} = \frac{(50)(18)}{100} = 9, \quad e_{12} = \frac{(50)(24)}{100} = 12, \quad \cdots, \quad e_{25} = \frac{(50)(12)}{100} = 6$$

$$\chi^2 = \frac{(4-9)^2}{9} + \frac{(10-12)^2}{12} + \cdots + \frac{(4-6)^2}{6} = 9.76$$

$\chi^2_{.05} = 9.48773$ (4 degrees of freedom)

Since $9.76 < 9.48773$, reject H_0.

Banking tends to have lower P/E ratios. We can conclude that industry type and P/E ratio are related.

36.   Expected Frequencies:

	Days of the Week							
County	Sun	Mon	Tues	Wed	Thur	Fri	Sat	Total
Urban	56.7	47.6	55.1	56.7	60.1	72.6	44.2	393
Rural	11.3	9.4	10.9	11.3	11.9	14.4	8.8	78
Total	68	57	66	68	72	87	53	471

$\chi^2 = 6.20$

$\chi^2_{.05} = 12.5916$ (6 degrees of freedom)

Do not reject H_0; the assumption of independence cannot be rejected.

37. $\overline{x} = 76.83 \quad s = 12.43$

Interval	Observed Frequency	Expected Frequency
less than 62.54	5	5
62.54 - 68.50	3	5
68.50 - 72.85	6	5
72.85 - 76.83	5	5
76.83 - 80.81	5	5
80.81 - 85.16	7	5
85.16 - 91.12	4	5
91.12 up	5	5

$\chi^2 = 2$

$\chi^2_{.05} = 11.0705$ (5 degrees of freedom)

Do not reject H_0; the assumption of a normal distribution cannot be rejected.

38.   Expected Frequencies:

	Los Angeles	San Diego	San Francisco	San Jose	Total
Occupied	165.7	124.3	186.4	165.7	642
Vacant	34.3	25.7	38.6	34.3	133
Total	200.0	150.0	225.0	200.0	775

$$\chi^2 = \frac{(160 - 165.7)^2}{165.7} + \frac{(116 - 124.3)^2}{124.3} + \cdots + \frac{(26 - 34.3)^2}{34.3}$$

$$= 7.78$$

$\chi_{.05}^2 = 7.81473$ with 3 degrees of freedom

Since $\chi^2 = 7.78 \le 7.81473$ Do not reject H_0.

We cannot conclude that office vacancies are dependent on metropolitan area, but it is close: the p-value is slightly larger than .05.

39. a.

x	Observed Frequencies	Binomial Prob. $n = 4, p = .30$	Expected Frequencies
0	30	.2401	24.01
1	32	.4116	41.16
2	25	.2646	26.46
3	10	.0756	7.56
4	3	.0081	.81
	100		100.00

The expected frequency of $x = 4$ is .81. Combine $x = 3$ and $x = 4$ into one category so that all expected frequencies are 5 or more.

x	Observed Frequencies	Expected Frequencies
0	30	24.01
1	32	41.16
2	25	26.46
3 or 4	13	8.37
	100	100.00

b. With 3 degrees of freedom, $\chi_{.05}^2 = 7.81473$. Reject H_0 if $\chi^2 > 7.81473$.

$$\chi^2 = \Sigma \frac{\left(f_i - e_i \right)^2}{e_i} = 6.17$$

Do not reject H_0; conclude that the assumption of a binomial distribution cannot be rejected.

Chapter 13
Analysis of Variance and Experimental Design

Learning Objectives

1. Understand how the analysis of variance procedure can be used to determine if the means of more than two populations are equal.

2. Know the assumptions necessary to use the analysis of variance procedure.

3. Understand the use of the F distribution in performing the analysis of variance procedure.

4. Know how to set up an ANOVA table and interpret the entries in the table.

5. Be able to use output from computer software packages to solve analysis of variance problems.

6. Know how to use Fisher's least significant difference (LSD) procedure and Fisher's LSD with the Bonferroni adjustment to conduct statistical comparisons between pairs of populations means.

7. Understand the difference between a completely randomized design, a randomized block design, and factorial experiments.

8. Know the definition of the following terms:

comparisonwise Type I error rate	partitioning
experimentwise Type I error rate	blocking
factor	main effect
level	interaction
treatment	
replication	

Solutions:

1. a. $\overline{\overline{x}} = (30 + 45 + 36)/3 = 37$

$$SSTR = \sum_{j=1}^{k} n_j \left(\overline{x}_j - \overline{\overline{x}} \right)^2 = 5(30 - 37)^2 + 5(45 - 37)^2 + 5(36 - 37)^2 = 570$$

MSTR = SSTR $/(k - 1) = 570/2 = 285$

b. $SSE = \sum_{j=1}^{k} (n_j - 1)s_j^2 = 4(6) + 4(4) + 4(6.5) = 66$

MSE = SSE $/(n_T - k) = 66/(15 - 3) = 5.5$

c. $F = MSTR /MSE = 285/5.5 = 51.82$

$F_{.05} = 3.89$ (2 degrees of freedom numerator and 12 denominator)

Since $F = 51.82 > F_{.05} = 3.89$, we reject the null hypothesis that the means of the three populations are equal.

d.

Source of Variation	Sum of Squares	Degrees of Freedom	Mean Square	F
Treatments	570	2	285	51.82
Error	66	12	5.5	
Total	636	14		

2. a. $\overline{\overline{x}} = (153 + 169 + 158)/3 = 160$

$$SSTR = \sum_{j=1}^{k} n_j \left(\overline{x}_j - \overline{\overline{x}} \right)^2 = 4(153 - 160)^2 + 4(169 - 160)^2 + 4(158 - 160)^2 = 536$$

MSTR = SSTR $/(k - 1) = 536/2 = 268$

b. $SSE = \sum_{j=1}^{k} (n_j - 1)s_j^2 = 3(96.67) + 3(97.33) + 3(82.00) = 828.00$

MSE = SSE $/(n_T - k) = 828.00 /(12 - 3) = 92.00$

c. $F = MSTR /MSE = 268/92 = 2.91$

$F_{.05} = 4.26$ (2 degrees of freedom numerator and 9 denominator)

Since $F = 2.91 < F_{.05} = 4.26$, we cannot reject the null hypothesis.

d.

Source of Variation	Sum of Squares	Degrees of Freedom	Mean Square	F
Treatments	536	2	268	2.91
Error	828	9	92	
Total	1364	11		

3. a. $\bar{\bar{x}} = \dfrac{4(100) + 6(85) + 5(79)}{15} = 87$

$\text{SSTR} = \displaystyle\sum_{j=1}^{k} n_j \left(\bar{x}_j - \bar{\bar{x}}\right)^2 = 4(100 - 87)^2 + 6(85 - 87)^2 + 5(79 - 87)^2 = 1{,}020$

$\text{MSTR} = \text{SSB}/(k - 1) = 1{,}020/2 = 510$

b. $\text{SSE} = \displaystyle\sum_{j=1}^{k} (n_j - 1)s_j^2 = 3(35.33) + 5(35.60) + 4(43.50) = 458$

$\text{MSE} = \text{SSE}/(n_T - k) = 458/(15 - 3) = 38.17$

c. $F = \text{MSTR}/\text{MSE} = 510/38.17 = 13.36$

$F_{.05} = 3.89$ (2 degrees of freedom numerator and 12 denominator)

Since $F = 13.36 > F_{.05} = 3.89$ we reject the null hypothesis that the means of the three populations are equal.

d.

Source of Variation	Sum of Squares	Degrees of Freedom	Mean Square	F
Treatments	1020	2	510	13.36
Error	458	12	38.17	
Total	1478	14		

4. a.

Source of Variation	Sum of Squares	Degrees of Freedom	Mean Square	F
Treatments	1200	3	400	80
Error	300	60	5	
Total	1500	63		

b. $F_{.05} = 2.76$ (3 degrees of freedom numerator and 60 denominator)

Since $F = 80 > F_{.05} = 2.76$ we reject the null hypothesis that the means of the 4 populations are equal.

5. a.

Source of Variation	Sum of Squares	Degrees of Freedom	Mean Square	F
Treatments	120	2	60	20
Error	216	72	3	
Total	336	74		

b. $F_{.05} = 3.15$ (2 numerator degrees of freedom and 60 denominator)

$F_{.05} = 3.07$ (2 numerator degrees of freedom and 120 denominator)

The critical value is between 3.07 and 3.15

Since $F = 20$ must exceed the critical value, no matter what its actual value, we reject the null hypothesis that the 3 population means are equal.

6.

	Manufacturer 1	Manufacturer 2	Manufacturer 3
Sample Mean	23	28	21
Sample Variance	6.67	4.67	3.33

$\bar{\bar{x}} = (23 + 28 + 21)/3 = 24$

$$\text{SSTR} = \sum_{j=1}^{k} n_j \left(\bar{x}_j - \bar{\bar{x}} \right)^2 = 4(23 - 24)^2 + 4(28 - 24)^2 + 4(21 - 24)^2 = 104$$

$\text{MSTR} = \text{SSTR} /(k - 1) = 104/2 = 52$

$$\text{SSE} = \sum_{j=1}^{k} (n_j - 1)s_j^2 = 3(6.67) + 3(4.67) + 3(3.33) = 44.01$$

$\text{MSE} = \text{SSE} /(n_T - k) = 44.01/(12 - 3) = 4.89$

$F = \text{MSTR} /\text{MSE} = 52/4.89 = 10.63$

$F_{.05} = 4.26$ (2 degrees of freedom numerator and 9 denominator)

Since $F = 10.63 > F_{.05} = 4.26$ we reject the null hypothesis that the mean time needed to mix a batch of material is the same for each manufacturer.

7.

	Superior	Peer	Subordinate
Sample Mean	5.75	5.5	5.25
Sample Variance	1.64	2.00	1.93

$\bar{\bar{x}} = (5.75 + 5.5 + 5.25)/3 = 5.5$

$$\text{SSTR} = \sum_{j=1}^{k} n_j \left(\bar{x}_j - \bar{\bar{x}} \right)^2 = 8(5.75 - 5.5)^2 + 8(5.5 - 5.5)^2 + 8(5.25 - 5.5)^2 = 1$$

$\text{MSTR} = \text{SSTR} /(k - 1) = 1/2 = .5$

$$\text{SSE} = \sum_{j=1}^{k} (n_j - 1)s_j^2 = 7(1.64) + 7(2.00) + 7(1.93) = 38.99$$

$\text{MSE} = \text{SSE} /(n_T - k) = 38.99/21 = 1.86$

$F = \text{MSTR} /\text{MSE} = 0.5/1.86 = 0.27$

$F_{.05} = 3.47$ (2 degrees of freedom numerator and 21 denominator)

Since $F = 0.27 < F_{.05} = 3.47$, we cannot reject the null hypothesis that the means of the three populations are equal; thus, the source of information does not significantly affect the dissemination of the information.

8.

	Marketing Managers	Marketing Research	Advertising
Sample Mean	5	4.5	6
Sample Variance	.8	.3	.4

$$\overline{\overline{x}} = (5 + 4.5 + 6)/3 = 5.17$$

$$\text{SSTR} = \sum_{j=1}^{k} n_j \left(\overline{x}_j - \overline{\overline{x}}\right)^2 = 6(5 - 5.17)^2 + 6(4.5 - 5.17)^2 + 6(6 - 5.17)^2 = 7.00$$

$$\text{MSTR} = \text{SSTR} / (k - 1) = 7.00/2 = 3.5$$

$$\text{SSE} = \sum_{j=1}^{k} (n_j - 1)s_j^2 = 5(.8) + 5(.3) + 5(.4) = 7.50$$

$$\text{MSE} = \text{SSE} / (n_T - k) = 7.50/(18 - 3) = .5$$

$$F = \text{MSTR} / \text{MSE} = 3.5/.50 = 7.00$$

$F_{.05} = 3.68$ (2 degrees of freedom numerator and 15 denominator)

Since $F = 7.00 > F_{.05} = 3.68$, we reject the null hypothesis that the mean perception score is the same for the three groups of specialists.

9.

	Real Estate Agent	Architect	Stockbroker
Sample Mean	67.73	61.13	65.80
Sample Variance	117.72	180.10	137.12

$$\overline{\overline{x}} = (67.73 + 61.13 + 65.80)/3 = 64.89$$

$$\text{SSTR} = \sum_{j=1}^{k} n_j \left(\overline{x}_j - \overline{\overline{x}}\right)^2 = 15(67.73 - 64.89)^2 + 15(61.13 - 64.89)^2 + 15(65.80 - 64.89)^2 = 345.47$$

$$\text{MSTR} = \text{SSTR} / (k - 1) = 345.47/2 = 172.74$$

$$\text{SSE} = \sum_{j=1}^{k} (n_j - 1)s_j^2 = 14(117.72) + 14(180.10) + 14(137.12) = 6089.16$$

$$\text{MSE} = \text{SSE} / (n_T - k) = 6089.16/(45-3) = 144.98$$

$$F = \text{MSTR} / \text{MSE} = 172.74/144.98 = 1.19$$

$F_{.05} = 3.22$ (2 degrees of freedom numerator and 42 denominator)

Note: Table 4 does not show a value for 2 degrees of freedom numerator and 42 denominator. However, the value of 3.23 corresponding to 2 degrees of freedom numerator and 40 denominator can be used as an approximation.

Since $F = 1.19 < F_{.05} = 3.23$, we cannot reject the null hypothesis that the job stress ratings are the same for the three occupations.

10.   The Mintab output is shown below:

```
ANALYSIS OF VARIANCE ON P/E
SOURCE      DF        SS         MS        F        p
Industry     2       40.8       20.4      0.94     0.403
ERROR       26      563.8       21.7
TOTAL       28      604.6
```

```
                                       INDIVIDUAL 95 PCT CI'S FOR MEAN
                                       BASED ON POOLED STDEV
LEVEL      N       MEAN       STDEV    ---------+---------+---------+-------
  1       12      15.250       5.463   (--------*-------)
  2        7      18.286       4.071              (-----------*-----------)
  3       10      16.300       3.889   (---------*---------)
                                       ---------+---------+---------+-------
POOLED STDEV =    4.657                   15.0      18.0      21.0
```

Since the p-value $= 0.403 > \alpha = 0.05$, we cannot reject the null hypothesis that that the mean price/earnings ratio is the same for these three groups of firms.

11. a $LSD = t_{\alpha/2}\sqrt{MSE\left(\dfrac{1}{n_i} + \dfrac{1}{n_j}\right)} = t_{.025}\sqrt{5.5\left(\dfrac{1}{5} + \dfrac{1}{5}\right)} = 2.179\sqrt{2.2} = 3.23$

$\left|\bar{x}_1 - \bar{x}_2\right| = \left|30 - 45\right| = 15 > LSD$; significant difference

$\left|\bar{x}_1 - \bar{x}_3\right| = \left|30 - 36\right| = 6 > LSD$; significant difference

$\left|\bar{x}_2 - \bar{x}_3\right| = \left|45 - 36\right| = 9 > LSD$; significant difference

b. $\bar{x}_1 - \bar{x}_2 \pm t_{\alpha/2}\sqrt{MSE\left(\dfrac{1}{n_1} + \dfrac{1}{n_2}\right)}$

$(30 - 45) \pm 2.179\sqrt{5.5\left(\dfrac{1}{n_1} + \dfrac{1}{n_2}\right)}$

$-15 \pm 3.23 = -18.23$ to -11.77

12. a.

	Sample 1	Sample 2	Sample 3
Sample Mean	51	77	58
Sample Variance	96.67	97.34	81.99

$\bar{\bar{x}} = (51 + 77 + 58)/3 = 62$

$SSTR = \sum_{j=1}^{k} n_j\left(\bar{x}_j - \bar{\bar{x}}\right)^2 = 4(51 - 62)^2 + 4(77 - 62)^2 + 4(58 - 62)^2 = 1{,}448$

MSTR = SSTR $/(k - 1)$ = 1,448/2 = 724

$$SSE = \sum_{j=1}^{k} (n_j - 1)s_j^2 = 3(96.67) + 3(97.34) + 3(81.99) = 828$$

MSE = SSE $/(n_T - k)$ = 828/(12 - 3) = 92

F = MSTR /MSE = 724/92 = 7.87

$F_{.05}$ = 4.26 (2 degrees of freedom numerator and 9 denominator)

Since $F = 7.87 > F_{.05} = 4.26$, we reject the null hypothesis that the means of the three populations are equal.

b. $$LSD = t_{\alpha/2}\sqrt{MSE\left(\frac{1}{n_i} + \frac{1}{n_j}\right)} = t_{.025}\sqrt{92\left(\frac{1}{4} + \frac{1}{4}\right)} = 2.262\sqrt{46} = 15.34$$

$|\bar{x}_1 - \bar{x}_2| = |51 - 77| = 26 > LSD$; significant difference

$|\bar{x}_1 - \bar{x}_3| = |51 - 58| = 7 < LSD$; no significant difference

$|\bar{x}_2 - \bar{x}_3| = |77 - 58| = 19 > LSD$; significant difference

13. $$LSD = t_{\alpha/2}\sqrt{MSE\left(\frac{1}{n_1} + \frac{1}{n_3}\right)} = t_{.025}\sqrt{4.89\left(\frac{1}{4} + \frac{1}{4}\right)} = 2.262\sqrt{2.45} = 3.54$$

Since $|\bar{x}_1 - \bar{x}_3| = |23 - 21| = 2 < 3.54$, there does not appear to be any significant difference between the means of population 1 and population 3.

14. $\bar{x}_1 - \bar{x}_2 \pm LSD$

23 - 28 $\pm$ 3.54

-5 $\pm$ 3.54 = -8.54 to -1.46

15.   Since there are only 3 possible pairwise comparisons we will use the Bonferroni adjustment.

α = .05/3 = .017

$t_{.017/2} = t_{.0085}$ which is approximately $t_{.01} = 2.602$

$$BSD = 2.602\sqrt{MSE\left(\frac{1}{n_i} + \frac{1}{n_j}\right)} = 2.602\sqrt{.5\left(\frac{1}{6} + \frac{1}{6}\right)} = 1.06$$

$|\bar{x}_1 - \bar{x}_2| = |5 - 4.5| = .5 < 1.06$; no significant difference

$|\bar{x}_1 - \bar{x}_3| = |5 - 6| = 1 < 1.06$; no significant difference

$\left|\overline{x}_2 - \overline{x}_3\right| = \left|4.5 - 6\right| = 1.5 > 1.06$; significant difference

16. a.

	Machine 1	Machine 2	Machine 3	Machine 4
Sample Mean	7.1	9.1	9.9	11.4
Sample Variance	1.21	.93	.70	1.02

$\overline{\overline{x}} = (7.1 + 9.1 + 9.9 + 11.4)/4 = 9.38$

$\mathrm{SSTR} = \sum_{j=1}^{k} n_j \left(\overline{x}_j - \overline{\overline{x}}\right)^2 = 6(7.1 - 9.38)^2 + 6(9.1 - 9.38)^2 + 6(9.9 - 9.38)^2 + 6(11.4 - 9.38)^2 = 57.77$

$\mathrm{MSTR} = \mathrm{SSTR}/(k-1) = 57.77/3 = 19.26$

$\mathrm{SSE} = \sum_{j=1}^{k} (n_j - 1)s_j^2 = 5(1.21) + 5(.93) + 5(.70) + 5(1.02) = 19.30$

$\mathrm{MSE} = \mathrm{SSE}/(n_T - k) = 19.30/(24 - 4) = .97$

$F = \mathrm{MSTR}/\mathrm{MSE} = 19.26/.97 = 19.86$

$F_{.05} = 3.10$ (3 degrees of freedom numerator and 20 denominator)

Since $F = 19.86 > F_{.05} = 3.10$, we reject the null hypothesis that the mean time between breakdowns is the same for the four machines.

b. Note: $t_{\alpha/2}$ is based upon 20 degrees of freedom

$$\mathrm{LSD} = t_{\alpha/2}\sqrt{\mathrm{MSE}\left(\frac{1}{n_i} + \frac{1}{n_j}\right)} = t_{.025}\sqrt{0.97\left(\frac{1}{6} + \frac{1}{6}\right)} = 2.086\sqrt{.3233} = 1.19$$

$\left|\overline{x}_2 - \overline{x}_4\right| = \left|9.1 - 11.4\right| = 2.3 > \mathrm{LSD}$; significant difference

17. $C = 6$ [(1,2), (1,3), (1,4), (2,3), (2,4), (3,4)]

$\alpha = .05/6 = .008$ and $\alpha/2 = .004$

Since the smallest value for $\alpha/2$ in the t table is .005, we will use $t_{.005} = 2.845$ as an approximation for $t_{.004}$ (20 degrees of freedom)

$$\mathrm{BSD} = 2.845\sqrt{0.97\left(\frac{1}{6} + \frac{1}{6}\right)} = 1.62$$

Thus, if the absolute value of the difference between any two sample means exceeds 1.62, there is sufficient evidence to reject the hypothesis that the corresponding population means are equal.

Means	(1,2)	(1,3)	(1,4)	(2,3)	(2,4)	(3,4)
| Difference |	2	2.8	4.3	0.8	2.3	1.5
Significant ?	Yes	Yes	Yes	No	Yes	No

18. $n_1 = 12$ $n_2 = 8$ $n_3 = 10$

$t_{\alpha/2}$ is based upon 27 degrees of freedom

Comparing 1 and 2

$$LSD = t_{.025}\sqrt{13\left(\frac{1}{12}+\frac{1}{8}\right)} = 2.052\sqrt{2.7083} = 3.38$$

$|9.95 - 14.75| = 4.8 > LSD$; significant difference

Comparing 1 and 3

$$LSD = 2.052\sqrt{13\left(\frac{1}{12}+\frac{1}{10}\right)} = 2.052\sqrt{2.3833} = 3.17$$

$|9.95 - 13.5| = 3.55 > LSD$; significant difference

Comparing 2 and 3

$$LSD = 2.052\sqrt{13\left(\frac{1}{8}+\frac{1}{10}\right)} = 2.052\sqrt{2.9250} = 3.51$$

$|14.75 - 13.5| = 1.25 < LSD$; no significant difference

Using the Bonferroni adjustment with C = 3

$\alpha = .05 / 3 = .0167$

$\alpha / 2 = .0083$ or approximately .01

$t_{.01} = 2.473$

Means	(1,2)	(1,3)	(2,3)
BSD	4.07	3.82	4.23
|Difference|	4.8	3.55	3.51
Significant ?	Yes	No	No

Thus, using the Bonferroni adjustment, the difference between the mean price/earnings ratios of banking firms and financial services firms is significant.

19. a. $\bar{\bar{x}} = (156 + 142 + 134)/3 = 144$

$$SSTR = \sum_{j=1}^{k} n_j\left(\bar{x}_j - \bar{\bar{x}}\right)^2 = 6(156 - 144)^2 + 6(142 - 144)^2 + 6(134 - 144)^2 = 1,488$$

b.   MSTR = SSTR /(k - 1) = 1488/2 = 744

c. $s_1^2 = 164.4$ $s_2^2 = 131.2$ $s_3^2 = 110.4$

$$SSE = \sum_{j=1}^{k} (n_j - 1)s_j^2 = 5(164.4) + 5(131.2) + 5(110.4) = 2030$$

d. MSE = SSE $/(n_T - k)$ = 2030/(12 - 3) = 135.3

e. F = MSTR /MSE = 744/135.3 = 5.50

$F_{.05}$ = 3.68 (2 degrees of freedom numerator and 15 denominator)

Since $F = 5.50 > F_{.05} = 3.68$, we reject the hypothesis that the means for the three treatments are equal.

20. a.

Source of Variation	Sum of Squares	Degrees of Freedom	Mean Square	F
Treatments	1488	2	744	5.50
Error	2030	15	135.3	
Total	3518	17		

b. $LSD = t_{\alpha/2}\sqrt{MSE\left(\dfrac{1}{n_i}+\dfrac{1}{n_j}\right)} = 2.131\sqrt{135.3\left(\dfrac{1}{6}+\dfrac{1}{6}\right)} = 14.31$

|156-142| = 14 < 14.31; no significant difference

|156-134| = 22 > 14.31; significant difference

|142-134| = 8 < 14.31; no significant difference

21.

Source of Variation	Sum of Squares	Degrees of Freedom	Mean Square	F
Treatments	300	4	75	14.07
Error	160	30	5.33	
Total	460	34		

22. a. $H_0: u_1 = u_2 = u_3 = u_4 = u_5$

H_a: Not all the population means are equal

b. $F_{.05}$ = 2.69 (4 degrees of freedom numerator and 30 denominator)

Since $F = 14.07 > 2.69$ we reject H_0

23.

Source of Variation	Sum of Squares	Degrees of Freedom	Mean Square	F
Treatments	150	2	75	4.80
Error	250	16	15.63	
Total	400	18		

$F_{.05}$ = 3.63 (2 degrees of freedom numerator and 16 denominator) Since $F = 4.80 > F_{.05} = 3.63$, we reject the null hypothesis that the means of the three treatments are equal.

24.

Source of Variation	Sum of Squares	Degrees of Freedom	Mean Square	F
Treatments	1200	2	600	43.99
Error	600	44	13.64	
Total	1800	46		

$F_{.05} = 3.23$ (2 degrees of freedom numerator and 40 denominator)

$F_{.05} = 3.15$ (2 degrees of freedom numerator and 60 denominator)

The critical F value is between 3.15 and 3.23.

Since $F = 43.99$ exceeds the critical value, we reject the hypothesis that the treatment means are equal.

25.

	A	B	C
Sample Mean	119	107	100
Sample Variance	146.89	96.43	173.78

$$\bar{\bar{x}} = \frac{8(119) + 10(107) + 10(100)}{28} = 107.93$$

$$\text{SSTR} = \sum_{j=1}^{k} n_j \left(\bar{x}_j - \bar{\bar{x}} \right)^2 = 8(119 - 107.93)^2 + 10(107 - 107.93)^2 + 10(100 - 107.93)^2 = 1617.9$$

$$\text{MSTR} = \text{SSTR}/(k-1) = 1617.9/2 = 809.95$$

$$\text{SSE} = \sum_{j=1}^{k} (n_j - 1)s_j^2 = 7(146.86) + 9(96.44) + 9(173.78) = 3,460$$

$$\text{MSE} = \text{SSE}/(n_T - k) = 3,460/(28 - 3) = 138.4$$

$$F = \text{MSTR}/\text{MSE} = 809.95/138.4 = 5.85$$

$F_{.05} = 3.39$ (2 degrees of freedom numerator and 25 denominator)

Since $F = 5.85 > F_{.05} = 3.39$, we reject the null hypothesis that the means of the three treatments are equal.

26. a.

Source of Variation	Sum of Squares	Degrees of Freedom	Mean Square	F
Treatments	4560	2	2280	9.87
Error	6240	27	231.11	
Total	10800	29		

b. $F_{.05} = 3.35$ (2 degrees of freedom numerator and 27 denominator)

Since $F = 9.87 > F_{.05} = 3.35$, we reject the null hypothesis that the means of the three assembly methods are equal.

27.

Source of Variation	Sum of Squares	Degrees of Freedom	Mean Square	F
Between	61.64	3	20.55	17.56
Error	23.41	20	1.17	
Total	85.05	23		

$F_{.05} = 3.10$ (3 degrees of freedom numerator and 20 denominator)

Since $F = 17.56 > F_{.05} = 3.10$, we reject the null hypothesis that the mean breaking strength of the four cables is the same.

28.

	50°	60°	70°
Sample Mean	33	29	28
Sample Variance	32	17.5	9.5

$\overline{\overline{x}} = (33 + 29 + 28)/3 = 30$

$SSTR = \sum_{j=1}^{k} n_j \left(\overline{x}_j - \overline{\overline{x}}\right)^2 = 5(33 - 30)^2 + 5(29 - 30)^2 + 5(28 - 30)^2 = 70$

$MSTR = SSTR /(k - 1) = 70 /2 = 35$

$SSE = \sum_{j=1}^{k} (n_j - 1)s_j^2 = 4(32) + 4(17.5) + 4(9.5) = 236$

$MSE = SSE /(n_T - k) = 236 /(15 - 3) = 19.67$

$F = MSTR /MSE = 35 /19.67 = 1.78$

$F_{.05} = 3.89$ (2 degrees of freedom numerator and 12 denominator)

Since $F = 1.78 < F_{.05} = 3.89$, we cannot reject the null hypothesis that the mean yields for the three temperatures are equal.

29.

	Direct Experience	Indirect Experience	Combination
Sample Mean	17.0	20.4	25.0
Sample Variance	5.01	6.26	4.01

$\overline{\overline{x}} = (17 + 20.4 + 25)/3 = 20.8$

$SSTR = \sum_{j=1}^{k} n_j \left(\overline{x}_j - \overline{\overline{x}}\right)^2 = 7(17 - 20.8)^2 + 7(20.4 - 20.8)^2 + 7(25 - 20.8)^2 = 225.68$

$MSTR = SSTR /(k - 1) = 225.68 /2 = 112.84$

$$SSE = \sum_{j=1}^{k} (n_j - 1)s_j^2 = 6(5.01) + 6(6.26) + 6(4.01) = 91.68$$

$$MSE = SSE /(n_T - k) = 91.68 /(21 - 3) = 5.09$$

$$F = MSTR /MSE = 112.84 /5.09 = 22.17$$

$F_{.05} = 3.55$ (2 degrees of freedom numerator and 18 denominator)

Since $F = 22.17 > F_{.05} = 3.55$, we reject the null hypothesis that the means for the three groups are equal.

30.

	Paint 1	Paint 2	Paint 3	Paint 4
Sample Mean	13.3	139	136	144
Sample Variance	47.5	.50	21	54.5

$$\overline{\overline{x}} = (133 + 139 + 136 + 144)/3 = 138$$

$$SSTR = \sum_{j=1}^{k} n_j \left(\overline{x}_j - \overline{\overline{x}} \right)^2 = 5(133 - 138)^2 + 5(139 - 138)^2 + 5(136 - 138)^2 + 5(144 - 138)^2 = 330$$

$$MSTR = SSTR /(k - 1) = 330 /3 = 110$$

$$SSE = \sum_{j=1}^{k} (n_j - 1)s_j^2 = 4(47.5) + 4(50) + 4(21) + 4(54.5) = 692$$

$$MSE = SSE /(n_T - k) = 692 /(20 - 4) = 43.25$$

$$F = MSTR /MSE = 110 /43.25 = 2.54$$

$F_{.05} = 3.24$ (3 degrees of freedom numerator and 16 denominator)

Since $F = 2.54 < F_{.05} = 3.24$, we cannot reject the null hypothesis that the mean drying times for the four paints are equal.

31.

	A	B	C
Sample Mean	20	21	25
Sample Variance	1	25	2.5

$$\overline{\overline{x}} = (20 + 21 + 25)/3 = 22$$

$$SSTR = \sum_{j=1}^{k} n_j \left(\overline{x}_j - \overline{\overline{x}} \right)^2 = 5(20 - 22)^2 + 5(21 - 22)^2 + 5(25 - 22)^2 = 70$$

$$MSTR = SSTR /(k - 1) = 70 /2 = 35$$

$$SSE = \sum_{j=1}^{k} (n_j - 1)s_j^2 = 4(1) + 4(2.5) + 4(2.5) = 24$$

$$MSE = SSE / (n_T - k) = 24 / (15 - 3) = 2$$

$$F = MSTR / MSE = 35 / 2 = 17.5$$

$F_{.05} = 3.89$ (2 degrees of freedom numerator and 12 denominator)

Since $F = 17.5 > F_{.05} = 3.89$, we reject the null hypothesis that the mean miles per gallon ratings are the same for the three automobiles.

32.   Note: degrees of freedom for $t_{\alpha/2}$ are 18

$$LSD = t_{\alpha/2}\sqrt{MSE\left(\frac{1}{n_i} + \frac{1}{n_j}\right)} = t_{.025}\sqrt{5.09\left(\frac{1}{7} + \frac{1}{7}\right)} = 2.101\sqrt{1.4543} = 2.53$$

$|\bar{x}_1 - \bar{x}_2| = |17.0 - 20.4| = 3.4 > 2.53$; significant difference

$|\bar{x}_1 - \bar{x}_3| = |17.0 - 25.0| = 8 > 2.53$; significant difference

$|\bar{x}_2 - \bar{x}_3| = |20.4 - 25| = 4.6 > 2.53$; significant difference

33.   Note: degrees of freedom for $t_{\alpha/2}$ are 12

$$LSD = t_{\alpha/2}\sqrt{MSE\left(\frac{1}{n_i} + \frac{1}{n_j}\right)} = t_{.025}\sqrt{2\left(\frac{1}{5} + \frac{1}{5}\right)} = 2.179\sqrt{.8} = 1.95$$

$|\bar{x}_1 - \bar{x}_2| = |20 - 21| = 1 < 1.95$; no significant difference

$|\bar{x}_1 - \bar{x}_3| = |20 - 25| = 5 > 1.95$; significant difference

$|\bar{x}_2 - \bar{x}_3| = |21 - 25| = 4 > 1.95$; significant difference

34.   <u>Treatment Means:</u>

$\bar{x}_{.1} = 13.6 \quad \bar{x}_{.2} = 11.0 \quad \bar{x}_{.3} = 10.6$

<u>Block Means:</u>

$\bar{x}_{1.} = 9 \quad \bar{x}_{2.} = 7.67 \quad \bar{x}_{3.} = 15.67 \quad \bar{x}_{4.} = 18.67 \quad \bar{x}_{5.} = 7.67$

<u>Overall Mean:</u>

$\bar{\bar{x}} = 176/15 = 11.73$

Step 1

$$SST = \sum_i \sum_j \left(x_{ij} - \overline{\overline{x}} \right)^2 = (10 - 11.73)^2 + (9 - 11.73)^2 + \cdots + (8 - 11.73)^2 = 354.93$$

Step 2

$$SSTR = b\sum_j \left(\overline{x}_{.j} - \overline{\overline{x}} \right)^2 = 5\left[(13.6 - 11.73)^2 + (11.0 - 11.73)^2 + (10.6 - 11.73)^2 \right] = 26.53$$

Step 3

$$SSBL = k\sum_i \left(\overline{x}_{i.} - \overline{\overline{x}} \right)^2 = 3\left[(9 - 11.73)^2 + (7.67 - 11.73)^2 + (15.67 - 11.73)^2 + \right.$$
$$\left. (18.67 - 11.73)^2 + (7.67 - 11.73)^2 \right] = 312.32$$

Step 4

SSE = SST - SSTR - SSBL = 354.93 - 26.53 - 312.32 = 16.08

Source of Variation	Sum of Squares	Degrees of Freedom	Mean Square	F
Treatments	26.53	2	13.27	6.60
Blocks	312.32	4	78.08	
Error	16.08	8	2.01	
Total	354.93	14		

$F_{.05} = 4.46$ (2 degrees of freedom numerator and 8 denominator)

Since $F = 6.60 > F_{.05} = 4.46$, we reject the null hypothesis that the means of the three treatments are equal.

35.

Source of Variation	Sum of Squares	Degrees of Freedom	Mean Square	F
Treatments	310	4	77.5	17.69
Blocks	85	2	42.5	
Error	35	8	4.38	
Total	430	14		

$F_{.05} = 3.84$ (4 degrees of freedom numerator and 8 denominator)

Since $F = 17.69 > F_{.05} = 3.84$, we reject the null hypothesis that the means of the treatments are equal.

36.

Source of Variation	Sum of Squares	Degrees of Freedom	Mean Square	F
Treatments	900	3	300	12.60
Blocks	400	7	57.14	
Error	500	21	23.81	
Total	1800	31		

$F_{.05} = 3.07$ (3 degrees of freedom numerator and 21 denominator)

Since $F = 12.60 > F_{.05} = 3.07$, we reject the null hypothesis that the means of the treatments are equal.

37. <u>Treatment Means:</u>

$\bar{x}_{.1} = 56 \quad \bar{x}_{.2} = 44$

<u>Block Means:</u>

$\bar{x}_{1.} = 46 \quad \bar{x}_{2.} = 49.5 \quad \bar{x}_{3.} = 54.5$

<u>Overall Mean:</u>

$\bar{\bar{x}} = 300/6 = 50$

<u>Step 1</u>

$$\text{SST} = \sum_i \sum_j \left(x_{ij} - \bar{\bar{x}} \right)^2 = (50 - 50)^2 + (42 - 50)^2 + \cdots + (46 - 50)^2 = 310$$

<u>Step 2</u>

$$\text{SSTR} = b \sum_j \left(\bar{x}_{.j} - \bar{\bar{x}} \right)^2 = 3 \left[(56 - 50)^2 + (44 - 50)^2 \right] = 216$$

<u>Step 3</u>

$$\text{SSBL} = k \sum_i \left(\bar{x}_{i.} - \bar{\bar{x}} \right)^2 = 2 \left[(46 - 50)^2 + (49.5 - 50)^2 + (54.5 - 50)^2 \right] = 73$$

<u>Step 4</u>

SSE = SST - SSTR - SSBL = 310 - 216 - 73 = 21

Source of Variation	Sum of Squares	Degrees of Freedom	Mean Square	F
Treatments	216	1	216	20.57
Blocks	73	2	36.5	
Error	21	2	10.5	
Total	310	5		

$F_{.05} = 18.51$ (1 degree of freedom numerator and 2 denominator)

Since $F = 20.57 > F_{.05} = 18.51$, we reject the null hypothesis that the mean tuneup times are the same for both analyzers.

38.

Source of Variation	Sum of Squares	Degrees of Freedom	Mean Square	F
Treatments	45	4	11.25	7.12
Blocks	36	3	12	
Error	19	12	1.58	
Total	100	19		

$F_{.05} = 3.26$ (4 degrees of freedom numerator and 12 denominator)

Since $F = 7.12 > F_{.05} = 3.26$, we reject the null hypothesis that the mean total audit times for the five auditing procedures are equal.

39.   Treatment Means:

$\bar{x}_{.1} = 16$ $\bar{x}_{.2} = 15$ $\bar{x}_{.3} = 21$

Block Means:

$\bar{x}_{1.} = 18.67$ $\bar{x}_{2.} = 19.33$ $\bar{x}_{3.} = 15.33$ $\bar{x}_{4.} = 14.33$ $\bar{x}_{5.} = 19$

Overall Mean:

$\bar{\bar{x}} = 260/15 = 17.33$

Step 1

$$SST = \sum_i \sum_j \left(x_{ij} - \bar{\bar{x}} \right)^2 = (16 - 17.33)^2 + (16 - 17.33)^2 + \cdots + (22 - 17.33)^2 = 175.33$$

Step 2

$$SSTR = b \sum_j \left(\bar{x}_{.j} - \bar{\bar{x}} \right)^2 = 5 \, [\, (16 - 17.33)^2 + (15 - 17.33)^2 + (21 - 17.33)^2 \,] = 103.33$$

Step 3

$$SSBL = k \sum_i \left(\bar{x}_{i.} - \bar{\bar{x}} \right)^2 = 3 \, [\, (18.67 - 17.33)^2 + (19.33 - 17.33)^2 + \cdots + (19 - 17.33)^2 \,] = 64.75$$

Step 4

SSE = SST - SSTR - SSBL = 175.33 - 103.33 - 64.75 = 7.25

Source of Variation	Sum of Squares	Degrees of Freedom	Mean Square	F
Treatments	100.33	2	51.67	56.78
Blocks	64.75	4	16.19	
Error	7.25	8	.91	
Total	175.33	14		

$F_{.05} = 4.46$ (2 degrees of freedom numerator and 8 denominator)

Since $F = 56.78 > F_{.05} = 4.46$, we reject the null hypothesis that the mean times for the three systems are equal.

40.   The Minitab output for these data is shown below:

```
ANALYSIS OF VARIANCE BPM

SOURCE          DF          SS          MS
Block            9        2796         311
Treat            3       19805        6602
ERROR           27        7949         294
TOTAL           39       30550
```

```
                          Individual 95% CI
Treat       Mean    ----+---------+---------+---------+-------
  1        178.0                              (-----*-----)
  2        171.0                         (-----*----)
  3        175.0                          (-----*----)
  4        123.6    (-----*----)
                    ----+---------+---------+---------+-------
                    120.0     140.0     160.0     180.0
```

$F_{.05} = 2.96$ (3 degrees of freedom numerator and 27 denominator)

Since $F = 6602/294 = 22.46 > 2.96$, we reject the null hypotheses that the mean heart rate for the four methods are equal.

41.

		Factor B			Factor A
		Level 1	Level 2	Level 3	Means
Factor A	Level 1	$\bar{x}_{11} = 150$	$\bar{x}_{12} = 78$	$\bar{x}_{13} = 84$	$\bar{x}_{1.} = 104$
	Level 2	$\bar{x}_{21} = 110$	$\bar{x}_{22} = 116$	$\bar{x}_{23} = 128$	$\bar{x}_{2.} = 118$
Factor B Means		$\bar{x}_{.1} = 130$	$\bar{x}_{.2} = 97$	$\bar{x}_{.3} = 106$	$\bar{\bar{x}} = 111$

Step 1

$$\text{SST} = \sum_i \sum_j \sum_k \left(x_{ijk} - \bar{\bar{x}} \right)^2 = (135 - 111)^2 + (165 - 111)^2 + \cdots + (136 - 111)^2 = 9{,}028$$

Step 2

$$\text{SSA} = br \sum_i \left(\bar{x}_{j.} - \bar{\bar{x}} \right)^2 = 3 \ (2) \ [\ (104 - 111)^2 + (118 - 111)^2 \ ] = 588$$

Step 3

$$SSB = ar\sum_{j}\left(\overline{x}_{.j} - \overline{\overline{x}}\right)^2 = 2\,(2)\,[\,(130 - 111)^2 + (97 - 111)^2 + (106 - 111)^2\,] = 2{,}328$$

Step 4

$$SSAB = r\sum_{i}\sum_{j}\left(\overline{x}_{ij} - \overline{x}_{i.} - \overline{x}_{.j} + \overline{\overline{x}}\right)^2 = 2\,[\,(150 - 104 - 130 + 111)^2 + (78 - 104 - 97 + 111)^2 +$$

$$\cdots + (128 - 118 - 106 + 111)^2\,] = 4{,}392$$

Step 5

SSE = SST - SSA - SSB - SSAB = 9,028 - 588 - 2,328 - 4,392 = 1,720

Source of Variation	Sum of Squares	Degrees of Freedom	Mean Square	F
Factor A	588	1	588	2.05
Factor B	2328	2	1164	4.06
Interaction	4392	2	2196	7.66
Error	1720	6	286.67	
Total	9028	11		

$F_{.05} = 5.99$ (1 degree of freedom numerator and 6 denominator)

$F_{.05} = 5.14$ (2 degrees of freedom numerator and 6 denominator)

Since $F = 2.05 < F_{.05} = 5.99$, Factor A is not significant.

Since $F = 4.06 < F_{.05} = 5.14$, Factor B is not significant.

Since $F = 7.66 > F_{.05} = 5.14$, Interaction is significant.

42.

Source of Variation	Sum of Squares	Degrees of Freedom	Mean Square	F
Factor A	26	3	8.67	3.72
Factor B	23	2	11.50	4.94
Interaction	175	6	29.17	12.52
Error	56	24	2.33	
Total	280	35		

$F_{.05} = 3.01$ (3 degrees of freedom numerator and 24 denominator)

Since $F = 3.72 > F_{.05} = 3.01$, Factor A is significant.

$F_{.05} = 3.40$ (2 degrees of freedom numerator and 24 denominator)

Since $F = 4.94 > F_{.05} = 3.40$, Factor B is significant.

$F_{.05} = 2.51$ (6 degrees of freedom numerator and 24 denominator)

Since $F = 12.52 > F_{.05} = 2.51$, Interaction is significant

43.

| | | Factor B | Factor B |
		Small	Large	Means
	A	$\bar{x}_{11} = 10$	$\bar{x}_{12} = 10$	$\bar{x}_{1.} = 10$
Factor A	B	$\bar{x}_{21} = 18$	$\bar{x}_{22} = 28$	$\bar{x}_{2.} = 23$
	C	$\bar{x}_{31} = 14$	$\bar{x}_{32} = 16$	$\bar{x}_{3.} = 15$
Factor B	Means	$\bar{x}_{.1} = 14$	$\bar{x}_{.2} = 18$	$\bar{\bar{x}} = 16$

Step 1

$$SST = \sum_i \sum_j \sum_k \left(x_{ijk} - \bar{\bar{x}}\right)^2 = (8 - 16)^2 + (12 - 16)^2 + (12 - 16)^2 + \cdots + (14 - 16)^2 = 544$$

Step 2

$$SSA = br\sum_i \left(\bar{x}_{i.} - \bar{\bar{x}}\right)^2 = 2\,(2)\,[\,(10 - 16)^2 + (23 - 16)^2 + (15 - 16)^2\,] = 344$$

Step 3

$$SSB = ar\sum_j \left(\bar{x}_{.j} - \bar{\bar{x}}\right)^2 = 3\,(2)\,[\,(14 - 16)^2 + (18 - 16)^2\,] = 48$$

Step 4

$$SSAB = r\sum_i \sum_j \left(\bar{x}_{ij} - \bar{x}_{i.} - \bar{x}_{.j} + \bar{\bar{x}}\right)^2 = 2\,[\,(10 - 10 - 14 + 16)^2 + \cdots + (16 - 15 - 18 + 16)^2\,] = 56$$

Step 5

SSE = SST - SSA - SSB - SSAB = 544 - 344 - 48 - 56 = 96

Source of Variation	Sum of Squares	Degrees of Freedom	Mean Square	F
Factor A	344	2	172	172/16 = 10.75
Factor B	48	1	48	48/16 = 3.00
Interaction	56	2	28	28/16 = 1.75
Error	96	6	16	
Total	544	11		

$F_{.05} = 5.14$ (2 degrees of freedom numerator and 6 denominator)

Since $F = 10.75 > F_{.05} = 5.14$, Factor A is significant, there is a difference due to the type of advertisement design.

$F_{.05} = 5.99$ (1 degree of freedom numerator and 6 denominator)

Since $F = 3 < F_{.05} = 5.99$, Factor B is not significant; there is not a significant difference due to size of advertisement.

Since $F = 1.75 < F_{.05} = 5.14$, Interaction is not significant.

44.

		Factor B Roller Coaster	Factor B Screaming Demon	Factor B Log Flume	Factor A Means
Factor A	Method 1	$\bar{x}_{11} = 42$	$\bar{x}_{12} = 48$	$\bar{x}_{13} = 48$	$\bar{x}_{1.} = 46$
	Method 2	$\bar{x}_{21} = 50$	$\bar{x}_{22} = 48$	$\bar{x}_{23} = 46$	$\bar{x}_{2.} = 48$
Factor B	Means	$\bar{x}_{.1} = 46$	$\bar{x}_{.2} = 48$	$\bar{x}_{.3} = 47$	$\bar{\bar{x}} = 47$

Step 1

$$SST = \sum_i \sum_j \sum_k \left(x_{ijk} - \bar{\bar{x}} \right)^2 = (41 - 47)^2 + (43 - 47)^2 + \cdots + (44 - 47)^2 = 136$$

Step 2

$$SSA = br \sum_i \left(\bar{x}_{i.} - \bar{\bar{x}} \right)^2 = 3\,(2)\,[\,(46 - 47)^2 + (48 - 47)^2\,] = 12$$

Step 3

$$SSB = ar \sum_j \left(\bar{x}_{.j} - \bar{\bar{x}} \right)^2 = 2\,(2)\,[\,(46 - 47)^2 + (48 - 47)^2 + (47 - 47)^2\,] = 8$$

Step 4

$$SSAB = r \sum_i \sum_j \left(\bar{x}_{ij} - \bar{x}_{i.} - \bar{x}_{.j} + \bar{\bar{x}} \right)^2 = 2\,[\,(41 - 46 - 46 + 47)^2 + \cdots + (44 - 48 - 47 + 47)^2\,] = 56$$

Step 5

SSE = SST - SSA - SSB - SSAB = 136 - 12 - 8 - 56 = 60

Source of Variation	Sum of Squares	Degrees of Freedom	Mean Square	F
Factor A	12	1	12	$12/10 = 1.2$
Factor B	8	2	4	$4/10 = .4$
Interaction	56	2	28	$28/10 = 2.8$
Error	60	6	10	
Total	136	11		

$F_{.05} = 5.99$ (1 numerator degree of freedom and 6 denominator)

$F_{.05} = 5.14$ (2 numerator degrees of freedom and 6 denominator)

Since none of the F values exceed the corresponding critical values, there is no significant effect due to the loading and unloading method, the type of ride, or interaction.

45.

		Factor B			Factor A
		Financial Manager	Computer Programmer	Pharmacist	Means
Factor A	Male	$\overline{x}_{11} = 979$	$\overline{x}_{12} = 797$	$\overline{x}_{13} = 1047$	$\overline{x}_{1.} = 941$
	Female	$\overline{x}_{21} = 635$	$\overline{x}_{22} = 741$	$\overline{x}_{23} = 931$	$\overline{x}_{2.} = 769$
Factor B Means		$\overline{x}_{.1} = 807$	$\overline{x}_{.2} = 769$	$\overline{x}_{.3} = 989$	$\overline{\overline{x}} = 855$

Step 1

$$SST = \sum_i \sum_j \sum_k \left(x_{ijk} - \overline{\overline{x}}\right)^2 = (872 - 979)^2 + (859 - 979)^2 + \cdots + (817 - 931)^2 = 864,432$$

Step 2

$$SSA = br \sum_i \left(\overline{x}_{i.} - \overline{\overline{x}}\right)^2 = 3(5)\,[(941 - 855)^2 + (769 - 855)^2] = 221,880$$

Step 3

$$SSB = ar \sum_j \left(\overline{x}_{.j} - \overline{\overline{x}}\right)^2 = 2(5)\,[(807 - 855)^2 + (769 - 855)^2 + (989 - 855)^2] = 276,560$$

Step 4

$$SSAB = r \sum_i \sum_j \left(\overline{x}_{ij} - \overline{x}_{i.} - \overline{x}_{.j} + \overline{\overline{x}}\right)^2 = 5[(979 - 941 - 807 - 855)^2 + (797 - 941 - 769 + 855)^2 +$$
$$\cdots + (989 - 769 - 989 + 855)^2] = 115,440$$

Step 5

SSE = SST - SSA - SSB - SSAB = 864,432 - 221,880 - 276,560 - 115,440 = 250,552

Source of Variation	Sum of Squares	Degrees of Freedom	Mean Square	F
Factor A	221,880	1	221,880	21.25
Factor B	276,560	2	138,280	13.25
Interaction	115,440	2	57,720	5.53
Error	250,552	24	10,440	
Total	864,432	29		

$F_{.05} = 4.26$ (1 degree of freedom numerator and 24 denominator)

$F_{.05} = 3.40$ (2 degrees of freedom numerator and 24 denominator)

Since $F = 21.25 > F_{.05} = 4.26$, Factor A (gender) is not significant.

Since $F = 13.25 > F_{.05} = 3.40$, Factor B (occupation) is significant.

Since $F = 5.53 > F_{.05} = 3.40$, Interaction is significant.

46. $\bar{x}_{1.} = (1.13 + 1.56 + 2.00)/3 = 1.563$

$\bar{x}_{2.} = (0.48 + 1.68 + 2.86)/3 = 1.673$

$\bar{x}_{.1} = (1.13 + 0.48)/2 = 0.805$

$\bar{x}_{.2} = (1.56 + 1.68)/2 = 1.620$

$\bar{x}_{.3} = (2.00 + 2.86)/2 = 2.43$

$\bar{\bar{x}} = (1.13 + 1.56 + 2.00 + 0.48 + 1.68 + 2.86)/6 = 1.618$

Step 1

SST = 327.50 (given in problem statement)

Step 2

$$SSA = br\sum_{i}\left(\bar{x}_{i.} - \bar{\bar{x}}\right)^2 = 3(25)[(1.563 - 1.618)^2 + (1.673 - 1.618)^2] = 0.4538$$

Step 3

$$SSB = ar\sum_{j}\left(\bar{x}_{.j} - \bar{\bar{x}}\right)^2 = 2(25)[(0.805 - 1.618)^2 + (1.62 - 1.618)^2 + (2.43 - 1.618)^2] = 66.0159$$

Step 4

$$SSAB = r \sum_i \sum_j \left(\bar{x}_{ij} - \bar{x}_{i.} - \bar{x}_{.j} + \bar{\bar{x}} \right)^2 = 25[(1.13 - 1.563 - 0.805 + 1.618)^2 + (1.56 - 1.563 - 1.62$$
$$+ 1.618)^2 + \cdots + (2.86 - 1.673 - 2.43 + 1.618)^2] = 14.2525$$

Step 5

$$SSE = SST - SSA - SSB - SSAB = 327.50 - 0.4538 - 66.0159 - 14.2525$$

Source of Variation	Sum of Squares	Degrees of Freedom	Mean Square	F
Factor A	0.4538	1	0.4538	0.2648
Factor B	66.1059	2	33.0080	19.2608
Interaction	14.2525	2	7.1263	4.1583
Error	246.7778	144	1.7137	
Total	327.5000	149		

$F_{.05}$ for 1 degree of freedom numerator and 144 degrees of freedom denominator is between 3.92 and 3.84.

$F_{.05}$ for 2 degrees of freedom numerator and 144 denominator is between 3.07 and 3.00.

Since $0.2648 < F_{.05} = 3.84$, Factor A is not significant

Since $19.2608 > F_{.05} = 3.07$, Factor B is significant

Since $4.1583 > F_{.05} = 3.07$, Interaction is significant

47. a.

	Area 1	Area 2
Sample Mean	96	94
Sample Variance	50	40

$$\text{pooled estimate} = \frac{s_1^2 + s_2^2}{2} = \frac{50 + 40}{2} = 45$$

$$\text{estimate of standard deviation of } \bar{x}_1 - \bar{x}_2 = \sqrt{45\left(\frac{1}{4} + \frac{1}{4}\right)} = 4.74$$

$$t = \frac{\bar{x}_1 - \bar{x}_2}{4.74} = \frac{96 - 94}{4.74} = .42$$

$t_{.025} = 2.447$ (6 degrees of freedom)

Since $t = .42 < t_{.025} = 2.477$, the means are not significantly different.

b. $\bar{\bar{x}} = (96 + 94)/2 = 95$

$$SSTR = \sum_{j=1}^{k} n_j \left(\bar{x}_j - \bar{\bar{x}} \right)^2 = 4(96 - 95)^2 + 4(94 - 95)^2 = 8$$

$$\text{MSTR} = \text{SSTR} /(k - 1) = 8 /1 = 8$$

$$\text{SSE} = \sum_{j=1}^{k} (n_j - 1)s_j^2 = 3(50) + 3(40) = 270$$

$$\text{MSE} = \text{SSE} /(n_T - k) = 270 /(8 - 2) = 45$$

$$F = \text{MSTR} /\text{MSE} = 8 /45 = .18$$

$F_{.05} = 5.99$ (1 degree of freedom numerator and 6 denominator)

Since $F = .18 < F_{.05} = 5.99$ the means are not significantly different.

c.

	Area 1	Area 2	Area 3
Sample Mean	96	94	83
Sample Variance	50	40	42

$$\overline{\overline{x}} = (96 + 94 + 83)/3 = 91$$

$$\text{SSTR} = \sum_{j=1}^{k} n_j \left(\overline{x}_j - \overline{\overline{x}}\right)^2 = 4(96 - 91)^2 + 4(94 - 91)^2 + 4(83 - 91)^2 = 392$$

$$\text{MSTR} = \text{SSTR} /(k - 1) = 392 /2 = 196$$

$$\text{SSE} = \sum_{j=1}^{k} (n_j - 1)s_j^2 = 3(50) + 3(40) + 3(42) = 396$$

$$\text{MSTR} = \text{SSE} /(n_T - k) = 396 /(12 - 3) = 44$$

$$F = \text{MSTR} /\text{MSE} = 196 /44 = 4.45$$

$F_{.05} = 4.26$ (2 degrees of freedom numerator and 6 denominator)

Since $F = 4.45 > F_{.05} = 4.26$ we reject the null hypothesis that the mean asking prices for all three areas are equal.

48.   The Minitab output for these data is shown below:

```
Analysis of Variance
Source       DF         SS         MS         F         P
Factor        2      753.3      376.6     18.59     0.000
Error        27      546.9       20.3
Total        29     1300.2
                                Individual 95% CIs For Mean
                                Based on Pooled StDev
Level        N       Mean      StDev   ---------+---------+---------+-------
SUV         10     58.600      4.575                        (-----*-----)
Small       10     48.800      4.211    (-----*----)
FullSize    10     60.100      4.701                          (-----*-----)
                                        ---------+---------+---------+-------
Pooled StDev =      4.501                    50.0      55.0      60.0
```

Because the p-value = .000 < α = .05, we can reject the null hypothesis that the mean resale value is the same. It appears that the mean resale value for small pickup trucks is much smaller than the mean resale value for sport utility vehicles or full-size pickup trucks.

49.

	Food	Personal Care	Retail
Sample Mean	52.25	62.25	55.75
Sample Variance	22.25	15.58	4.92

$\bar{\bar{x}} = (52.25 + 62.25 + 55.75)/3 = 56.75$

$$\text{SSTR} = \sum_{j=1}^{k} n_j \left(\bar{x}_j - \bar{\bar{x}}\right)^2 = 4(52.25 - 56.75)^2 + 4(62.25 - 56.75)^2 + 4(55.75 - 56.75)^2 = 206$$

$\text{MSTR} = \text{SSTR}/(k - 1) = 206/2 = 103$

$$\text{SSE} = \sum_{j=1}^{k} (n_j - 1)s_j^2 = 3(22.25) + 3(15.58) + 3(4.92) = 128.25$$

$\text{MSE} = \text{SSE}/(n_T - k) = 128.25/(12 - 3) = 14.25$

$F = \text{MSTR}/\text{MSE} = 103/14.25 = 7.23$

$F_{.05} = 4.26$ (2 degrees of freedom numerator and 9 denominator)

Since $F = 7.23$ exceeds the critical F value, we reject the null hypothesis that the mean age of executives is the same in the three categories of companies.

50.

	Lawyer	Physical Therapist	Cabinet Maker	Systems Analyst
Sample Mean	50.0	63.7	69.1	61.2
Sample Variance	124.22	164.68	105.88	136.62

$\bar{\bar{x}} = \dfrac{50.0 + 63.7 + 69.1 + 61.2}{4} = 61$

$$\text{SSTR} = \sum_{j=1}^{k} n_j \left(\bar{x}_j - \bar{\bar{x}}\right)^2 = 10(50.0 - 61)^2 + 10(63.7 - 61)^2 + 10(69.1 - 61)^2 + 10(61.2 - 61)^2 = 1939.4$$

$\text{MSTR} = \text{SSTR}/(k - 1) = 1939.4/3 = 646.47$

$$\text{SSE} = \sum_{j=1}^{k} (n_j - 1)s_j^2 = 9(124.22) + 9(164.68) + 9(105.88) + 9(136.62) = 4,782.60$$

$\text{MSE} = \text{SSE}/(n_T - k) = 4782.6/(40 - 4) = 132.85$

$F = \text{MSTR}/\text{MSE} = 646.47/132.85 = 4.87$

$F_{.05} = 2.84$ (3 degrees of numerator and 40 denominator)

$F_{.05} = 2.76$ (3 degrees of freedom numerator and 60 denominator)

Thus, the critical F value is between 2.76 and 2.84.

Since $F = 4.87$ exceeds the critical F value, we reject the null hypothesis that the mean job satisfaction rating is the same for the four professions.

51. The Minitab output for these data is shown below:

```
Analysis of Variance
Source      DF        SS        MS        F        P
Factor       2      4339      2169     3.66    0.039
Error       27     15991       592
Total       29     20330
                                      Individual 95% CIs For Mean
                                      Based on Pooled StDev
Level        N      Mean     StDev    ---+---------+---------+---------+---
West        10    108.00     23.78              (-------*-------)
South       10     91.70     19.62    (-------*-------)
NE          10    121.10     28.75                 (-------*------)
                                      ---+---------+---------+---------+---
Pooled StDev =    24.34              80        100       120       140
```

Because the p-value $= .039 < \alpha = .05$, we can reject the null hypothesis that the mean rate for the three regions is the same.

52. The Mintab output is shown below:

```
ANALYSIS OF VARIANCE
SOURCE      DF        SS        MS        F        p
FACTOR       3    1271.0     423.7     8.74    0.000
ERROR       36    1744.2      48.4
TOTAL       39    3015.2
                                      INDIVIDUAL 95 PCT CI'S FOR MEAN
                                      BASED ON POOLED STDEV
 LEVEL       N      MEAN     STDEV    --+---------+---------+---------+----
West        10    60.000     7.218                    (------*-----)
South       10    45.400     7.610    (------*-----)
N.Cent      10    47.300     6.778     (------*-----)
N.East      10    52.100     6.152          (-----*------)
                                      --+---------+---------+---------+----
POOLED STDEV =     6.961            42.0      49.0      56.0      63.0
```

Since the p-value $= 0.000 < \alpha = 0.05$, we can reject the null hypothesis that that the mean base salary for art directors is the same for each of the four regions.

53.   The Minitab output for these data is shown below:

```
Analysis of Variance
Source      DF        SS          MS         F         P
Factor       2     12.402       6.201      9.33     0.001
Error       37     24.596       0.665
Total       39     36.998
                                    Individual 95% CIs For Mean
                                    Based on Pooled StDev
Level       N       Mean       StDev   ------+---------+---------+---------+
Receiver    15     7.4133      0.8855                        (-------*------)
Guard       13     6.1077      0.7399   (-------*------)
Tackle      12     7.0583      0.8005                  (-------*-------)
                                        ------+---------+---------+---------+
Pooled StDev =     0.8153                   6.00      6.60      7.20      7.80
```

Because the p-value = .001 < α = .05, we can reject the null hypothesis that the mean rating for the three positions is the same. It appears that wide receivers and tackles have a higher mean rating than guards.

54.

	X	Y	Z
Sample Mean	92	97	84
Sample Variance	30	6	35.33

$\overline{\overline{x}} = (92 + 97 + 44)/3 = 91$

$$\text{SSTR} = \sum_{j=1}^{k} n_j \left(\overline{x}_j - \overline{\overline{x}}\right)^2 = 4(92 - 91)^2 + 4(97 - 91)^2 + 4(84 - 91)^2 = 344$$

$\text{MSTR} = \text{SSTR}/(k-1) = 344/2 = 172$

$$\text{SSE} = \sum_{j=1}^{k} (n_j - 1)s_j^2 = 3(30) + 3(6) + 3(35.33) = 213.99$$

$\text{MSE} = \text{SSE}/(n_T - k) = 213.99/(12 - 3) = 23.78$

$F = \text{MSTR}/\text{MSE} = 172/23.78 = 7.23$

$F_{.05} = 4.26$ (2 degrees of freedom numerator and 9 denominator)

Since $F = 7.23 > F_{.05} = 4.26$, we reject the null hypothesis that the mean absorbency ratings for the three brands are equal.

55.

	First Year	Second Year	Third Year	Fourth Year
Sample Mean	1.03	-0.99	15.24	9.81
Sample Variance	416.93	343.04	159.31	55.43

$\overline{\overline{x}} = (1.03 - .99 + 15.24 + 9.81)/4 = 6.27$

$$\text{SSTR} = \sum_{j=1}^{k} n_j \left(\overline{x}_j - \overline{\overline{x}} \right)^2 = 7(1.03 - 6.27)^2 + 7(-.99 - 6.27)^2 + 7(15.24 - 6.27)^2 + (9.81 - 6.27)^2$$

$$= 1,212.10$$

$$\text{MSTR} = \text{SSTR} / (k - 1) = 1,212.10 / 3 = 404.03$$

$$\text{SSE} = \sum_{j=1}^{k} (n_j - 1) s_j^2 = 6(416.93) + 6(343.04) + 6(159.31) + 6(55.43) = 5,848.26$$

$$\text{MSE} = \text{SSE} / (n_T - k) = 5,848.26 / (28 - 4) = 243.68$$

$$F = \text{MSTR} / \text{MSE} = 404.03 / 243.68 = 1.66$$

$F_{.05} = 3.01$ (3 degrees of freedom numerator and 24 denominator)

Since $F = 1.66 < F_{.05} = 3.01$, we can not reject the null hypothesis that the mean percent changes in each of the four years are equal.

56.

	Method A	Method B	Method C
Sample Mean	90	84	81
Sample Variance	98.00	168.44	159.78

$$\overline{\overline{x}} = (90 + 84 + 81) / 3 = 85$$

$$\text{SSTR} = \sum_{j=1}^{k} n_j \left(\overline{x}_j - \overline{\overline{x}} \right)^2 = 10(90 - 85)^2 + 10(84 - 85)^2 + 10(81 - 85)^2 = 420$$

$$\text{MSTR} = \text{SSTR} / (k - 1) = 420 / 2 = 210$$

$$\text{SSE} = \sum_{j=1}^{k} (n_j - 1) s_j^2 = 9(98.00) + 9(168.44) + 9(159.78) = 3,836$$

$$\text{MSE} = \text{SSE} / (n_T - k) = 3,836 / (30 - 3) = 142.07$$

$$F = \text{MSTR} / \text{MSE} = 210 / 142.07 = 1.48$$

$F_{.05} = 3.35$ (2 degrees of freedom numerator and 27 denominator)

Since $F = 1.48 < F_{.05} = 3.35$, we can not reject the null hypothesis that the means are equal.

57.

	Type A	Type B	Type C	Type D
Sample Mean	32,000	27,500	34,200	30,300
Sample Variance	2,102,500	2,325,625	2,722,500	1,960,000

$$\overline{\overline{x}} = (32,000 + 27,500 + 34,200 + 30,000) / 4 = 31,000$$

$$\text{SSTR} = \sum_{j=1}^{k} n_j \left(\overline{x}_j - \overline{\overline{x}}\right)^2 = 30(32{,}000 - 31{,}000)^2 + 30(27{,}500 - 31{,}000)^2 + 30(34{,}200 - 31{,}000)^2 +$$

$$30(30{,}300 - 31{,}000)^2 = 719{,}400{,}000$$

$$\text{MSTR} = \text{SSTR}/(k - 1) = 719{,}400{,}000/3 = 239{,}800{,}000$$

$$\text{SSE} = \sum_{j=1}^{k} (n_j - 1)s_j^2 = 29(2{,}102{,}500) + 29(2{,}325{,}625) + 29(2{,}722{,}500) + 29(1{,}960{,}000)$$

$$= 264{,}208{,}125$$

$$\text{MSE} = \text{SSE}/(n_T - k) = 264{,}208{,}125/(120 - 4) = 2{,}277{,}656.25$$

$$F = \text{MSTR}/\text{MSE} = 239{,}800{,}000/2{,}277{,}656.25 = 105.28$$

$F_{.05}$ is approximately 2.68, the table value for 3 degrees of freedom numerator and 120 denominator; the value we would look up, if it were available, would correspond to 116 denominator degrees of freedom. Since $F = 105.28$ exceeds $F_{.05}$, whatever its value actually is, we reject the null hypothesis that the population means are equal.

58.

	Design A	Design B	Design C
Sample Mean	90	107	109
Sample Variance	82.67	68.67	100.67

$$\overline{\overline{x}} = (90 + 107 + 109)/3 = 102$$

$$\text{SSTR} = \sum_{j=1}^{k} n_j \left(\overline{x}_j - \overline{\overline{x}}\right)^2 = 4(90 - 102)^2 + 4(107 - 102)^2 + (109 - 102)^2 = 872$$

$$\text{MSTR} = \text{SSTR}/(k - 1) = 872/2 = 436$$

$$\text{SSE} = \sum_{j=1}^{k} (n_j - 1)s_j^2 = 3(82.67) + 3(68.67) + 3(100.67) = 756.03$$

$$\text{MSE} = \text{SSE}/(n_T - k) = 756.03/(12 - 3) = 84$$

$$F = \text{MSTR}/\text{MSE} = 436/84 = 5.19$$

$F_{.05} = 4.26$ (2 degrees of freedom numerator and 9 denominator)

Since $F = 5.19 > F_{.05} = 4.26$, we reject the null hypothesis that the mean lifetime in hours is the same for the three designs.

59. a.

	Nonbrowser	Light Browser	Heavy Browser
Sample Mean	4.25	5.25	5.75
Sample Variance	1.07	1.07	1.36

$$\overline{\overline{x}} = (4.25 + 5.25 + 5.75)/3 = 5.08$$

$$SSTR = \sum_{j=1}^{k} n_j \left(\overline{x}_j - \overline{\overline{x}} \right)^2 = 8(4.25 - 5.08)^2 + 8(5.25 - 5.08)^2 + 8(5.75 - 5.08)^2 = 9.33$$

$$MSB = SSB/(k-1) = 9.33/2 = 4.67$$

$$SSW = \sum_{j=1}^{k} (n_j - 1)s_j^2 = 7(1.07) + 7(1.07) + 7(1.36) = 24.5$$

$$MSW = SSW/(n_T - k) = 24.5/(24 - 3) = 1.17$$

$$F = MSB/MSW = 4.67/1.17 = 3.99$$

$F_{.05} = 3.47$ (2 degrees of freedom numerator and 21 denominator)

Since $F = 3.99 > F_{.05} = 3.47$, we reject the null hypothesis that the mean comfort scores are the same for the three groups.

b.　$$LSD = t_{\alpha/2} \sqrt{MSW \left(\frac{1}{n_i} + \frac{1}{n_j} \right)} = 2.080 \sqrt{1.17 \left(\frac{1}{8} + \frac{1}{8} \right)} = 1.12$$

Since the absolute value of the difference between the sample means for nonbrowsers and light browsers is $\left| 4.25 - 5.25 \right| = 1$, we cannot reject the null hypothesis that the two population means are equal.

60.　　Treatment Means:

$$\overline{x}_{.1} = 22.8 \quad \overline{x}_{.2} = 24.8 \quad \overline{x}_{.3} = 25.80$$

Block Means:

$$\overline{x}_{1.} = 19.67 \quad \overline{x}_{2.} = 25.67 \quad \overline{x}_{3.} = 31 \quad \overline{x}_{4.} = 23.67 \quad \overline{x}_{5.} = 22.33$$

Overall Mean:

$$\overline{\overline{x}} = 367/15 = 24.47$$

Step 1

$$SST = \sum_i \sum_j \left(x_{ij} - \overline{\overline{x}} \right)^2 = (18 - 24.47)^2 + (21 - 24.47)^2 + \cdots + (24 - 24.47)^2 = 253.73$$

Step 2

$$SSTR = b \sum_j \left(\overline{x}_{.j} - \overline{\overline{x}} \right)^2 = 5 \left[(22.8 - 24.47)^2 + (24.8 - 24.47)^2 + (25.8 - 24.47)^2 \right] = 23.33$$

<u>Step 3</u>

$$SSBL = k\sum_{i}\left(\bar{x}_{i.} - \bar{\bar{x}}\right)^2 = 3\,[\,(19.67 - 24.47)^2 + (25.67 - 24.47)^2 + \cdots + (22.33 - 24.47)^2\,] = 217.02$$

<u>Step 4</u>

SSE = SST - SSTR - SSBL = 253.73 - 23.33 - 217.02 = 13.38

Source of Variation	Sum of Squares	Degrees of Freedom	Mean Square	F
Treatment	23.33	2	11.67	6.99
Blocks	217.02	4	54.26	32.49
Error	13.38	8	1.67	
Total	253.73	14		

$F_{.05} = 4.46$ (2 degrees of freedom numerator and 8 denominator)

Since $F = 6.99 > F_{.05} = 4.46$ we reject the null hypothesis that the mean miles per gallon ratings for the three brands of gasoline are equal.

61.

	I	II	III
Sample Mean	22.8	24.8	25.8
Sample Variance	21.2	9.2	27.2

$\bar{\bar{x}} = (22.8 + 24.8 + 25.8)\,/3 = 24.47$

$$SSTR = \sum_{j=1}^{k} n_j\left(\bar{x}_j - \bar{\bar{x}}\right)^2 = 5(22.8 - 24.47)^2 + 5(24.8 - 24.47)^2 + 5(25.8 - 24.47)^2 = 23.33$$

$MSTR = SSTR\,/(k - 1) = 23.33\,/2 = 11.67$

$$SSE = \sum_{j=1}^{k}(n_j - 1)s_j^2 = 4(21.2) + 4(9.2) + 4(27.2) = 230.4$$

$MSE = SSE\,/(n_T - k) = 230.4\,/(15 - 3) = 19.2$

$F = MSTR\,/MSE = 11.67\,/19.2 = .61$

$F_{.05} = 3.89$ (2 degrees of freedom numerator and 12 denominator)

Since $F = .61 < F_{.05} = 3.89$, we cannot reject the null hypothesis that the mean miles per gallon ratings for the three brands of gasoline are equal.

Thus, we must remove the block effect in order to detect a significant difference due to the brand of gasoline. The following table illustrates the relationship between the randomized block design and the completely randomized design.

Sum of Squares	Randomized Block Design	Completely Randomized Design
SST	253.73	253.73
SSTR	23.33	23.33
SSBL	217.02	does not exist
SSE	13.38	230.4

Note that SSE for the completely randomized design is the sum of SSBL (217.02) and SSE (13.38) for the randomized block design. This illustrates that the effect of blocking is to remove the block effect from the error sum of squares; thus, the estimate of σ^2 for the randomized block design is substantially smaller than it is for the completely randomized design.

62. The Minitab output for these data is shown below:

```
Analysis of Variance
Source     DF        SS        MS        F         P
Factor      2    731.75    365.88    93.16     0.000
Error      63    247.42      3.93
Total      65    979.17
                                    Individual 95% CIs For Mean
                                    Based on Pooled StDev
Level       N      Mean     StDev   ---+---------+---------+---------+---
UK         22    12.052     1.393   (--*--)
US         22    14.957     1.847                (--*--)
Europe     22    20.105     2.536                                  (--*--)
                                    ---+---------+---------+---------+---
Pooled StDev =    1.982            12.0      15.0      18.0      21.0
```

Because the *p*-value = .000 < α = .05, we can reject the null hypothesis that the mean download time is the same for web sites located in the three countries. Note that the mean download time for web sites located in the United Kingdom (12.052 seconds) is less than the mean download time for web sites in the United States (14.957) and web sites located in Europe (20.105).

63.

			Factor B		Factor A
		Spanish	French	German	Means
Factor A	System 1	$\bar{x}_{11} = 10$	$\bar{x}_{12} = 12$	$\bar{x}_{13} = 14$	$\bar{x}_{1.} = 12$
	System 2	$\bar{x}_{21} = 8$	$\bar{x}_{22} = 15$	$\bar{x}_{23} = 19$	$\bar{x}_{2.} = 14$
Factor B Means		$\bar{x}_{.1} = 9$	$\bar{x}_{.2} = 13.5$	$\bar{x}_{.3} = 16.5$	$\bar{\bar{x}} = 13$

Step 1

$$SST = \sum_i \sum_j \sum_k \left(x_{ijk} - \bar{\bar{x}} \right)^2 = (8 - 13)^2 + (12 - 13)^2 + \cdots + (22 - 13)^2 = 204$$

Step 2

$$SSA = br\sum_i \left(\bar{x}_{i.} - \bar{\bar{x}}\right)^2 = 3\,(2)\,[\,(12 - 13)^2 + (14 - 13)^2\,] = 12$$

Step 3

$$SSB = ar\sum_j \left(\bar{x}_{.j} - \bar{\bar{x}}\right)^2 = 2\,(2)\,[\,(9 - 13)^2 + (13.5 - 13)^2 + (16.5 - 13)^2\,] = 114$$

Step 4

$$SSAB = r\sum_i\sum_j \left(\bar{x}_{ij} - \bar{x}_{i.} - \bar{x}_{.j} + \bar{\bar{x}}\right)^2 = 2\,[(8 - 12 - 9 + 13)^2 + \cdots + (22 - 14 - 16.5 + 13)^2] = 26$$

Step 5

$$SSE = SST - SSA - SSB - SSAB = 204 - 12 - 114 - 26 = 52$$

Source of Variation	Sum of Squares	Degrees of Freedom	Mean Square	F
Factor A	12	1	12	1.38
Factor B	114	2	57	6.57
Interaction	26	2	12	1.50
Error	52	6	8.67	
Total	204	11		

$F_{.05} = 5.99$ (1 degree of freedom numerator and 6 denominator)

$F_{.05} = 5.14$ (2 degrees of freedom numerator and 6 denominator)

Since $F = 6.57 > F_{.05} = 5.14$, Factor B is significant; that is, there is a significant difference due to the language translated.

Type of system and interaction are not significant since both F values are less than the critical value.

64.

		Factor B Manual	Factor B Automatic	Factor B Means
Factor A	Machine 1	$\bar{x}_{11} = 32$	$\bar{x}_{12} = 28$	$\bar{x}_{1.} = 36$
	Machine 2	$\bar{x}_{21} = 21$	$\bar{x}_{22} = 26$	$\bar{x}_{2.} = 23.5$
Factor B Means		$\bar{x}_{.1} = 26.5$	$\bar{x}_{.2} = 27$	$\bar{\bar{x}} = 26.75$

Step 1

$$SST = \sum_i \sum_j \sum_k \left(x_{ijk} - \overline{\overline{x}}\right)^2 = (30 - 26.75)^2 + (34 - 26.75)^2 + \cdots + (28 - 26.75)^2 = 151.5$$

Step 2

$$SSA = br\sum_i \left(\overline{x}_{i.} - \overline{\overline{x}}\right)^2 = 2\,(2)\,[\,(30 - 26.75)^2 + (23.5 - 26.75)^2\,] = 84.5$$

Step 3

$$SSB = ar\sum_j \left(\overline{x}_{.j} - \overline{\overline{x}}\right)^2 = 2\,(2)\,[\,(26.5 - 26.75)^2 + (27 - 26.75)^2\,] = 0.5$$

Step 4

$$SSAB = r\sum_i \sum_j \left(\overline{x}_{ij} - \overline{x}_{i.} - \overline{x}_{.j} + \overline{\overline{x}}\right)^2 = 2[(30 - 30 - 26.5 + 26.75)^2 + \cdots + (28 - 23.5 - 27 + 26.75)^2]$$

$$= 40.5$$

Step 5

SSE = SST - SSA - SSB - SSAB = 151.5 - 84.5 - 0.5 - 40.5 = 26

Source of Variation	Sum of Squares	Degrees of Freedom	Mean Square	F
Factor A	84.5	1	84.5	13
Factor B	.5	1	.5	.08
Interaction	40.5	1	40.5	6.23
Error	26	4	6.5	
Total	151.5	7		

$F_{.05} = 7.71$ (1 degree of freedom numerator and 4 denominator)

Since $F = 13 > F_{.05} = 7.71$, Factor A (Type of Machine) is significant.

Type of Loading System and Interaction are not significant since both F values are less than the critical value.

Chapter 14
Simple Linear Regression

Learning Objectives

1. Understand how regression analysis can be used to develop an equation that estimates mathematically how two variables are related.

2. Understand the differences between the regression model, the regression equation, and the estimated regression equation.

3. Know how to fit an estimated regression equation to a set of sample data based upon the least-squares method.

4. Be able to determine how good a fit is provided by the estimated regression equation and compute the sample correlation coefficient from the regression analysis output.

5. Understand the assumptions necessary for statistical inference and be able to test for a significant relationship.

6. Learn how to use a residual plot to make a judgement as to the validity of the regression assumptions, recognize outliers, and identify influential observations.

7. Know how to develop confidence interval estimates of y given a specific value of x in both the case of a mean value of y and an individual value of y.

8. Be able to compute the sample correlation coefficient from the regression analysis output.

9. Know the definition of the following terms:

   independent and dependent variable
   simple linear regression
   regression model
   regression equation and estimated regression equation
   scatter diagram
   coefficient of determination
   standard error of the estimate
   confidence interval
   prediction interval
   residual plot
   standardized residual plot
   outlier
   influential observation
   leverage

Solutions:

1   a.

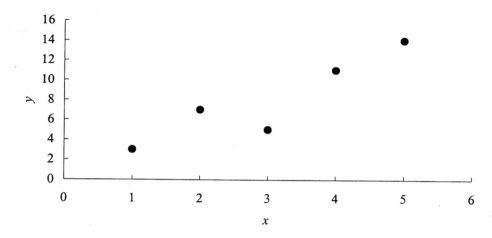

b.   There appears to be a linear relationship between x and y.

c.   Many different straight lines can be drawn to provide a linear approximation of the relationship between x *and* y; in part d we will determine the equation of a straight line that "best" represents the relationship according to the least squares criterion.

d.   Summations needed to compute the slope and y-intercept are:

$$\Sigma x_i = 15 \quad \Sigma y_i = 40 \quad \Sigma(x_i - \overline{x})(y_i - \overline{y}) = 26 \quad \Sigma(x_i - \overline{x})^2 = 10$$

$$b_1 = \frac{\Sigma(x_i - \overline{x})(y_i - \overline{y})}{\Sigma(x_i - \overline{x})^2} = \frac{26}{10} = 2.6$$

$$b_0 = \overline{y} - b_1\overline{x} = 8 - (2.6)(3) = 0.2$$

$$\hat{y} = 0.2 - 2.6x$$

e. $\hat{y} = 0.2 - 2.6(4) = 10.6$

2. a.

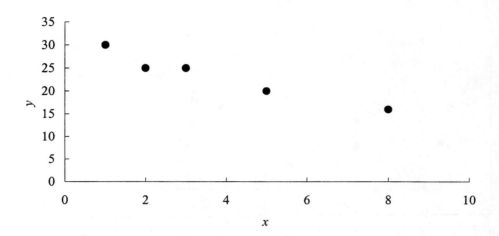

b. There appears to be a linear relationship between x and y.

c. Many different straight lines can be drawn to provide a linear approximation of the relationship between x *and* y; in part d we will determine the equation of a straight line that "best" represents the relationship according to the least squares criterion.

d. Summations needed to compute the slope and y-intercept are:

$$\Sigma x_i = 19 \quad \Sigma y_i = 116 \quad \Sigma(x_i - \overline{x})(y_i - \overline{y}) = -57.8 \quad \Sigma(x_i - \overline{x})^2 = 30.8$$

$$b_1 = \frac{\Sigma(x_i - \overline{x})(y_i - \overline{y})}{\Sigma(x_i - \overline{x})^2} = \frac{-57.8}{30.8} = -1.8766$$

$$b_0 = \overline{y} - b_1\overline{x} = 23.2 - (-1.8766)(3.8) = 30.3311$$

$$\hat{y} = 30.33 - 1.88x$$

e. $\hat{y} = 30.33 - 1.88(6) = 19.05$

3. a.

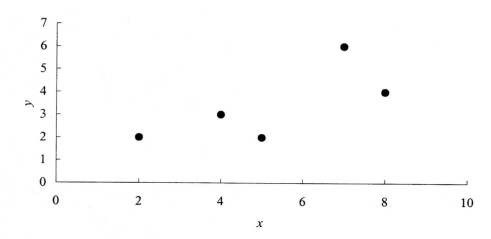

b. Summations needed to compute the slope and y-intercept are:

$$\Sigma x_i = 26 \quad \Sigma y_i = 17 \quad \Sigma(x_i - \bar{x})(y_i - \bar{y}) = 11.6 \quad \Sigma(x_i - \bar{x})^2 = 22.8$$

$$b_1 = \frac{\Sigma(x_i - \bar{x})(y_i - \bar{y})}{\Sigma(x_i - \bar{x})^2} = \frac{11.6}{22.8} = 0.5088$$

$$b_0 = \bar{y} - b_1\bar{x} = 3.4 - (0.5088)(5.2) = 0.7542$$

$$\hat{y} = 0.75 + 0.51x$$

c. $\hat{y} = 0.75 + 0.51(4) = 2.79$

4. a.

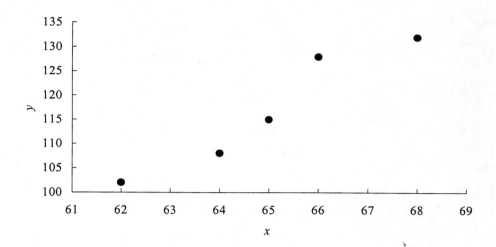

b. There appears to be a linear relationship between x and y.

c. Many different straight lines can be drawn to provide a linear approximation of the relationship between x and y; in part d we will determine the equation of a straight line that "best" represents the relationship according to the least squares criterion.

d. Summations needed to compute the slope and y-intercept are:

$$\Sigma x_i = 325 \quad \Sigma y_i = 585 \quad \Sigma(x_i - \bar{x})(y_i - \bar{y}) = 110 \quad \Sigma(x_i - \bar{x})^2 = 20$$

$$b_1 = \frac{\Sigma(x_i - \bar{x})(y_i - \bar{y})}{\Sigma(x_i - \bar{x})^2} = \frac{110}{20} = 5.5$$

$$b_0 = \bar{y} - b_1\bar{x} = 117 - (5.5)(65) = -240.5$$

$$\hat{y} = -240.5 + 5.5x$$

e. $\hat{y} = -240.5 + 5.5x = -240.5 + 5.5(63) = 106$ pounds

5. a.

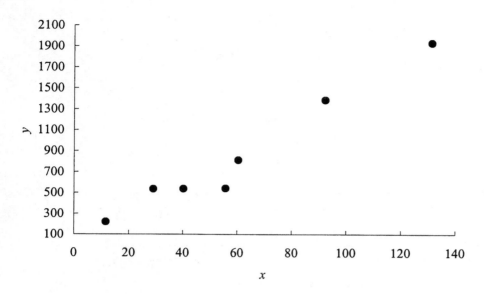

b. There appears to be a linear relationship between x and y.

c. Many different straight lines can be drawn to provide a linear approximation of the relationship between x and y; in part d we will determine the equation of a straight line that "best" represents the relationship according to the least squares criterion.

Summations needed to compute the slope and y-intercept are:

$$\Sigma x_i = 420.6 \quad \Sigma y_i = 5958.7 \quad \Sigma(x_i - \overline{x})(y_i - \overline{y}) = 142,040.3443 \quad \Sigma(x_i - \overline{x})^2 = 9847.6486$$

$$b_1 = \frac{\Sigma(x_i - \overline{x})(y_i - \overline{y})}{\Sigma(x_i - \overline{x})^2} = \frac{142,040.3443}{9847.6486} = 14.4238$$

$$b_0 = \overline{y} - b_1\overline{x} = 851.2429 - (14.4238)(60.0857) = -15.42$$

$$\hat{y} = -15.42 + 14.42x$$

d. A one million dollar increase in media expenditures will increase case sales by approximately 14.42 million.

e. $\hat{y} = -15.42 + 14.42x = -15.42 + 14.42(70) = 993.98$

6. a.

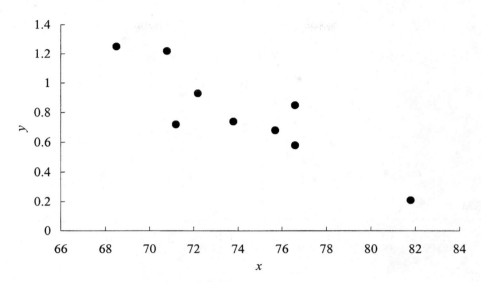

b. There appears to be a linear relationship between x and y.

c. Summations needed to compute the slope and y-intercept are:

$$\Sigma x_i = 667.2 \quad \Sigma y_i = 7.18 \quad \Sigma(x_i - \bar{x})(y_i - \bar{y}) = -9.0623 \quad \Sigma(x_i - \bar{x})^2 = 128.7$$

$$b_1 = \frac{\Sigma(x_i - \bar{x})(y_i - \bar{y})}{\Sigma(x_i - \bar{x})^2} = \frac{-9.0623}{128.7} = -0.0704$$

$$b_0 = \bar{y} - b_1\bar{x} = 0.7978 - (-0.0704)(74.1333) = 6.02$$

$$\hat{y} = 6.02 - 0.07x$$

d. A one percent increase in the percentage of flights arriving on time will decrease the number of complaints per 100,000 passengers by 0.07.

e $\hat{y} = 6.02 - 0.07x = 6.02 - 0.07(80) = 0.42$

7. a.

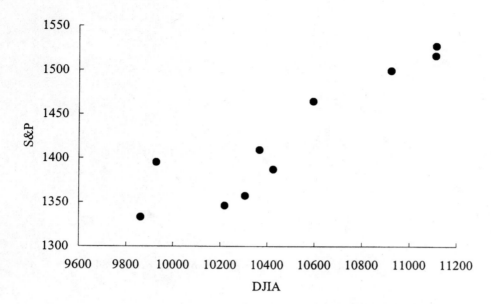

b. Let x = DJIA and y = S&P. Summations needed to compute the slope and y-intercept are:

$$\Sigma x_i = 104,850 \quad \Sigma y_i = 14,233 \quad \Sigma(x_i - \bar{x})(y_i - \bar{y}) = 268,921 \quad \Sigma(x_i - \bar{x})^2 = 1,806,384$$

$$b_1 = \frac{\Sigma(x_i - \bar{x})(y_i - \bar{y})}{\Sigma(x_i - \bar{x})^2} = \frac{268,921}{1,806,384} = 0.14887$$

$$b_0 = \bar{y} - b_1\bar{x} = 1423.3 - (.14887)(10,485) = -137.629$$

$$\hat{y} = -137.63 + 0.1489x$$

c. $\hat{y} = -137.63 + 0.1489(11,000) = 1500.27$ or approximately 1500

8. a. Summations needed to compute the slope and y-intercept are:

$$\Sigma x_i = 121 \quad \Sigma y_i = 1120.9 \quad \Sigma(x_i - \bar{x})(y_i - \bar{y}) = 544.0429 \quad \Sigma(x_i - \bar{x})^2 = 177.4286$$

$$b_1 = \frac{\Sigma(x_i - \bar{x})(y_i - \bar{y})}{\Sigma(x_i - \bar{x})^2} = \frac{544.0429}{177.4286} = 3.0663$$

$$b_0 = \bar{y} - b_1\bar{x} = 160.1286 - (3.0663)(17.2857) = 107.13$$

$$\hat{y} = 107.13 + 3.07x$$

b. Increasing the number of times an ad is aired by one will increase the number of household exposures by approximately 3.07 million.

c. $\hat{y} = 107.13 + 3.07x = 107.13 + 3.07(15) = 153.2$

9. a.

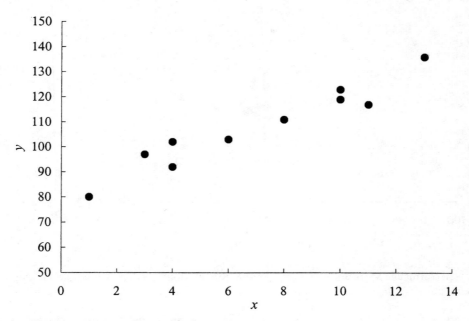

b. Summations needed to compute the slope and y-intercept are:

$$\Sigma x_i = 70 \quad \Sigma y_i = 1080 \quad \Sigma(x_i - \overline{x})(y_i - \overline{y}) = 568 \quad \Sigma(x_i - \overline{x})^2 = 142$$

$$b_1 = \frac{\Sigma(x_i - \overline{x})(y_i - \overline{y})}{\Sigma(x_i - \overline{x})^2} = \frac{568}{142} = 4$$

$$b_0 = \overline{y} - b_1 \overline{x} = 108 - (4)(7) = 80$$

$$\hat{y} = 80 + 4x$$

c. $\hat{y} = 80 + 4x = 80 + 4(9) = 116$

10. a.

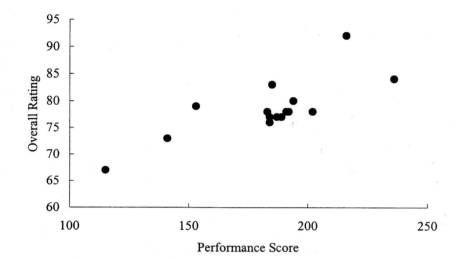

b. Let x = performance score and y = overall rating. Summations needed to compute the slope and y-intercept are:

$$\Sigma x_i = 2752 \quad \Sigma y_i = 1177 \quad \Sigma(x_i - \overline{x})(y_i - \overline{y}) = 1723.73 \quad \Sigma(x_i - \overline{x})^2 = 11,867.73$$

$$b_1 = \frac{\Sigma(x_i - \overline{x})(y_i - \overline{y})}{\Sigma(x_i - \overline{x})^2} = \frac{1723.73}{11,867.73} = 0.1452$$

$$b_0 = \overline{y} - b_1\overline{x} = 78.4667 - (.1452)(183.4667) = 51.82$$

$$\hat{y} = 51.82 + 0.145x$$

c. $\hat{y} = 51.82 + 0.145(225) = 84.4$ or approximately 84

11. a.

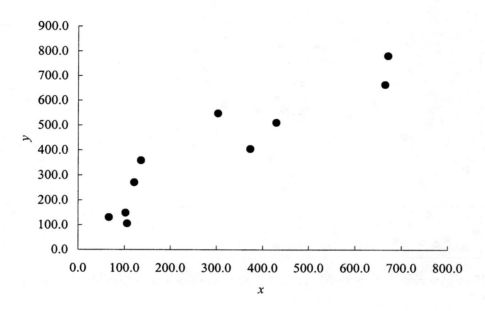

b. There appears to be a linear relationship between the variables.

c. The summations needed to compute the slope and the y-intercept are:

$$\Sigma x_i = 2973.3 \quad \Sigma y_i = 3925.6 \quad \Sigma(x_i - \overline{x})(y_i - \overline{y}) = 453,345.042 \quad \Sigma(x_i - \overline{x})^2 = 483,507.581$$

$$b_1 = \frac{\Sigma(x_i - \overline{x})(y_i - \overline{y})}{\Sigma(x_i - \overline{x})^2} = \frac{453,345.042}{483,507.581} = 0.9385$$

$$b_0 = \overline{y} - b_1\overline{x} = 392.56 - (0.9385)(297.33) = 113.52$$

$$\hat{y} = 113.52 + 0.94x$$

d. $\hat{y} = 113.52 + 0.94x = 113.52 + 0.94(500) = 583.5$

12. a.

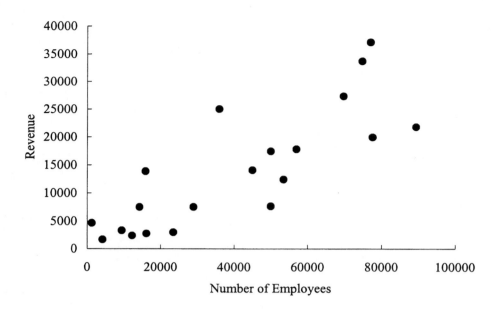

b.   There appears to be a positive linear relationship between the number of employees and the revenue.

c.   Let x = number of employees and y = revenue. Summations needed to compute the slope and y-intercept are:

$$\Sigma x_i = 4200 \quad \Sigma y_i = 1669 \quad \Sigma(x_i - \bar{x})(y_i - \bar{y}) = 4,658,594,168 \quad \Sigma(x_i - \bar{x})^2 = 14,718,343,803$$

$$b_1 = \frac{\Sigma(x_i - \bar{x})(y_i - \bar{y})}{\Sigma(x_i - \bar{x})^2} = \frac{4,658,594,168}{14,718,343,803} = 0.316516$$

$$b_0 = \bar{y} - b_1\bar{x} = 14,048 - (.316516)(40,299) = 1293$$

$$\hat{y} = 1293 + 0.3165x$$

d. $\hat{y} = 1293 + .3165(75,000) = 25,031$

13. a.

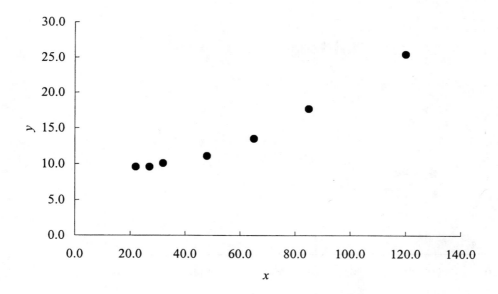

b. The summations needed to compute the slope and the y-intercept are:

$$\Sigma x_i = 399 \quad \Sigma y_i = 97.1 \quad \Sigma(x_i - \overline{x})(y_i - \overline{y}) = 1233.7 \quad \Sigma(x_i - \overline{x})^2 = 7648$$

$$b_1 = \frac{\Sigma(x_i - \overline{x})(y_i - \overline{y})}{\Sigma(x_i - \overline{x})^2} = \frac{1233.7}{7648} = 0.16131$$

$$b_0 = \overline{y} - b_1\overline{x} = 13.87143 - (0.16131)(57) = 4.67675$$

$$\hat{y} = 4.68 + 0.16x$$

c. $\hat{y} = 4.68 + 0.16x = 4.68 + 0.16(52.5) = 13.08$ or approximately \$13,080.

The agent's request for an audit appears to be justified.

14. a.

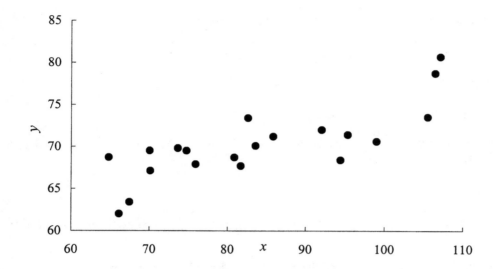

b. The summations needed to compute the slope and the y-intercept are:

$$\Sigma x_i = 1677.25 \quad \Sigma y_i = 1404.3 \quad \Sigma(x_i - \overline{x})(y_i - \overline{y}) = 897.9493 \quad \Sigma(x_i - \overline{x})^2 = 3657.4568$$

$$b_1 = \frac{\Sigma(x_i - \overline{x})(y_i - \overline{y})}{\Sigma(x_i - \overline{x})^2} = \frac{897.9493}{3657.4568} = 0.2455$$

$$b_0 = \overline{y} - b_1\overline{x} = 70.215 - (0.2455)(83.8625) = 49.63$$

$$\hat{y} = 49.63 + .2455x$$

c. $\hat{y} = 49.63 + .2455x = 49.63 + .2455(80) = 69.3\%$

15. a. The estimated regression equation and the mean for the dependent variable are:

$$\hat{y}_i = 0.2 + 2.6x_i \qquad \overline{y} = 8$$

The sum of squares due to error and the total sum of squares are

$$SSE = \Sigma(y_i - \hat{y}_i)^2 = 12.40 \qquad SST = \Sigma(y_i - \overline{y})^2 = 80$$

Thus, SSR = SST - SSE = 80 - 12.4 = 67.6

b. $r^2 = SSR/SST = 67.6/80 = .845$

The least squares line provided a very good fit; 84.5% of the variability in y has been explained by the least squares line.

c. $r = \sqrt{.845} = +.9192$

16. a.　The estimated regression equation and the mean for the dependent variable are:

$$\hat{y}_i = 30.33 - 1.88x \qquad \bar{y} = 23.2$$

The sum of squares due to error and the total sum of squares are

$$SSE = \Sigma(y_i - \hat{y}_i)^2 = 6.33 \qquad SST = \Sigma(y_i - \bar{y})^2 = 114.80$$

Thus,　$SSR = SST - SSE = 114.80 - 6.33 = 108.47$

b.　$r^2 = SSR/SST = 108.47/114.80 = .945$

The least squares line provided an excellent fit; 94.5% of the variability in y has been explained by the estimated regression equation.

c.　$r = \sqrt{.945} = -.9721$

Note: the sign for r is negative because the slope of the estimated regression equation is negative. ($b_1 = -1.88$)

17.　The estimated regression equation and the mean for the dependent variable are:

$$\hat{y}_i = .75 + .51x \qquad \bar{y} = 3.4$$

The sum of squares due to error and the total sum of squares are

$$SSE = \Sigma(y_i - \hat{y}_i)^2 = 5.3 \qquad SST = \Sigma(y_i - \bar{y})^2 = 11.2$$

Thus,　$SSR = SST - SSE = 11.2 - 5.3 = 5.9$

$r^2 = SSR/SST = 5.9/11.2 = .527$

We see that 52.7% of the variability in y has been explained by the least squares line.

$r = \sqrt{.527} = +.7259$

18. a.　The estimated regression equation and the mean for the dependent variable are:

$$\hat{y} = 1790.5 + 581.1x \qquad \bar{y} = 3650$$

The sum of squares due to error and the total sum of squares are

$$SSE = \Sigma(y_i - \hat{y}_i)^2 = 85,135.14 \qquad SST = \Sigma(y_i - \bar{y})^2 = 335,000$$

Thus,　$SSR = SST - SSE = 335,000 - 85,135.14 = 249,864.86$

b.　$r^2 = SSR/SST = 249,864.86/335,000 = .746$

We see that 74.6% of the variability in y has been explained by the least squares line.

c.　$r = \sqrt{.746} = +.8637$

19. a. The estimated regression equation and the mean for the dependent variable are:

$$\hat{y} = -137.63 + .1489x \qquad \bar{y} = 1423.3$$

The sum of squares due to error and the total sum of squares are

$$SSE = \Sigma(y_i - \hat{y}_i)^2 = 7547.14 \qquad SST = \Sigma(y_i - \bar{y})^2 = 47,582.10$$

Thus, SSR = SST - SSE = 47,582.10 - 7547.14 = 40,034.96

   b. r^2 = SSR/SST = 40,034.96/47,582.10 = .84

We see that 84% of the variability in y has been explained by the least squares line.

   c. $r = \sqrt{.84} = +.92$

20. a. Let x = income and y = home price. Summations needed to compute the slope and y-intercept are:

$$\Sigma x_i = 1424 \quad \Sigma y_i = 2455.5 \quad \Sigma(x_i - \bar{x})(y_i - \bar{y}) = 4011 \quad \Sigma(x_i - \bar{x})^2 = 1719.618$$

$$b_1 = \frac{\Sigma(x_i - \bar{x})(y_i - \bar{y})}{\Sigma(x_i - \bar{x})^2} = \frac{4011}{1719.618} = 2.3325$$

$$b_0 = \bar{y} - b_1\bar{x} = 136.4167 - (2.3325)(79.1111) = -48.11$$

$$\hat{y} = -48.11 + 2.3325x$$

   b. The sum of squares due to error and the total sum of squares are

$$SSE = \Sigma(y_i - \hat{y}_i)^2 = 2017.37 \qquad SST = \Sigma(y_i - \bar{y})^2 = 11,373.09$$

Thus, SSR = SST - SSE = 11,373.09 - 2017.37 = 9355.72

$$r^2 = SSR/SST = 9355.72/11,373.09 = .82$$

We see that 82% of the variability in y has been explained by the least squares line.

$$r = \sqrt{.82} = +.91$$

   c. $\hat{y} = -48.11 + 2.3325(95) = 173.5$ or approximately $173,500

21. a. The summations needed in this problem are:

$$\Sigma x_i = 3450 \quad \Sigma y_i = 33,700 \quad \Sigma(x_i - \bar{x})(y_i - \bar{y}) = 712,500 \quad \Sigma(x_i - \bar{x})^2 = 93,750$$

$$b_1 = \frac{\Sigma(x_i - \bar{x})(y_i - \bar{y})}{\Sigma(x_i - \bar{x})^2} = \frac{712,500}{93,750} = 7.6$$

$$b_0 = \bar{y} - b_1\bar{x} = 5616.67 - (7.6)(575) = 1246.67$$

$$\hat{y} = 1246.67 + 7.6x$$

b. $7.60

c. The sum of squares due to error and the total sum of squares are:

$$SSE = \Sigma(y_i - \hat{y}_i)^2 = 233,333.33 \qquad SST = \Sigma(y_i - \overline{y})^2 = 5,648,333.33$$

Thus, SSR = SST - SSE = 5,648,333.33 - 233,333.33 = 5,415,000

r^2 = SSR/SST = 5,415,000/5,648,333.33 = .9587

We see that 95.87% of the variability in y has been explained by the estimated regression equation.

d. $\hat{y} = 1246.67 + 7.6x = 1246.67 + 7.6(500) = \$5046.67$

22. a. The summations needed in this problem are:

$$\Sigma x_i = 613.1 \quad \Sigma y_i = 70 \quad \Sigma(x_i - \overline{x})(y_i - \overline{y}) = 5766.7 \quad \Sigma(x_i - \overline{x})^2 = 45,833.9286$$

$$b_1 = \frac{\Sigma(x_i - \overline{x})(y_i - \overline{y})}{\Sigma(x_i - \overline{x})^2} = \frac{5766.7}{45,833.9286} = 0.1258$$

$$b_0 = \overline{y} - b_1\overline{x} = 10 - (0.1258)(87.5857) = -1.0183$$

$$\hat{y} = -1.0183 + 0.1258x$$

b. The sum of squares due to error and the total sum of squares are:

$$SSE = \Sigma(y_i - \hat{y}_i)^2 = 1272.4495 \qquad SST = \Sigma(y_i - \overline{y})^2 = 1998$$

Thus, SSR = SST - SSE = 1998 - 1272.4495 = 725.5505

r^2 = SSR/SST = 725.5505/1998 = 0.3631

Approximately 37% of the variability in change in executive compensation is explained by the two-year change in the return on equity.

c. $r = \sqrt{0.3631} = +0.6026$

It reflects a linear relationship that is between weak and strong.

23. a. $s^2 = MSE = SSE / (n - 2) = 12.4 / 3 = 4.133$

b. $s = \sqrt{MSE} = \sqrt{4.133} = 2.033$

c. $\Sigma(x_i - \overline{x})^2 = 10$

$$s_{b_1} = \frac{s}{\sqrt{\Sigma(x_i - \overline{x})^2}} = \frac{2.033}{\sqrt{10}} = 0.643$$

d. $t = \dfrac{b_1}{s_{b_1}} = \dfrac{2.6}{.643} = 4.04$

$t_{.025} = 3.182$ (3 degrees of freedom)

Since $t = 4.04 > t_{.05} = 3.182$ we reject H_0: $\beta_1 = 0$

e. $MSR = SSR / 1 = 67.6$

$F = MSR / MSE = 67.6 / 4.133 = 16.36$

$F_{.05} = 10.13$ (1 degree of freedom numerator and 3 denominator)

Since $F = 16.36 > F_{.05} = 10.13$ we reject H_0: $\beta_1 = 0$

Source of Variation	Sum of Squares	Degrees of Freedom	Mean Square	F
Regression	67.6	1	67.6	16.36
Error	12.4	3	4.133	
Total	80.0	4		

24. a. $s^2 = MSE = SSE / (n - 2) = 6.33 / 3 = 2.11$

b. $s = \sqrt{MSE} = \sqrt{2.11} = 1.453$

c. $\Sigma(x_i - \overline{x})^2 = 30.8$

$s_{b_1} = \dfrac{s}{\sqrt{\Sigma(x_i - \overline{x})^2}} = \dfrac{1.453}{\sqrt{30.8}} = 0.262$

d. $t = \dfrac{b_1}{s_{b_1}} = \dfrac{-1.88}{.262} = -7.18$

$t_{.025} = 3.182$ (3 degrees of freedom)

Since $t = -7.18 < -t_{.025} = -3.182$ we reject H_0: $\beta_1 = 0$

e. $MSR = SSR / 1 = 8.47$

$F = MSR / MSE = 108.47 / 2.11 = 51.41$

$F_{.05} = 10.13$ (1 degree of freedom numerator and 3 denominator)

Since $F = 51.41 > F_{.05} = 10.13$ we reject H_0: $\beta_1 = 0$

Source of Variation	Sum of Squares	Degrees of Freedom	Mean Square	F
Regression	108.47	1	108.47	51.41
Error	6.33	3	2.11	
Total	114.80	4		

25. a. $s^2 = MSE = SSE / (n - 2) = 5.30 / 3 = 1.77$

$s = \sqrt{MSE} = \sqrt{1.77} = 1.33$

b. $\Sigma(x_i - \overline{x})^2 = 22.8$

$$s_{b_1} = \frac{s}{\sqrt{\Sigma(x_i - \overline{x})^2}} = \frac{1.33}{\sqrt{22.8}} = 0.28$$

$$t = \frac{b_1}{s_{b_1}} = \frac{.51}{.28} = 1.82$$

$t_{.025} = 3.182$ (3 degrees of freedom)

Since $t = 1.82 < t_{.025} = 3.182$ we cannot reject H_0: $\beta_1 = 0$; x and y do not appear to be related.

c. MSR = SSR/1 = 5.90 /1 = 5.90

F = MSR/MSE = 5.90/1.77 = 3.33

$F_{.05} = 10.13$ (1 degree of freedom numerator and 3 denominator)

Since $F = 3.33 < F_{.05} = 10.13$ we cannot reject H_0: $\beta_1 = 0$; x and y do not appear to be related.

26. a. $s^2 = $ MSE $ = $ SSE / $(n - 2) = 85,135.14 / 4 = 21,283.79$

$$s = \sqrt{\text{MSE}} = \sqrt{21,283.79} = 145.89$$

$$\Sigma(x_i - \overline{x})^2 = 0.74$$

$$s_{b_1} = \frac{s}{\sqrt{\Sigma(x_i - \overline{x})^2}} = \frac{145.89}{\sqrt{0.74}} = 169.59$$

$$t = \frac{b_1}{s_{b_1}} = \frac{581.08}{169.59} = 3.43$$

$t_{.025} = 2.776$ (4 degrees of freedom)

Since $t = 3.43 > t_{.025} = 2.776$ we reject H_0: $\beta_1 = 0$

b. MSR $ = $ SSR / 1 $ = 249,864.86 / 1 = 249.864.86$

F = MSR / MSE = $249,864.86 / 21,283.79 = 11.74$

$F_{.05} = 7.71$ (1 degree of freedom numerator and 4 denominator)

Since $F = 11.74 > F_{.05} = 7.71$ we reject H_0: $\beta_1 = 0$

c.

Source of Variation	Sum of Squares	Degrees of Freedom	Mean Square	F
Regression	249864.86	1	249864.86	11.74
Error	85135.14	4	21283.79	
Total	335000	5		

27. The sum of squares due to error and the total sum of squares are:

SSE = $\Sigma(y_i - \hat{y}_i)^2 = 170$ SST = 2442

Thus, SSR = SST - SSE = 2442 - 170 = 2272

MSR = SSR / 1 = 2272

SSE = SST - SSR = 2442 - 2272 = 170

MSE = SSE / $(n - 2)$ = 170 / 8 = 21.25

F = MSR / MSE = 2272 / 21.25 = 106.92

$F_{.05}$ = 5.32 (1 degree of freedom numerator and 8 denominator)

Since F = 106.92 > $F_{.05}$ = 5.32 we reject H_0: $\beta_1 = 0$.

Years of experience and sales are related.

28.   SST = 411.73   SSE = 161.37   SSR = 250.36

MSR = SSR / 1 = 250.36

MSE = SSE / $(n - 2)$ = 161.37 / 13 = 12.413

F = MSR / MSE = 250.36 / 12.413 = 20.17

$F_{.05}$ = 4.67 (1 degree of freedom numerator and 13 denominator)

Since F = 20.17 > $F_{.05}$ = 4.67 we reject H_0: $\beta_1 = 0$.

29.   SSE = 233,333.33   SST = 5,648,333.33   SSR = 5,415,000

MSE = SSE/$(n - 2)$ = 233,333.33/(6 - 2) = 58,333.33

MSR = SSR/1 = 5,415,000

F = MSR / MSE = 5,415,000 / 58,333.25 = 92.83

Source of Variation	Sum of Squares	Degrees of Freedom	Mean Square	F
Regression	5,415,000.00	1	5,415,000	92.83
Error	233,333.33	4	58,333.33	
Total	5,648,333.33	5		

$F_{.05}$ = 7.71 (1 degree of freedom numerator and 4 denominator)

Since F = 92.83 > 7.71 we reject H_0: $\beta_1 = 0$. Production volume and total cost are related.

30.   Using the computations from Exercise 22,

SSE = 1272.4495   SST = 1998   SSR = 725.5505

$s = \sqrt{254.4899} = 15.95$

$\sum (x_i - \bar{x})^2 = 45,833.9286$

$$s_{b_1} = \frac{s}{\sqrt{\Sigma(x_i - \overline{x})^2}} = \frac{15.95}{\sqrt{45,833.9286}} = 0.0745$$

$$t = \frac{b_1}{s_{b_1}} = \frac{0.1258}{0.0745} = 1.69$$

$$t_{.025} = 2.571$$

Since $t = 1.69 < 2.571$, we cannot reject H_0: $\beta_1 = 0$

There is no evidence of a significant relationship between x and y.

31.   SST = 11,373.09   SSE = 2017.37   SSR = 9355.72

MSR = SSR / 1 = 9355.72

MSE = SSE / $(n - 2)$ = 2017.37/ 16 = 126.0856

F = MSR / MSE = 9355.72/ 126.0856 = 74.20

$F_{.01}$ = 8.53 (1 degree of freedom numerator and 16 denominator)

Since $F = 74.20 > F_{.01} = 8.53$ we reject H_0: $\beta_1 = 0$.

32. a. $s = 2.033$

$\overline{x} = 3$ $\Sigma(x_i - \overline{x})^2 = 10$

$$s_{\hat{y}_p} = s\sqrt{\frac{1}{n} + \frac{(x_p - \overline{x})^2}{\Sigma(x_i - \overline{x})^2}} = 2.033\sqrt{\frac{1}{5} + \frac{(4-3)^2}{10}} = 1.11$$

b. $\hat{y} = 0.2 + 2.6x = 0.2 + 2.6(4) = 10.6$

$\hat{y}_p \pm t_{\alpha/2} s_{\hat{y}_p}$

$10.6 \pm 3.182 \,(1.11) = 10.6 \pm 3.53$

or 7.07 to 14.13

c. $$s_{ind} = s\sqrt{1 + \frac{1}{n} + \frac{(x_p - \overline{x})^2}{\Sigma(x_i - \overline{x})^2}} = 2.033\sqrt{1 + \frac{1}{5} + \frac{(4-3)^2}{10}} = 2.32$$

d. $\hat{y}_p \pm t_{\alpha/2} s_{ind}$

$10.6 \pm 3.182 \,(2.32) = 10.6 \pm 7.38$

or 3.22 to 17.98

33. a. $s = 1.453$

    b. $\bar{x} = 3.8 \quad \Sigma(x_i - \bar{x})^2 = 30.8$

    $$s_{\hat{y}_p} = s\sqrt{\frac{1}{n} + \frac{(x_p - \bar{x})^2}{\Sigma(x_i - \bar{x})^2}} = 1.453\sqrt{\frac{1}{5} + \frac{(3-3.8)^2}{30.8}} = .068$$

    $$\hat{y} = 30.33 - 1.88x = 30.33 - 1.88(3) = 24.69$$

    $$\hat{y}_p \pm t_{\alpha/2}s_{\hat{y}_p}$$

    $24.69 \pm 3.182 (.68) = 24.69 \pm 2.16$

    or 22.53 to 26.85

    c. $$s_{ind} = s\sqrt{1 + \frac{1}{n} + \frac{(x_p - \bar{x})^2}{\Sigma(x_i - \bar{x})^2}} = 1.453\sqrt{1 + \frac{1}{5} + \frac{(3-3.8)^2}{30.8}} = 1.61$$

    d. $$\hat{y}_p \pm t_{\alpha/2}s_{ind}$$

    $24.69 \pm 3.182 (1.61) = 24.69 \pm 5.12$

    or 19.57 to 29.81

34. $s = 1.33$

    $\bar{x} = 5.2 \quad \Sigma(x_i - \bar{x})^2 = 22.8$

    $$s_{\hat{y}_p} = s\sqrt{\frac{1}{n} + \frac{(x_p - \bar{x})^2}{\Sigma(x_i - \bar{x})^2}} = 1.33\sqrt{\frac{1}{5} + \frac{(3-5.2)^2}{22.8}} = 0.85$$

    $$\hat{y} = 0.75 + 0.51x = 0.75 + 0.51(3) = 2.28$$

    $$\hat{y}_p \pm t_{\alpha/2}s_{\hat{y}_p}$$

    $2.28 \pm 3.182 (.85) = 2.28 \pm 2.70$

    or -.40 to 4.98

    $$s_{ind} = s\sqrt{1 + \frac{1}{n} + \frac{(x_p - \bar{x})^2}{\Sigma(x_i - \bar{x})^2}} = 1.33\sqrt{1 + \frac{1}{5} + \frac{(3-5.2)^2}{22.8}} = 1.58$$

    $$\hat{y}_p \pm t_{\alpha/2}s_{ind}$$

    $2.28 \pm 3.182 (1.58) = 2.28 \pm 5.03$

    or -2.27 to 7.31

35. a. $s = 145.89$

$\overline{x} = 3.2 \quad \Sigma(x_i - \overline{x})^2 = 0.74$

$$s_{\hat{y}_p} = s\sqrt{\frac{1}{n} + \frac{(x_p - \overline{x})^2}{\Sigma(x_i - \overline{x})^2}} = 145.89\sqrt{\frac{1}{6} + \frac{(3-3.2)^2}{0.74}} = 68.54$$

$\hat{y} = 290.54 + 581.08x = 290.54 + 581.08(3) = 2033.78$

$\hat{y}_p \pm t_{\alpha/2}s_{\hat{y}_p}$

$2,033.78 \pm 2.776 (68.54) = 2,033.78 \pm 190.27$

or \$1,843.51 to \$2,224.05

b. $s_{\text{ind}} = s\sqrt{1 + \frac{1}{n} + \frac{(x_p - \overline{x})^2}{\Sigma(x_i - \overline{x})^2}} = 145.89\sqrt{1 + \frac{1}{6} + \frac{(3-3.2)^2}{0.74}} = 161.19$

$\hat{y}_p \pm t_{\alpha/2}s_{\text{ind}}$

$2,033.78 \pm 2.776 (161.19) = 2,033.78 \pm 447.46$

or \$1,586.32 to \$2,481.24

36. a. $\hat{y} = 51.819 + .1452x = 51.819 + .1452(200) = 80.859$

b. $s = 3.5232$

$\overline{x} = 183.4667 \quad \Sigma(x_i - \overline{x})^2 = 11,867.73$

$$s_{\hat{y}_p} = s\sqrt{\frac{1}{n} + \frac{(x_p - \overline{x})^2}{\Sigma(x_i - \overline{x})^2}} = 3.5232\sqrt{\frac{1}{15} + \frac{(200-183.4667)^2}{11,867.73}} = 1.055$$

$\hat{y}_p \pm t_{\alpha/2}s_{\hat{y}_p}$

$80.859 \pm 2.160 (1.055) = 80.859 \pm 2.279$

or 78.58 to 83.14

c. $s_{\text{ind}} = s\sqrt{1 + \frac{1}{n} + \frac{(x_p - \overline{x})^2}{\Sigma(x_i - \overline{x})^2}} = 3.5232\sqrt{1 + \frac{1}{15} + \frac{(200-183.4667)^2}{11,867.73}} = 3.678$

$\hat{y}_p \pm t_{\alpha/2}s_{\text{ind}}$

$80.859 \pm 2.160 (3.678) = 80.859 \pm 7.944$

or 72.92 to 88.80

37. a. $\bar{x} = 57$ $\Sigma(x_i - \bar{x})^2 = 7648$

   $s^2 = 1.88$ $s = 1.37$

   $$s_{\hat{y}_p} = s\sqrt{\frac{1}{n} + \frac{(x_p - \bar{x})^2}{\Sigma(x_i - \bar{x})^2}} = 1.37\sqrt{\frac{1}{7} + \frac{(52.5 - 57)^2}{7648}} = 0.52$$

   $$\hat{y}_p \pm t_{\alpha/2}s_{\hat{y}_p}$$

   $13.08 \pm 2.571\,(.52) = 13.08 \pm 1.34$

   or 11.74 to 14.42 or \$11,740 to \$14,420

   b. $s_{ind} = 1.47$

   $13.08 \pm 2.571\,(1.47) = 13.08 \pm 3.78$

   or 9.30 to 16.86 or \$9,300 to \$16,860

   c. Yes, \$20,400 is much larger than anticipated.

   d. Any deductions exceeding the \$16,860 upper limit could suggest an audit.

38. a. $\hat{y} = 1246.67 + 7.6(500) = \$5046.67$

   b. $\bar{x} = 575$ $\Sigma(x_i - \bar{x})^2 = 93,750$

   $s^2 = \text{MSE} = 58,333.33$ $s = 241.52$

   $$s_{ind} = s\sqrt{1 + \frac{1}{n} + \frac{(x_p - \bar{x})^2}{\Sigma(x_i - \bar{x})^2}} = 241.52\sqrt{1 + \frac{1}{6} + \frac{(500 - 575)^2}{93,750}} = 267.50$$

   $$\hat{y}_p \pm t_{\alpha/2}s_{ind}$$

   $5046.67 \pm 4.604\,(267.50) = 5046.67 \pm 1231.57$

   or \$3815.10 to \$6278.24

   c. Based on one month, \$6000 is not out of line since \$3815.10 to \$6278.24 is the prediction interval. However, a sequence of five to seven months with consistently high costs should cause concern.

39. a. Summations needed to compute the slope and y-intercept are:

   $\Sigma x_i = 227$ $\Sigma y_i = 2281.7$ $\Sigma(x_i - \bar{x})(y_i - \bar{y}) = 6003.41$ $\Sigma(x_i - \bar{x})^2 = 1032.1$

   $$b_1 = \frac{\Sigma(x_i - \bar{x})(y_i - \bar{y})}{\Sigma(x_i - \bar{x})^2} = \frac{6003.41}{1032.1} = 5.816694$$

   $$b_0 = \bar{y} - b_1\bar{x} = 228.17 - (5.816694)(27.7) = 67.047576$$

$\hat{y} = 67.0476 + 5.8167x$

b. SST = 39,065.14   SSE = 4145.141   SSR = 34,920.000

$r^2 = $ SSR/SST $= 34,920.000/39,065.141 = 0.894$

The estimated regression equation explained 89.4% of the variability in y; a very good fit.

c. $s^2 = $ MSE $= 4145.141/8 = 518.143$

$s = \sqrt{518.143} = 22.76$

$s_{\hat{y}_p} = s\sqrt{\dfrac{1}{n} + \dfrac{(x_p - \overline{x})^2}{\Sigma(x_i - \overline{x})^2}} = 22.76\sqrt{\dfrac{1}{10} + \dfrac{(35 - 27.7)^2}{1032.1}} = 8.86$

$\hat{y} = 67.0476 + 5.8167x = 67.0476 + 5.8167(35) = 270.63$

$\hat{y}_p \pm t_{\alpha/2}s_{\hat{y}_p}$

$270.63 \pm 2.262\,(8.86) = 270.63 \pm 20.04$

or 250.59 to 290.67

d. $s_{\text{ind}} = s\sqrt{1 + \dfrac{1}{n} + \dfrac{(x_p - \overline{x})^2}{\Sigma(x_i - \overline{x})^2}} = 22.76\sqrt{1 + \dfrac{1}{10} + \dfrac{(35 - 27.7)^2}{1032.1}} = 24.42$

$\hat{y}_p \pm t_{\alpha/2}s_{\text{ind}}$

$270.63 \pm 2.262\,(24.42) = 270.63 \pm 55.24$

or 215.39 to 325.87

40. a. 9

b. $\hat{y} = 20.0 + 7.21x$

c. 1.3626

d. SSE = SST - SSR = 51,984.1 - 41,587.3 = 10,396.8

MSE = 10,396.8/7 = 1,485.3

$F = $ MSR / MSE $= 41,587.3 / 1,485.3 = 28.00$

$F_{.05} = 5.59$ (1 degree of freedom numerator and 7 denominator)

Since $F = 28 > F_{.05} = 5.59$ we reject $H_0: B_1 = 0$.

e. $\hat{y} = 20.0 + 7.21(50) = 380.5$ or \$380,500

41. a. $\hat{y} = 6.1092 + .8951x$

   b. $t = \dfrac{b_1 - B_1}{s_{b_1}} = \dfrac{.8951 - 0}{.149} = 6.01$

   $t_{.025} = 2.306$ (1 degree of freedom numerator and 8 denominator)

   Since $t = 6.01 > t_{.025} = 2.306$ we reject H_0: $B_1 = 0$

   c. $\hat{y} = 6.1092 + .8951(25) = 28.49$ or $28.49 per month

42 a. $\hat{y} = 80.0 + 50.0x$

   b.   30

   c. $F = \text{MSR} / \text{MSE} = 6828.6/82.1 = 83.17$

   $F_{.05} = 4.20$ (1 degree of freedom numerator and 28 denominator)

   Since $F = 83.17 > F_{.05} = 4.20$ we reject H_0: $B_1 = 0$.

   Branch office sales are related to the salespersons.

   d. $\hat{y} = 80 + 50\,(12) = 680$ or $680,000

43. a.   The Minitab output is shown below:

```
The regression equation is
Price = - 11.8 + 2.18 Income

Predictor          Coef        SE Coef           T          P
Constant          -11.80         12.84        -0.92      0.380
Income            2.1843        0.2780         7.86      0.000

S = 6.634       R-Sq = 86.1%       R-Sq(adj) = 84.7%

Analysis of Variance

Source            DF            SS           MS          F          P
Regression         1         2717.9       2717.9      61.75      0.000
Residual Error    10          440.1         44.0
Total             11         3158.0

Predicted Values for New Observations

New Obs      Fit      SE Fit        95.0% CI              95.0% PI
1          75.79       2.47    (  70.29,   81.28)   (   60.02,    91.56)
```

   b. $r^2 = .861$. The least squares line provided a very good fit.

   c.   The 95% confidence interval is 70.29 to 81.28 or $70,290 to $81,280.

   d.   The 95% prediction interval is 60.02 to 91.56 or $60,020 to $91,560.

44. a/b. The scatter diagram shows a linear relationship between the two variables.

   c.   The Minitab output is shown below:

```
The regression equation is
Rental$ = 37.1 - 0.779 Vacancy%

Predictor          Coef      SE Coef           T          P
Constant         37.066        3.530       10.50      0.000
Vacancy%        -0.7791        0.2226       -3.50      0.003

S = 4.889      R-Sq = 43.4%      R-Sq(adj) = 39.8%

Analysis of Variance

Source              DF           SS           MS          F          P
Regression           1       292.89       292.89      12.26      0.003
Residual Error      16       382.37        23.90
Total               17       675.26

Predicted Values for New Observations

New Obs      Fit      SE Fit         95.0% CI               95.0% PI
1          17.59        2.51    ( 12.27,    22.90)   (    5.94,    29.23)
2          28.26        1.42    (.25.26,    31.26)   (   17.47,    39.05)

Values of Predictors for New Observations

New Obs  Vacancy%
1            25.0
2            11.3
```

   d.   Since the p-value = 0.003 is less than $\alpha = .05$, the relationship is significant.

   e. $r^2 = .434$. The least squares line does not provide a very good fit.

   f.   The 95% confidence interval is 12.27 to 22.90 or $12.27 to $22.90.

   g.   The 95% prediction interval is 17.47 to 39.05 or $17.47 to $39.05.

45. a. $\Sigma x_i = 14$ $\Sigma y_i = 76$ $\Sigma(x_i - \overline{x})(y_i - \overline{y}) = 200$ $\Sigma(x_i - \overline{x})^2 = 126$

$$b_1 = \frac{\Sigma(x_i - \overline{x})(y_i - \overline{y})}{\Sigma(x_i - \overline{x})^2} = \frac{200}{126} = 1.5873$$

$$b_0 = \overline{y} - b_1\overline{x} = 15.2 - (1.5873)(14) = -7.0222$$

$$\hat{y} = -7.02 + 1.59x$$

   b.   The residuals are 3.48, -2.47, -4.83, -1.6, and 5.22

c.

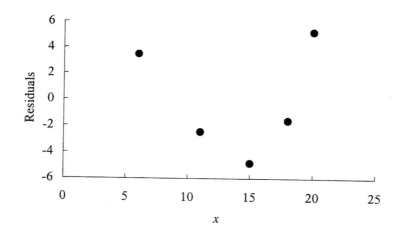

With only 5 observations it is difficult to determine if the assumptions are satisfied. However, the plot does suggest curvature in the residuals that would indicate that the error term assumptions are not satisfied. The scatter diagram for these data also indicates that the underlying relationship between x and y may be curvilinear.

d. $s^2 = 23.78$

$$h_i = \frac{1}{n} + \frac{(x_i - \bar{x})^2}{\Sigma(x_i - \bar{x})^2} = \frac{1}{5} + \frac{(x_i - 14)^2}{126}$$

The standardized residuals are 1.32, -.59, -1.11, -.40, 1.49.

e.   The standardized residual plot has the same shape as the original residual plot. The curvature observed indicates that the assumptions regarding the error term may not be satisfied.

46. a. $\hat{y} = 2.32 + .64x$

b.

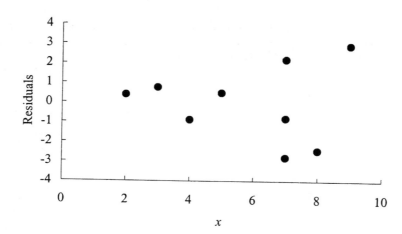

The assumption that the variance is the same for all values of x is questionable. The variance appears to increase for larger values of x.

47. a. Let x = advertising expenditures and y = revenue

$\hat{y} = 29.4 + 1.55x$

b. SST = 1002   SSE = 310.28   SSR = 691.72

MSR = SSR / 1 = 691.72

MSE = SSE / $(n - 2)$ = 310.28/ 5 = 62.0554

F = MSR / MSE = 691.72/ 62.0554= 11.15

$F_{.05}$ = 6.61 (1 degree of freedom numerator and 5 denominator)

Since F = 11.15 > $F_{.05}$ = 6.61 we conclude that the two variables are related.

c.

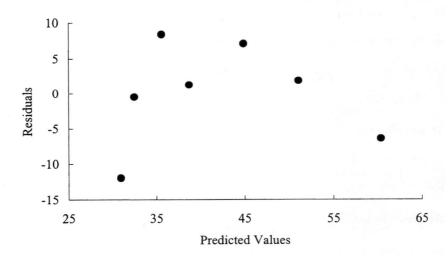

d. The residual plot leads us to question the assumption of a linear relationship between x and y. Even though the relationship is significant at the .05 level of significance, it would be extremely dangerous to extrapolate beyond the range of the data.

48. a. $\hat{y} = 80 + 4x$

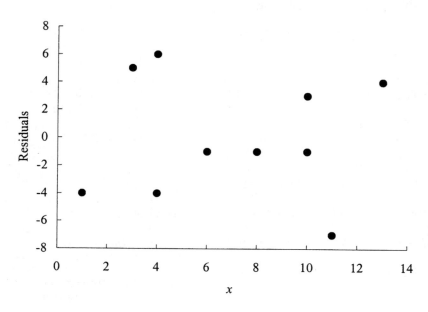

b. The assumptions concerning the error term appear reasonable.

49. a. Let x = return on investment (ROE) and y = price/earnings (P/E) ratio.

$\hat{y} = -32.13 + 3.22x$

b.

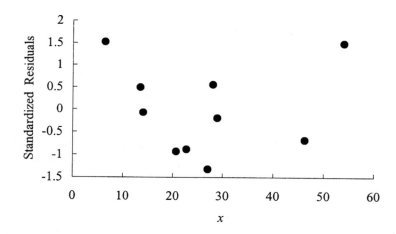

c. There is an unusual trend in the residuals. The assumptions concerning the error term appear questionable.

50. a.   The MINITAB output is shown below:

```
The regression equation is
Y = 66.1 + 0.402 X

Predictor         Coef       Stdev     t-ratio         p
Constant         66.10       32.06        2.06     0.094
X               0.4023      0.2276        1.77     0.137

s = 12.62        R-sq = 38.5%      R-sq(adj) = 26.1%

Analysis of Variance

SOURCE          DF           SS          MS         F         p
Regression       1        497.2       497.2      3.12     0.137
Error            5        795.7       159.1
Total            6       1292.9

Unusual Observations
Obs.        X           Y        Fit Stdev.Fit   Residual     St.Resid
  1       135      145.00     120.42      4.87      24.58         2.11R

R denotes an obs. with a large st. resid.
```

The standardized residuals are: 2.11, -1.08, .14, -.38, -.78, -.04, -.41

The first observation appears to be an outlier since it has a large standardized residual.

b.

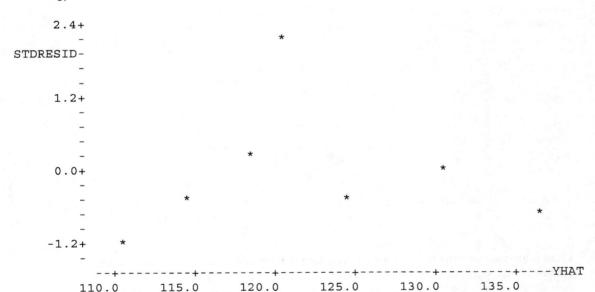

The standardized residual plot indicates that the observation $x = 135, y = 145$ may be an outlier; note that this observation has a standardized residual of 2.11.

c.   The scatter diagram is shown below

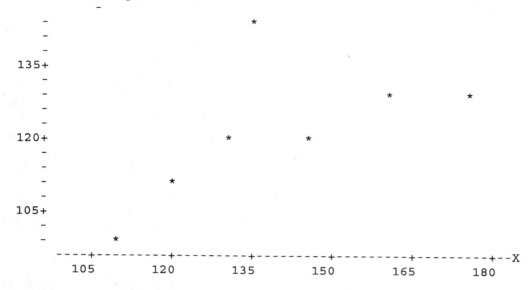

The scatter diagram also indicates that the observation $x = 135, y = 145$ may be an outlier; the implication is that for simple linear regression an outlier can be identified by looking at the scatter diagram.

51. a.   The Minitab output is shown below:

```
The regression equation is
Y = 13.0 + 0.425 X

Predictor        Coef        Stdev      t-ratio           p
Constant       13.002        2.396         5.43       0.002
X              0.4248       0.2116         2.01       0.091

s = 3.181        R-sq = 40.2%      R-sq(adj) = 30.2%

Analysis of Variance

SOURCE          DF            SS            MS          F         p
Regression       1         40.78         40.78       4.03     0.091
Error            6         60.72         10.12
Total            7        101.50

Unusual Observations
Obs.         X            Y          Fit Stdev.Fit   Residual    St.Resid
   7      12.0        24.00        18.10       1.20       5.90       2.00R
   8      22.0        19.00        22.35       2.78      -3.35      -2.16RX

R denotes an obs. with a large st. resid.
X denotes an obs. whose X value gives it large influence.
```

The standardized residuals are: -1.00, -.41, .01, -.48, .25, .65, -2.00, -2.16

The last two observations in the data set appear to be outliers since the standardized residuals for these observations are 2.00 and -2.16, respectively.

b. Using MINITAB, we obtained the following leverage values:

.28, .24, .16, .14, .13, .14, .14, .76

MINITAB identifies an observation as having high leverage if $h_i > 6/n$; for these data, $6/n = 6/8 = .75$. Since the leverage for the observation $x = 22$, $y = 19$ is .76, MINITAB would identify observation 8 as a high leverage point. Thus, we conclude that observation 8 is an influential observation.

c.

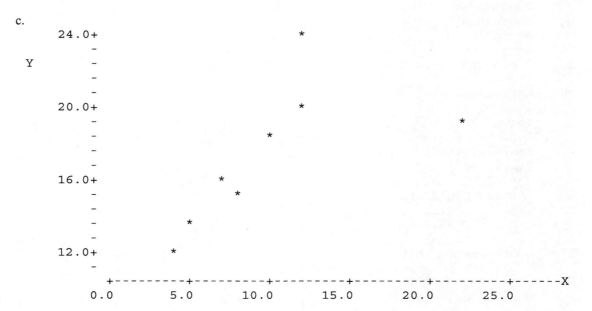

The scatter diagram indicates that the observation $x = 22$, $y = 19$ is an influential observation.

52. a. The Minitab output is shown below:

```
The regression equation is
Amount = 4.09 + 0.196 MediaExp

Predictor          Coef      SE Coef          T          P
Constant          4.089        2.168       1.89      0.096
MediaExp        0.19552      0.03635       5.38      0.001

S = 5.044       R-Sq = 78.3%      R-Sq(adj) = 75.6%

Analysis of Variance

Source              DF           SS           MS          F          P
Regression           1       735.84       735.84      28.93      0.001
Residual Error       8       203.51        25.44
Total                9       939.35

Unusual Observations
Obs    MediaExp      Amount         Fit      SE Fit     Residual      St Resid
  1         120       36.30       27.55        3.30         8.75         2.30R

R denotes an observation with a large standardized residual
```

b. Minitab identifies observation 1 as having a large standardized residual; thus, we would consider observation 1 to be an outlier.

53. a. The Minitab output is shown below:

```
The regression equation is
Exposure = - 8.6 + 7.71 Aired

Predictor        Coef      SE Coef           T          P
Constant        -8.55        21.65       -0.39      0.703
Aired          7.7149       0.5119        15.07      0.000

S = 34.88       R-Sq = 96.6%      R-Sq(adj) = 96.2%

Analysis of Variance

Source            DF          SS          MS          F          P
Regression         1       276434      276434     227.17      0.000
Residual Error     8         9735        1217
Total              9       286169

Unusual Observations
Obs     Aired    Exposure       Fit      SE Fit     Residual     St Resid
  1      95.0      758.8      724.4        32.0         34.4       2.46RX

R denotes an observation with a large standardized residual
X denotes an observation whose X value gives it large influence.
```

b. Minitab identifies observation 1 as having a large standardized residual; thus, we would consider observation 1 to be an outlier. Minitab also identifies observation 1 as an influential observation.

54. a. The Minitab output is shown below:

```
The regression equation is
Salary = 707 + 0.00482 MktCap

Predictor        Coef      SE Coef           T          P
Constant        707.0        118.0        5.99      0.000
MktCap       0.0048154    0.0008076        5.96      0.000

S = 379.8       R-Sq = 66.4%      R-Sq(adj) = 64.5%

Analysis of Variance

Source            DF          SS          MS          F          P
Regression         1      5129071     5129071      35.55      0.000
Residual Error    18      2596647      144258
Total             19      7725718

Unusual Observations
Obs    MktCap     Salary       Fit      SE Fit     Residual     St Resid
  6    507217     3325.0     3149.5       338.6        175.5       1.02 X
 17    120967      116.2     1289.5        86.4      -1173.3      -3.17R

R denotes an observation with a large standardized residual
X denotes an observation whose X value gives it large influence.
```

b. Minitab identifies observation 6 as having a large standardized residual and observation 17 as an observation whose x value gives it large influence. A standardized residual plot against the predicted values is shown below:

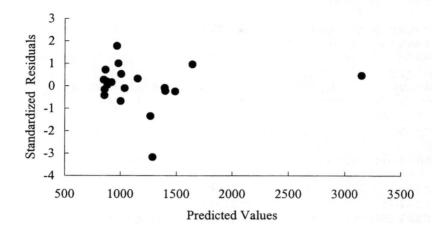

55. No. Regression or correlation analysis can never prove that two variables are casually related.

56. The estimate of a mean value is an estimate of the average of all y values associated with the same x. The estimate of an individual y value is an estimate of only one of the y values associated with a particular x.

57. To determine whether or not there is a significant relationship between x and y. However, if we reject $B_1 = 0$, it does not imply a good fit.

58. a. The Minitab output is shown below:

```
The regression equation is
Price = 9.26 + 0.711 Shares

Predictor        Coef      SE Coef          T          P
Constant        9.265        1.099       8.43      0.000
Shares         0.7105       0.1474       4.82      0.001

S = 1.419      R-Sq = 74.4%      R-Sq(adj) = 71.2%

Analysis of Variance

Source            DF          SS          MS         F          P
Regression         1      46.784      46.784     23.22      0.001
Residual Error     8      16.116       2.015
Total              9      62.900
```

b. Since the p-value corresponding to F = 23.22 = .001 < α = .05, the relationship is significant.

c. $r^2 = .744$; a good fit. The least squares line explained 74.4% of the variability in Price.

d. $\hat{y} = 9.26 + .711(6) = 13.53$

59. a.   The Minitab output is shown below:

```
The regression equation is
Options = - 3.83 + 0.296 Common

Predictor          Coef       SE Coef              T             P
Constant         -3.834         5.903          -0.65         0.529
Common          0.29567       0.02648          11.17         0.000

S = 11.04        R-Sq = 91.9%      R-Sq(adj) = 91.2%

Analysis of Variance

Source               DF             SS           MS           F            P
Regression            1          15208        15208       124.72        0.000
Residual Error       11           1341          122
Total                12          16550
```

b. $\hat{y} = -3.83 + .296(150) = 40.57$; approximately 40.6 million shares of options grants outstanding.

c. $r^2 = .919$; a very good fit. The least squares line explained 91.9% of the variability in Options.

60. a.   The Minitab output is shown below:

```
The regression equation is
IBM = 0.275 + 0.950 S&P 500

Predictor          Coef        StDev              T             P
Constant         0.2747       0.9004           0.31         0.768
S&P 500          0.9498       0.3569           2.66         0.029

S = 2.664        R-Sq = 47.0%      R-Sq(adj) = 40.3%

Analysis of Variance

Source         DF             SS           MS           F           P
Regression      1         50.255       50.255        7.08       0.029
Error           8         56.781        7.098
Total           9        107.036
```

b.   Since the p-value $= 0.029$ is less than $\alpha = .05$, the relationship is significant.

c. $r^2 = .470$. The least squares line does not provide a very good fit.

d.   Woolworth has higher risk with a market beta of 1.25.

61. a.

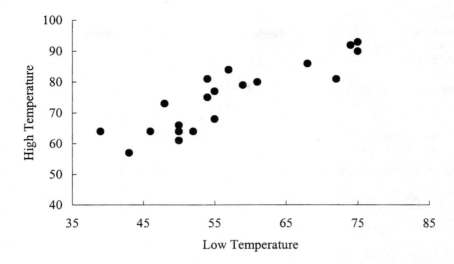

b. It appears that there is a positive linear relationship between the two variables.

c. The Minitab output is shown below:

```
The regression equation is
High = 23.9 + 0.898 Low

Predictor          Coef       SE Coef              T          P
Constant         23.899         6.481           3.69      0.002
Low              0.8980        0.1121           8.01      0.000

S = 5.285        R-Sq = 78.1%      R-Sq(adj) = 76.9%

Analysis of Variance

Source             DF            SS             MS          F          P
Regression          1        1792.3         1792.3      64.18      0.000
Residual Error     18         502.7           27.9
Total              19        2294.9
```

d. Since the p-value corresponding to $F = 64.18 = .000 < \alpha = .05$, the relationship is significant.

e. $r^2 = .781$; a good fit. The least squares line explained 78.1% of the variability in high temperature.

f. $r = \sqrt{.781} = +.88$

62. The MINITAB output is shown below:

```
The regression equation is
Y = 10.5 + 0.953 X

Predictor          Coef         Stdev      t-ratio          p
Constant         10.528         3.745         2.81      0.023
X                0.9534        0.1382         6.90      0.000

s = 4.250        R-sq = 85.6%      R-sq(adj) = 83.8%
```

```
Analysis of Variance

SOURCE          DF              SS              MS              F           p
Regression      1           860.05          860.05          47.62       0.000
Error           8           144.47           18.06
Total           9          1004.53


  Fit    Stdev.Fit          95% C.I.              95% P.I.
39.13         1.49      ( 35.69,   42.57)    ( 28.74,   49.52)
```

a. $\hat{y} = 10.5 + .953\, x$

b. Since the *p*-value corresponding to $F = 47.62 = .000 < \alpha = .05$, we reject $H_0\colon \beta_1 = 0$.

c. The 95% prediction interval is 28.74 to 49.52 or $2874 to $4952

d. Yes, since the expected expense is $3913.

63. a. The Minitab output is shown below:

```
The regression equation is
Defects = 22.2 - 0.148 Speed

Predictor          Coef        SE Coef            T           P
Constant         22.174         1.653         13.42       0.000
Speed           -0.14783       0.04391        -3.37       0.028

S = 1.489        R-Sq = 73.9%       R-Sq(adj) = 67.4%

Analysis of Variance

Source          DF              SS              MS              F           P
Regression      1           25.130          25.130          11.33       0.028
Residual Error  4            8.870           2.217
Total           5           34.000

Predicted Values for New Observations

New Obs    Fit    SE Fit           95.0% CI               95.0% PI
1       14.783    0.896      ( 12.294,   17.271)    (  9.957,   19.608)
```

b. Since the *p*-value corresponding to $F = 11.33 = .028 < \alpha = .05$, the relationship is significant.

c. $r^2 = .739$; a good fit. The least squares line explained 73.9% of the variability in the number of defects.

d. Using the Minitab output in part (a), the 95% confidence interval is 12.294 to 17.271.

64. a. There appears to be a negative linear relationship between distance to work and number of days absent.

b.   The MINITAB output is shown below:

```
The regression equation is
Y = 8.10 - 0.344 X

Predictor        Coef        Stdev      t-ratio         p
Constant       8.0978       0.8088        10.01     0.000
X             -0.34420      0.07761       -4.43     0.002

s = 1.289       R-sq = 71.1%      R-sq(adj) = 67.5%

Analysis of Variance

SOURCE         DF           SS           MS          F         p
Regression      1        32.699       32.699      19.67     0.002
Error           8        13.301        1.663
Total           9        46.000

       Fit   Stdev.Fit           95% C.I.           95% P.I.
      6.377      0.512    (  5.195,   7.559)  (  3.176,   9.577)
```

c.   Since the p-value corresponding to F = 419.67 is .002 < α = .05. We reject $H_0 : \beta_1 = 0$.

d. r^2 = .711. The estimated regression equation explained 71.1% of the variability in y; this is a reasonably good fit.

e.   The 95% confidence interval is 5.195 to 7.559 or approximately 5.2 to 7.6 days.

65. a.   Let X = the age of a bus and Y = the annual maintenance cost.

The MINITAB output is shown below:

```
The regression equation is
Y = 220 + 132 X

Predictor        Coef        Stdev      t-ratio         p
Constant       220.00       58.48         3.76      0.006
X              131.67       17.80         7.40      0.000

s = 75.50       R-sq = 87.3%      R-sq(adj) = 85.7%

Analysis of Variance

SOURCE         DF           SS           MS          F         p
Regression      1       312050       312050      54.75     0.000
Error           8        45600         5700
Total           9       357650

       Fit   Stdev.Fit           95% C.I.           95% P.I.
      746.7      29.8     (  678.0,   815.4)  (  559.5,   933.9)
```

b.   Since the p-value corresponding to F = 54.75 is .000 < α = .05, we reject $H_0: \beta_1 = 0$.

c. r^2 = .873. The least squares line provided a very good fit.

d.   The 95% prediction interval is 559.5 to 933.9 or $559.50 to $933.90

66. a. Let X = hours spent studying and Y = total points earned

The MINITAB output is shown below:

```
The regression equation is
Y = 5.85 + 0.830 X

Predictor          Coef        Stdev     t-ratio           p
Constant          5.847        7.972        0.73       0.484
X                0.8295       0.1095        7.58       0.000

s = 7.523       R-sq = 87.8%      R-sq(adj) = 86.2%

Analysis of Variance

SOURCE          DF           SS          MS          F          p
Regression       1       3249.7      3249.7      57.42      0.000
Error            8        452.8        56.6
Total            9       3702.5

      Fit   Stdev.Fit          95% C.I.            95% P.I.
    84.65        3.67     ( 76.19,   93.11)    ( 65.35, 103.96)
```

b. Since the p-value corresponding to $F = 57.42$ is .000 $< \alpha$ = .05, we reject H_0: $\beta_1 = 0$.

c. 84.65 points

d. The 95% prediction interval is 65.35 to 103.96

67. a. The Minitab output is shown below:

```
The regression equation is
Audit% = - 0.471 +0.000039 Income

Predictor          Coef       SE Coef            T          P
Constant       -0.4710        0.5842        -0.81      0.431
Income      0.00003868    0.00001731         2.23      0.038

S = 0.2088      R-Sq = 21.7%      R-Sq(adj) = 17.4%

Analysis of Variance

Source           DF           SS          MS          F          P
Regression        1      0.21749     0.21749        4.99      0.038
Residual Error   18      0.78451     0.04358
Total            19      1.00200

Predicted Values for New Observations

New Obs     Fit     SE Fit          95.0% CI             95.0% PI
1        0.8828     0.0523    ( 0.7729,  0.9927)   ( 0.4306,  1.3349)
```

b. Since the p-value = 0.038 is less than α = .05, the relationship is significant.

c. r^2 = .217. The least squares line does not provide a very good fit.

d. The 95% confidence interval is .7729 to .9927.

Chapter 15
Multiple Regression

Learning Objectives

1. Understand how multiple regression analysis can be used to develop relationships involving one dependent variable and several independent variables.

2. Be able to interpret the coefficients in a multiple regression analysis.

3. Know the assumptions necessary to conduct statistical tests involving the hypothesized regression model.

4. Understand the role of computer packages in performing multiple regression analysis.

5. Be able to interpret and use computer output to develop the estimated regression equation.

6. Be able to determine how good a fit is provided by the estimated regression equation.

7. Be able to test for the significance of the regression equation.

8. Understand how multicollinearity affects multiple regression analysis.

9. Know how residual analysis can be used to make a judgement as to the appropriateness of the model, identify outliers, and determine which observations are influential.

Solutions:

1. a. $b_1 = .5906$ is an estimate of the change in y corresponding to a 1 unit change in x_1 when x_2 is held constant.

    $b_2 = .4980$ is an estimate of the change in y corresponding to a 1 unit change in x_2 when x_1 is held constant.

2. a. The estimated regression equation is

    $$\hat{y} = 45.06 + 1.94x_1$$

    An estimate of y when $x_1 = 45$ is

    $$\hat{y} = 45.06 + 1.94(45) = 132.36$$

    b. The estimated regression equation is

    $$\hat{y} = 85.22 + 4.32x_2$$

    An estimate of y when $x_2 = 15$ is

    $$\hat{y} = 85.22 + 4.32(15) = 150.02$$

    c. The estimated regression equation is

    $$\hat{y} = -18.37 + 2.01x_1 + 4.74x_2$$

    An estimate of y when $x_1 = 45$ and $x_2 = 15$ is

    $$\hat{y} = -18.37 + 2.01(45) + 4.74(15) = 143.18$$

3. a. $b_1 = 3.8$ is an estimate of the change in y corresponding to a 1 unit change in x_1 when x_2, x_3, and x_4 are held constant.

    $b_2 = -2.3$ is an estimate of the change in y corresponding to a 1 unit change in x_2 when x_1, x_3, and x_4 are held constant.

    $b_3 = 7.6$ is an estimate of the change in y corresponding to a 1 unit change in x_3 when x_1, x_2, and x_4 are held constant.

    $b_4 = 2.7$ is an estimate of the change in y corresponding to a 1 unit change in x_4 when x_1, x_2, and x_3 are held constant.

4. a. $\hat{y} = 235 + 10(15) + 8(10) = 255$; sales estimate: \$255,000

    b. Sales can be expected to increase by \$10 for every dollar increase in inventory investment when advertising expenditure is held constant. Sales can be expected to increase by \$8 for every dollar increase in advertising expenditure when inventory investment is held constant.

5. a. The Minitab output is shown below:

```
The regression equation is
Revenue = 88.6 + 1.60 TVAdv

Predictor          Coef        SE Coef            T           P
Constant         88.638          1.582        56.02       0.000
TVAdv            1.6039          0.4778         3.36       0.015

S = 1.215        R-Sq = 65.3%      R-Sq(adj) = 59.5%

Analysis of Variance

Source              DF            SS           MS           F          P
Regression           1        16.640       16.640       11.27      0.015
Residual Error       6         8.860        1.477
Total                7        25.500
```

b. The Minitab output is shown below:

```
The regression equation is
Revenue = 83.2 + 2.29 TVAdv + 1.30 NewsAdv

Predictor          Coef        SE Coef            T           P
Constant         83.230          1.574        52.88       0.000
TVAdv            2.2902          0.3041         7.53       0.001
NewsAdv          1.3010          0.3207         4.06       0.010

S = 0.6426       R-Sq = 91.9%      R-Sq(adj) = 88.7%

Analysis of Variance

Source              DF            SS           MS           F          P
Regression           2        23.435       11.718       28.38      0.002
Residual Error       5         2.065        0.413
Total                7        25.500

Source          DF      Seq SS
TVAdv            1      16.640
NewsAdv          1       6.795
```

c. No, it is 1.60 in part 2(a) and 2.99 above. In this exercise it represents the marginal change in revenue due to an increase in television advertising with newspaper advertising held constant.

d. Revenue = 83.2 + 2.29(3.5) + 1.30(1.8) = $93.56 or $93,560

6. a. The Minitab output is shown below:

```
The regression equation is
Speed = 49.8 + 0.0151 Weight

Predictor          Coef        SE Coef            T           P
Constant         49.78          19.11         2.61       0.021
Weight           0.015104       0.006005      2.52       0.025
```

```
S = 7.000           R-Sq = 31.1%      R-Sq(adj) = 26.2%
```

Analysis of Variance

Source	DF	SS	MS	F	P
Regression	1	309.95	309.95	6.33	0.025
Error	14	686.00	49.00		
Total	15	995.95			

b. The Minitab output is shown below:

```
The regression equation is
Speed = 80.5 - 0.00312 Weight + 0.105 Horsepwr
```

Predictor	Coef	SE Coef	T	P
Constant	80.487	9.139	8.81	0.000
Weight	-0.003122	0.003481	-0.90	0.386
Horsepwr	0.10471	0.01331	7.86	0.000

```
S = 3.027        R-Sq = 88.0%      R-Sq(adj) = 86.2%
```

Analysis of Variance

Source	DF	SS	MS	F	P
Regression	2	876.80	438.40	47.83	0.000
Residual Error	13	119.15	9.17		
Total	15	995.95			

7. a. The Minitab output is shown below:

```
The regression equation is
Sales = 66.5 + 0.414 Compet$ - 0.270 Heller$
```

Predictor	Coef	SE Coef	T	P
Constant	66.52	41.88	1.59	0.156
Compet$	0.4139	0.2604	1.59	0.156
Heller$	-0.26978	0.08091	-3.33	0.013

```
S = 18.74        R-Sq = 65.3%      R-Sq(adj) = 55.4%
```

Analysis of Variance

Source	DF	SS	MS	F	P
Regression	2	4618.8	2309.4	6.58	0.025
Residual Error	7	2457.3	351.0		
Total	9	7076.1			

b. $b_1 = .414$ is an estimate of the change in the quantity sold (1000s) of the Heller mower with respect to a $1 change in price in competitor's mower with the price of the Heller mower held constant. $b_2 = -.270$ is an estimate of the change in the quantity sold (1000s) of the Heller mower with respect to a $1 change in its price with the price of the competitor's mower held constant.

c. $\hat{y} = 66.5 + 0.414(170) - 0.270(160) = 93.68$ or 93,680 units

8. a. The Minitab output is shown below:

```
The regression equation is
Return = 247 - 32.8 Safety + 34.6 ExpRatio

Predictor          Coef      SE Coef            T          P
Constant          247.4        110.4         2.24      0.039
Safety           -32.84        13.95        -2.35      0.031
ExpRatio          34.59        14.13         2.45      0.026

S = 16.98      R-Sq = 58.2%      R-Sq(adj) = 53.3%

Analysis of Variance

Source             DF           SS           MS          F          P
Regression          2        6823.2       3411.6      11.84      0.001
Residual Error     17        4899.7        288.2
Total              19       11723.0
```

b. $\hat{y} = 247 - 32.8(7.5) + 34.6(2) = 70.2$

9. a. The Minitab output is shown below:

```
The regression equation is
%College = 26.7 - 1.43 Size + 0.0757 SatScore

Predictor          Coef      SE Coef            T          P
Constant          26.71        51.67         0.52      0.613
Size            -1.4298       0.9931        -1.44      0.170
SatScore        0.07574      0.03906         1.94      0.072

S = 12.42      R-Sq = 38.2%      R-Sq(adj) = 30.0%

Analysis of Variance

Source             DF           SS           MS          F          P
Regression          2        1430.4        715.2       4.64      0.027
Residual Error     15        2312.7        154.2
Total              17        3743.1
```

b. $\hat{y} = 26.7 - 1.43(20) + 0.0757(1000) = 73.8$

Estimate is 73.8%

10. a. The Minitab output is shown below:

```
The regression equation is
Revenue = 33.3 + 7.98 Cars

Predictor          Coef      SE Coef            T          P
Constant          33.34        83.08         0.40      0.695
Cars             7.9840       0.6323        12.63      0.000
S = 226.7      R-Sq = 92.5%      R-Sq(adj) = 91.9%
```

Analysis of Variance

Source	DF	SS	MS	F	P
Regression	1	8192067	8192067	159.44	0.000
Error	13	667936	51380		
Total	14	8860003			

b. An increase of 1000 cars in service will result in an increase in revenue of $7.98 million.

c. The Minitab output is shown below:

The regression equation is
Revenue = 106 + 8.94 Cars - 0.191 Location

Predictor	Coef	SE Coef	T	P
Constant	105.97	85.52	1.24	0.239
Cars	8.9427	0.7746	11.55	0.000
Location	-0.1914	0.1026	-1.87	0.087

S = 207.7   R-Sq = 94.2%   R-Sq(adj) = 93.2%

Analysis of Variance

Source	DF	SS	MS	F	P
Regression	2	8342186	4171093	96.66	0.000
Error	12	517817	43151		
Total	14	8860003			

11. a. SSE = SST - SSR = 6,724.125 - 6,216.375 = 507.75

   b. $R^2 = \dfrac{SSR}{SST} = \dfrac{6,216.375}{6,724.125} = .924$

   c. $R_a^2 = 1 - (1 - R^2)\dfrac{n-1}{n-p-1} = 1 - (1-.924)\dfrac{10-1}{10-2-1} = .902$

   d. The estimated regression equation provided an excellent fit.

12. a. $R^2 = \dfrac{SSR}{SST} = \dfrac{14,052.2}{15,182.9} = .926$

   b. $R_a^2 = 1 - (1 - R^2)\dfrac{n-1}{n-p-1} = 1 - (1-.926)\dfrac{10-1}{10-2-1} = .905$

   c. Yes; after adjusting for the number of independent variables in the model, we see that 90.5% of the variability in y has been accounted for.

13. a. $R^2 = \dfrac{SSR}{SST} = \dfrac{1760}{1805} = .975$

b. $R_a^2 = 1 - (1 - R^2)\dfrac{n-1}{n-p-1} = 1 - (1 - .975)\dfrac{30-1}{30-4-1} = .971$

c. The estimated regression equation provided an excellent fit.

14. a. $R^2 = \dfrac{SSR}{SST} = \dfrac{12,000}{16,000} = .75$

b. $R_a^2 = 1 - (1 - R^2)\dfrac{n-1}{n-p-1} = 1 - .25\dfrac{9}{7} = .68$

c. The adjusted coefficient of determination shows that 68% of the variability has been explained by the two independent variables; thus, we conclude that the model does not explain a large amount of variability.

15. a. $R^2 = \dfrac{SSR}{SST} = \dfrac{23.435}{25.5} = .919$

$R_a^2 = 1 - (1 - R^2)\dfrac{n-1}{n-p-1} = 1 - (1 - .919)\dfrac{8-1}{8-2-1} = .887$

b. Multiple regression analysis is preferred since both R^2 and R_a^2 show an increased percentage of the variability of y explained when both independent variables are used.

16. Note: the Minitab output is shown with the solution to Exercise 6.

a. No; R-Sq = 31.1%

b. Multiple regression analysis is preferred since both R-Sq and R-Sq(adj) show an increased percentage of the variability of y explained when both independent variables are used.

17. a. $R^2 = \dfrac{SSR}{SST} = \dfrac{1430.4}{3743.1} = .382$

$R_a^2 = 1 - (1 - R^2)\dfrac{n-1}{n-p-1} = 1 - (1 - .382)\dfrac{18-1}{18-2-1} = .30$

b. The fit is not very good

18. Note: The Minitab output is shown with the solution to Exercise 10.

a. R-Sq = 94.2% R-Sq(adj) = 93.2%

b. The fit is very good.

19. a. MSR = SSR/p = 6,216.375/2 = 3,108.188

$MSE = \dfrac{SSE}{n-p-1} = \dfrac{507.75}{10-2-1} = 72.536$

b. $F = \text{MSR/MSE} = 3,108.188/72.536 = 42.85$

$F_{.05} = 4.74$ (2 degrees of freedom numerator and 7 denominator)

Since $F = 42.85 > F_{.05} = 4.74$ the overall model is significant.

c. $t = .5906/.0813 = 7.26$

$t_{.025} = 2.365$ (7 degrees of freedom)

Since t = 2.365 > $t_{.025}$ = 2.365, β_1 is significant.

d. $t = .4980/.0567 = 8.78$

Since $t = 8.78 > t_{.025} = 2.365$, β_2 is significant.

20. A portion of the Minitab output is shown below.

```
The regression equation is
Y = - 18.4 + 2.01 X1 + 4.74 X2

Predictor          Coef       SE Coef            T           P
Constant          -18.37        17.97        -1.02       0.341
X1                2.0102        0.2471         8.13       0.000
X2                4.7378        0.9484         5.00       0.002

S = 12.71        R-Sq = 92.6%      R-Sq(adj) = 90.4%

Analysis of Variance

Source             DF           SS           MS           F           P
Regression          2       14052.2       7026.1       43.50       0.000
Residual Error      7        1130.7        161.5
Total               9       15182.9
```

a. Since the p-value corresponding to $F = 43.50$ is .000 < $\alpha = .05$, we reject H_0: $\beta_1 = \beta_2 = 0$; there is a significant relationship.

b. Since the p-value corresponding to $t = 8.13$ is .000 < $\alpha = .05$, we reject H_0: $\beta_1 = 0$; β_1 is significant.

c. Since the p-value corresponding to $t = 5.00$ is .002 < $\alpha = .05$, we reject H_0: $\beta_2 = 0$; β_2 is significant.

21. a. In the two independent variable case the coefficient of x_1 represents the expected change in y corresponding to a one unit increase in x_1 when x_2 is held constant. In the single independent variable case the coefficient of x_1 represents the expected change in y corresponding to a one unit increase in x_1.

b. Yes. If x_1 and x_2 are correlated one would expect a change in x_1 to be accompanied by a change in x_2.

22. a. SSE = SST - SSR = 16000 - 12000 = 4000

$$s^2 = \frac{SSE}{n-p-1} = \frac{4000}{7} = 571.43$$

$$MSR = \frac{SSR}{p} = \frac{12000}{2} = 6000$$

    b. F = MSR/MSE = 6000/571.43 = 10.50

$F_{.05}$ = 4.74 (2 degrees of freedom numerator and 7 denominator)

Since F = 10.50 > $F_{.05}$ = 4.74, we reject H_0. There is a significant relationship among the variables.

23. a. F = 28.38

$F_{.01}$ = 13.27 (2 degrees of freedom, numerator and 1 denominator)

Since $F > F_{.01}$ = 13.27, reject H_0.

Alternatively, the p-value of .002 leads to the same conclusion.

    b. t = 7.53

$t_{.025}$ = 2.571

Since $t > t_{.025}$ = 2.571, β_1 is significant and x_1 should not be dropped from the model.

    c. t = 4.06

$t_{.025}$ = 2.571

Since $t > t_{.025}$ = 2.571, β_2 is significant and x_2 should not be dropped from the model.

24.   Note: The Minitab output is shown in part (b) of Exercise 6

    a. F = 47.83

$F_{.05}$ = 3.81 (2 degrees of freedom numerator and 13 denominator)

Since F = 47.83 > $F_{.05}$ = 3.81, we reject H_0: $\beta_1 = \beta_2 = 0$.

Alternatively, since the p-value = .000 < α = .05 we can reject H_0.

    b. For Weight:

H_0: $\beta_1 = 0$ H_a: $\beta_1 \neq 0$

Since the p-value = 0.386 > α = 0.05, we cannot reject H_0

For Horsepower:

$H_0: \beta_2 = 0 \qquad H_a: \beta_2 \neq 0$

Since the p-value $= 0.000 < \alpha = 0.05$, we can reject H_0

25. a. The Minitab output is shown below:

```
The regression equation is
P/E = 6.04 + 0.692 Profit% + 0.265 Sales%

Predictor          Coef      SE Coef          T          P
Constant          6.038        4.589       1.32      0.211
Profit%          0.6916       0.2133       3.24      0.006
Sales%           0.2648       0.1871       1.42      0.180

S = 5.456       R-Sq = 47.2%      R-Sq(adj) = 39.0%

Analysis of Variance

Source            DF           SS          MS          F          P
Regression         2       345.28      172.64       5.80      0.016
Residual Error    13       387.00       29.77
Total             15       732.28
```

b. Since the p-value $= 0.016 < \alpha = 0.05$, there is a significant relationship among the variables.

c. For Profit%: Since the p-value $= 0.006 < \alpha = 0.05$, Profit% is significant.

For Sales%: Since the p-value $= 0.180 > \alpha = 0.05$, Sales% is not significant.

26. Note: The Minitab output is shown with the solution to Exercise 10.

a. Since the p-value corresponding to $F = 96.66$ is $0.000 < \alpha = .05$, there is a significant relationship among the variables.

b. For Cars: Since the p-value $= 0.000 < \alpha = 0.05$, Cars is significant

c. For Location: Since the p-value $= 0.087 > \alpha = 0.05$, Location is not significant

27. a. $\hat{y} = 29.1270 + .5906(180) + .4980(310) = 289.8150$

b. The point estimate for an individual value is $\hat{y} = 289.8150$, the same as the point estimate of the mean value.

28. a. Using Minitab, the 95% confidence interval is 132.16 to 154.16.

b. Using Minitab, the 95% prediction interval is 111.13 to 175.18.

29. a. $\hat{y} = 83.2 + 2.29(3.5) + 1.30(1.8) = 93.555$ or $93,555

Note: In Exercise 5b, the Minitab output also shows that $b_0 = 83.230$, $b_1 = 2.2902$, and $b_2 = 1.3010$; hence, $\hat{y} = 83.230 + 2.2902x_1 + 1.3010x_2$. Using this estimated regression equation, we obtain

$\hat{y} = 83.230 + 2.2902(3.5) + 1.3010(1.8) = 93.588$ or $93,588

The difference ($93,588 - $93,555 = $33) is simply due to the fact that additional significant digits are used in the computations. From a practical point of view, however, the difference is not enough to be concerned about. In practice, a computer software package is always used to perform the computations and this will not be an issue.

The Minitab output is shown below:

```
    Fit   Stdev.Fit        95% C.I.              95% P.I.
 93.588       0.291  ( 92.840,  94.335)   ( 91.774,  95.401)
```

Note that the value of FIT ($\hat{y}$) is 93.588.

b. Confidence interval estimate: 92.840 to 94.335 or $92,840 to $94,335

c. Prediction interval estimate: 91.774 to 95.401 or $91,774 to $95,401

30. a. Since weight is not statistically significant (see Exercise 24), we will use an estimated regression equation which uses only Horsepower to predict the speed at 1/4 mile. The Minitab output is shown below:

```
The regression equation is
Speed = 72.6 + 0.0968 Horsepwr

Predictor         Coef    SE Coef          T          P
Constant        72.650      2.655      27.36      0.000
Horsepwr      0.096756   0.009865       9.81      0.000

S = 3.006       R-Sq = 87.3%     R-Sq(adj) = 86.4%

Analysis of Variance

Source             DF           SS          MS          F          P
Regression          1       869.43      869.43      96.21      0.000
Residual Error     14       126.52        9.04
Total              15       995.95

Unusual Observations
Obs    Horsepwr     Speed         Fit      SE Fit     Residual     St Resid
  2         290   108.000     100.709       0.814        7.291       2.52R
  6         450   116.200     116.190       2.036        0.010       0.00 X

R denotes an observation with a large standardized residual
X denotes an observation whose X value gives it large influence.
```

The output shows that the point estimate is a speed of 101.290 miles per hour.

Chapter 15

b. The 95% confidence interval is 99.490 to 103.089 miles per hour.

c. The 95% prediction interval is 94.596 to 107.984 miles per hour.

31. a. Using Minitab the 95% confidence interval is 58.37% to 75.03%.

b. Using Minitab the 95% prediction interval is 35.24% to 90.59%.

32. a. $E(y) = \beta_0 + \beta_1 x_1 + \beta_2 x_2$ where

$x_2 = 0$ if level 1 and 1 if level 2

b. $E(y) = \beta_0 + \beta_1 x_1 + \beta_2(0) = \beta_0 + \beta_1 x_1$

c. $E(y) = \beta_0 + \beta_1 x_1 + \beta_2(1) = \beta_0 + \beta_1 x_1 + \beta_2$

d. $\beta_2 = E(y \mid \text{level 2}) - E(y \mid \text{level 1})$

β_1 is the change in $E(y)$ for a 1 unit change in x_1 holding x_2 constant.

33. a. two

b. $E(y) = \beta_0 + \beta_1 x_1 + \beta_2 x_2 + \beta_3 x_3$ where

x_2	x_3	Level
0	0	1
1	0	2
0	1	3

c. $E(y \mid \text{level 1}) = \beta_0 + \beta_1 x_1 + \beta_2(0) + \beta_3(0) = \beta_0 + \beta_1 x_1$

$E(y \mid \text{level 2}) = \beta_0 + \beta_1 x_1 + \beta_2(1) + \beta_3(0) = \beta_0 + \beta_1 x_1 + \beta_2$

$E(y \mid \text{level 3}) = \beta_0 + \beta_1 x_1 + \beta_2(0) + \beta_3(0) = \beta_0 + \beta_1 x_1 + \beta_3$

$\beta_2 = E(y \mid \text{level 2}) - E(y \mid \text{level 1})$

$\beta_3 = E(y \mid \text{level 3}) - E(y \mid \text{level 1})$

β_1 is the change in $E(y)$ for a 1 unit change in x_1 holding x_2 and x_3 constant.

34. a. $15,300

b. Estimate of sales $= 10.1 - 4.2(2) + 6.8(8) + 15.3(0) = 56.1$ or $56,100

c. Estimate of sales $= 10.1 - 4.2(1) + 6.8(3) + 15.3(1) = 41.6$ or $41,600

35. a. Let Type = 0 if a mechanical repair
Type = 1 if an electrical repair

The Minitab output is shown below:

```
The regression equation is
Time = 3.45 + 0.617 Type

Predictor         Coef      SE Coef           T          P
Constant        3.4500       0.5467        6.31      0.000
Type            0.6167       0.7058        0.87      0.408

S = 1.093       R-Sq = 8.7%       R-Sq(adj) = 0.0%

Analysis of Variance

Source            DF           SS          MS          F          P
Regression         1        0.913       0.913       0.76      0.408
Residual Error     8        9.563       1.195
Total              9       10.476
```

b. The estimated regression equation did not provide a good fit. In fact, the p-value of .408 shows that the relationship is not significant for any reasonable value of α.

c. Person = 0 if Bob Jones performed the service and Person = 1 if Dave Newton performed the service. The Minitab output is shown below:

```
The regression equation is
Time = 4.62 - 1.60 Person

Predictor         Coef      SE Coef           T          P
Constant        4.6200       0.3192       14.47      0.000
Person         -1.6000       0.4514       -3.54      0.008

S = 0.7138      R-Sq = 61.1%       R-Sq(adj) = 56.2%

Analysis of Variance

Source            DF           SS          MS          F          P
Regression         1       6.4000      6.4000      12.56      0.008
Residual Error     8       4.0760      0.5095
Total              9      10.4760
```

d. We see that 61.1% of the variability in repair time has been explained by the repair person that performed the service; an acceptable, but not good, fit.

36. a. The Minitab output is shown below:

```
The regression equation is
Time = 1.86 + 0.291 Months + 1.10 Type - 0.609 Person

Predictor         Coef      SE Coef           T          P
Constant        1.8602       0.7286        2.55      0.043
Months          0.29144      0.08360       3.49      0.013
Type            1.1024       0.3033        3.63      0.011
Person         -0.6091       0.3879       -1.57      0.167

S = 0.4174      R-Sq = 90.0%       R-Sq(adj) = 85.0%
```

```
Analysis of Variance

Source            DF            SS           MS          F          P
Regression         3        9.4305       3.1435      18.04      0.002
Residual Error     6        1.0455       0.1743
Total              9       10.4760
```

b. Since the p-value corresponding to $F = 18.04$ is $.002 < \alpha = .05$, the overall model is statistically significant.

c. The p-value corresponding to $t = -1.57$ is $.167 > \alpha = .05$; thus, the addition of Person is not statistically significant. Person is highly correlated with Months (the sample correlation coefficient is -.691); thus, once the effect of Months has been accounted for, Person will not add much to the model.

37. a. Let Position = 0 if a guard
         Position = 1 if an offensive tackle.

b. The Minitab output is shown below:

```
The regression equation is
Rating = 11.2 + 0.732 Position + 0.0222 Weight - 2.28 Speed

Predictor        Coef       SE Coef           T          P
Constant       11.223         4.523        2.48      0.022
Position       0.7324        0.2893        2.53      0.019
Weight        0.02219       0.01039        2.14      0.045
Speed         -2.2775        0.9290       -2.45      0.023

S = 0.6936      R-Sq = 47.5%      R-Sq(adj) = 40.1%

Analysis of Variance

Source            DF            SS           MS          F          P
Regression         3        9.1562       3.0521       6.35      0.003
Residual Error    21       10.1014       0.4810
Total             24       19.2576
```

c. Since the p-value corresponding to $F = 6.35$ is $.003 < \alpha = .05$, there is a significant relationship between rating and the independent variables.

d. The value of R-Sq (adj) is 40.1%; the estimated regression equation did not provide a very good fit.

e. Since the p-value for Position is $t = 2.53 < \alpha = .05$, position is a significant factor in the player's rating.

f. $\hat{y} = 11.2 + .732(1) + .0222(300) - 2.28(5.1) = 6.96$

38. a. The Minitab output is shown below:

```
The regression equation is
Risk = - 91.8 + 1.08 Age + 0.252 Pressure + 8.74 Smoker

Predictor        Coef      SE Coef          T          P
Constant       -91.76        15.22      -6.03      0.000
Age            1.0767       0.1660       6.49      0.000
Pressure      0.25181      0.04523       5.57      0.000
Smoker          8.740        3.001       2.91      0.010

S = 5.757        R-Sq = 87.3%      R-Sq(adj) = 85.0%

Analysis of Variance

Source           DF           SS          MS          F          P
Regression        3       3660.7      1220.2      36.82      0.000
Residual Error   16        530.2        33.1
Total            19       4190.9
```

b. Since the p-value corresponding to $t = 2.91$ is $.010 < \alpha = .05$, smoking is a significant factor.

c. Using Minitab, the point estimate is 34.27; the 95% prediction interval is 21.35 to 47.18. Thus, the probability of a stroke (.2135 to .4718 at the 95% confidence level) appears to be quite high. The physician would probably recommend that Art quit smoking and begin some type of treatment designed to reduce his blood pressure.

39. a. The Minitab output is shown below:

```
The regression equation is
Y = 0.20 + 2.60 X

Predictor        Coef      SE Coef          T          P
Constant        0.200        2.132       0.09      0.931
X              2.6000       0.6429       4.04      0.027

S = 2.033        R-Sq = 84.5%      R-Sq(adj) = 79.3%

Analysis of Variance

Source           DF           SS          MS          F          P
Regression        1       67.600      67.600      16.35      0.027
Residual Error    3       12.400       4.133
Total             4       80.000
```

b. Using Minitab we obtained the following values:

x_i	y_i	$\hat{y}_i$	Standardized Residual
1	3	2.8	.16
2	7	5.4	.94
3	5	8.0	-1.65
4	11	10.6	.24
5	14	13.2	.62

The point (3,5) does not appear to follow the trend of remaining data; however, the value of the standardized residual for this point, -1.65, is not large enough for us to conclude that (3, 5) is an outlier.

c. Using Minitab, we obtained the following values:

x_i	y_i	Studentized Deleted Residual
1	3	.13
2	7	.91
3	5	- 4.42
4	11	.19
5	14	.54

$t_{.025} = 4.303$ ($n - p - 2 = 5 - 1 - 2 = 2$ degrees of freedom)

Since the studentized deleted residual for (3, 5) is -4.42 < -4.303, we conclude that the 3rd observation is an outlier.

40. a. The Minitab output is shown below:

```
The regression equation is
Y = -53.3 + 3.11 X

Predicator            Coef       Stdev     t-ratio        p
Constant           -53.280       5.786       -9.21    0.003
X                   3.1100      0.2016       15.43    0.001

s = 2.851   R-sq = 98.8%   R-sq (adj) = 98.3%
Analysis of Variance

SOURCE             DF          SS          MS          F        p
Regression          1      1934.4      1934.4     238.03    0.001
Error               3        24.4         8.1
Total               4      1598.8
```

b. Using the Minitab we obtained the following values:

x_i	y_i	Studentized Deleted Residual
22	12	-1.94
24	21	-.12
26	31	1.79
28	35	.40
40	70	-1.90

$t_{.025} = 4.303$ ($n - p - 2 = 5 - 1 - 2 = 2$ degrees of freedom)

Since none of the studentized deleted residuals are less than -4.303 or greater than 4.303, none of the observations can be classified as an outlier.

c. Using Minitab we obtained the following values:

x_i	y_i	h_i
22	12	.38
24	21	.28
26	31	.22
28	35	.20
40	70	.92

The critical value is

$$\frac{3(p+1)}{n} = \frac{3(1+1)}{5} = 1.2$$

Since none of the values exceed 1.2, we conclude that there are no influential observations in the data.

d. Using Minitab we obtained the following values:

x_i	y_i	D_i
22	12	.60
24	21	.00
26	31	.26
28	35	.03
40	70	11.09

Since $D_5 = 11.09 > 1$ (rule of thumb critical value), we conclude that the fifth observation is influential.

41. a. The Minitab output appears in the solution to part (b) of Exercise 5; the estimated regression equation is:

Revenue = 83.2 + 2.29 TVAdv + 1.30 NewsAdv

b. Using Minitab we obtained the following values:

$\hat{y}_i$	Standardized Residual
96.63	-1.62
90.41	-1.08
94.34	1.22
92.21	- .37
94.39	1.10
94.24	- .40
94.42	-1.12
93.35	1.08

With the relatively few observations, it is difficult to determine if any of the assumptions regarding the error term have been violated. For instance, an argument could be made that there does not appear to be any pattern in the plot; alternatively an argument could be made that there is a curvilinear pattern in the plot.

c. The values of the standardized residuals are greater than -2 and less than +2; thus, using test, there are no outliers. As a further check for outliers, we used Minitab to compute the following studentized deleted residuals:

Observation	Studentized Deleted Residual
1	-2.11
2	-1.10
3	1.31
4	- .33
5	1.13
6	- .36
7	-1.16
8	1.10

$t_{.025} = 2.776$ ($n - p - 2 = 8 - 2 - 2 = 4$ degrees of freedom)

Since none of the studentized deleted residuals is less tan -2.776 or greater than 2.776, we conclude that there are no outliers in the data.

d. Using Minitab we obtained the following values:

Observation	h_i	D_i
1	.63	1.52
2	.65	.70
3	.30	.22
4	.23	.01
5	.26	.14
6	.14	.01
7	.66	.81
8	.13	.06

The critical average value is

$$\frac{3(p+1)}{n} = \frac{3(2+1)}{8} = 1.125$$

Since none of the values exceed 1.125, we conclude that there are no influential observations. However, using Cook's distance measure, we see that $D_1 > 1$ (rule of thumb critical value); thus, we conclude the first observation is influential. Final Conclusion: observations 1 is an influential observation.

42. a. The Minitab output is shown below:

```
The regression equation is
Speed = 71.3 + 0.107 Price + 0.0845 Horsepwr

Predictor          Coef        SE Coef           T          P
Constant         71.328          2.248       31.73      0.000
Price           0.10719        0.03918        2.74      0.017
Horsepwr       0.084496       0.009306        9.08      0.000

S = 2.485        R-Sq = 91.9%       R-Sq(adj) = 90.7%
```

```
Analysis of Variance

Source              DF            SS           MS          F          P
Regression           2        915.66       457.83      74.12      0.000
Residual Error      13         80.30         6.18
Total               15        995.95

Source          DF      Seq SS
Price            1      406.39
Horsepwr         1      509.27

Unusual Observations
Obs      Price       Speed        Fit      SE Fit    Residual     St Resid
  2       93.8     108.000    105.882       2.007       2.118       1.45 X
```

X denotes an observation whose X value gives it large influence.

b. The standardized residual plot is shown below. There appears to be a very unusual trend in the standardized residuals.

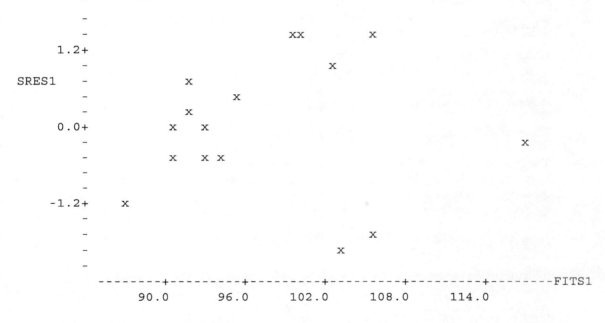

c. The Minitab output shown in part (a) did not identify any observations with a large standardized residual; thus, there does not appear to be any outliers in the data.

d. The Minitab output shown in part (a) identifies observation 2 as an influential observation.

43. a. The Minitab output is shown below:

```
The regression equation is
%College = - 26.6 + 0.0970 SatScore

Predictor          Coef       SE Coef            T          P
Constant         -26.61         37.22        -0.72      0.485
SatScore        0.09703        0.03734         2.60      0.019

S = 12.83        R-Sq = 29.7%       R-Sq(adj) = 25.3%
```

```
Analysis of Variance

Source              DF          SS          MS          F          P
Regression          1        1110.8      1110.8      6.75      0.019
Residual Error     16        2632.3       164.5
Total              17        3743.1

Unusual Observations
Obs    SatScore    %College    Fit     SE Fit    Residual    St Resid
 3          716       40.00   42.86     10.79       -2.86      -0.41 X
```

X denotes an observation whose X value gives it large influence.

b. The Minitab output shown in part a identifies observation 3 as an influential observation.

c. The Minitab output appears in the solution to Exercise 9; the estimates regression equation is
    %College = 26.7 - 1.43 Size + 0.0757 SATScore

d. The following Minitab output was also provided as part of the regression output for part c.

Unusual Observations

```
Obs.    Size    %College    Fit    Stdev.Fit    Residual    St.Resid
 3      30.0       40.0    38.04       10.97        1.96       0.34 X
```

X denotes an obs. whose X value gives it large influence.

Observation 3 is still identified as an influential observation.

44. a. The expected increase in final college grade point average corresponding to a one point increase in high school grade point average is .0235 when SAT mathematics score does not change. Similarly, the expected increase in final college grade point average corresponding to a one point increase in the SAT mathematics score is .00486 when the high school grade point average does not change.

b. $\hat{y} = -1.41 + .0235(84) + .00486(540) = 3.19$

45. a. Job satisfaction can be expected to decrease by 8.69 units with a one unit increase in length of service if the wage rate does not change. A dollar increase in the wage rate is associated with a 13.5 point increase in the job satisfaction score when the length of service does not change.

b. $\hat{y} = 14.4 - 8.69(4) + 13.5(6.5) = 67.39$

46. a. The computer output with the missing values filled in is as follows:

```
The regression equation is

Y = 8.103 + 7.602 X1 + 3.111 X2

    Predicator      Coef      Stdev      t-ratio
    Constant       8.103      2.667        3.04
    X1             7.602      2.105        3.61
    X2             3.111      0.613        5.08

s = 3.35      R-sq = 92.3%       R-sq (adj) = 91.0%
```

Analysis of Variance

SOURCE	DF	SS	MS	F
Regression	2	1612	806	71.82
Error	12	134,67	11.2225	
Total	14	1746.67		

b. $t_{.025} = 2.179$ (12 DF)

for β_1: 3.61 > 2.179; reject $H_0 : \beta_1 = 0$

for β_2: 5.08 > 2.179; reject $H_0 : \beta_2 = 0$

c. See computer output.

d. $R_a^2 = 1 - (1 - .923)\dfrac{14}{12} = .91$

47. a. The regression equation is

Y = -1.41 + .0235 X1 + .00486 X2

Predictor	Coef	Stdev	t-ratio
Constant	-1.4053	0.4848	-2.90
X1	0.023467	0.008666	2.71
X2	.00486	0.001077	4.51

s = 0.1298   R-sq = 93.7%   R-sq (adj) = 91.9%

Analysis of Variance

SOURCE	DF	SS	MS	F
Regression	2	1.76209	.881	52.44
Error	7	.1179	.0168	
Total	9	1.88000		

b. $F_{.05} = 4.74$ (2 DF numerator, 7 DF denominator)

$F = 52.44 > F_{.05}$; significant relationship.

c. $R^2 = \dfrac{\text{SSR}}{\text{SST}} = .937$

$R_a^2 = 1 - (1 - .937)\dfrac{9}{7} = .919$

good fit

d. $t_{.025} = 2.365$ (7 DF)

for B_1: $t = 2.71 > 2.365$; reject $H_0 : B_1 = 0$

for B_2: $t = 4.51 > 2.365$; reject $H_0 : B_2 = 0$

48. a. The regression equation is

```
Y = 14.4 - 8.69 X1 + 13.52 X2

Predictor          Coef        Stdev       t-ratio
Constant         14.448        8.191          1.76
X1                -8.69        1.555         -5.59
X2               13.517        2.085          6.48

 s = 3.773    R-sq = 90.1%      R-sq (adj) = 86.1%

Analysis of Variance

SOURCE          DF           SS            MS           F
Regression       2       648.83       324.415       22.79
Error            5        71.17        14.234
Total            7       720.00
```

b. $F_{.05} = 5.79$ (5 DF)

$F = 22.79 > F_{.05}$; significant relationship.

c. $R^2 = \dfrac{\text{SSR}}{\text{SST}} = .901$

$R_a^2 = 1 - (1 - .901)\dfrac{7}{5} = .861$

good fit

d. $t_{.025} = 2.571$ (5 DF)

for β_1: $t = -5.59 < -2.571$; reject $H_0 : \beta_1 = 0$

for β_2: $t = 6.48 > 2.571$; reject $H_0 : \beta_2 = 0$

49. a. The Minitab output is shown below:

```
The regression equation is
Price = 12.8 + 2.26 BookVal

Predictor         Coef      SE Coef           T          P
Constant        12.793        6.624        1.93      0.064
BookVal         2.2649       0.6631        3.42      0.002

S = 19.50       R-Sq = 29.4%      R-Sq(adj) = 26.9%

Analysis of Variance

Source          DF           SS           MS          F         P
Regression       1       4433.9       4433.9      11.67     0.002
Error           28      10642.3        380.1
Total           29      15076.1
```

b. The value of R-sq is 29.4%; the estimated regression equation does not provide a good fit.

c. The Minitab output is shown below:

```
The regression equation is
Price = 5.88 + 2.54 BookVal + 0.484 ReturnEq

Predictor        Coef       SE Coef          T          P
Constant        5.877         5.545       1.06      0.299
BookVal        2.5356        0.5331       4.76      0.000
ReturnEq       0.4841        0.1174       4.12      0.000

S = 15.55        R-Sq = 56.7%       R-Sq(adj) = 53.5%

Analysis of Variance

Source          DF           SS          MS          F          P
Regression       2       8544.2      4272.1      17.66      0.000
Error           27       6531.9       241.9
Total           29      15076.1
```

Since the p-value corresponding to the F test is 0.000, the relationship is significant.

50. a. The Minitab output is shown below:

```
The regression equation is
Speed = 97.6 + 0.0693 Price - 0.00082 Weight + 0.0590
Horsepwr - 2.48 Zero60

Predictor        Coef       SE Coef          T          P
Constant        97.57         11.79       8.27      0.000
Price         0.06928       0.03805       1.82      0.096
Weight       -0.000816      0.002593     -0.31      0.759
Horsepwr      0.05901       0.01543       3.82      0.003
Zero60        -2.4836        0.9601      -2.59      0.025

S = 2.127        R-Sq = 95.0%       R-Sq(adj) = 93.2%

Analysis of Variance

Source            DF          SS          MS          F          P
Regression         4      946.18      236.55      52.28      0.000
Residual Error    11       49.77        4.52
Total             15      995.95
```

b. Since the p-value corresponding to the F test is 0.000, the relationship is significant.

c. Since the p-values corresponding to the t test for both Horsepwr (p-value = .003) and Zero60 (p-value = .025) are less than .05, both of these independent variables are significant.

d.　The Minitab output is shown below:

```
The regression equation is
Speed = 103 + 0.0558 Horsepwr - 3.19 Zero60

Predictor          Coef       SE Coef            T          P
Constant        103.103         9.448        10.91      0.000
Horsepwr        0.05582       0.01452         3.84      0.002
Zero60          -3.1876        0.9658        -3.30      0.006

S = 2.301        R-Sq = 93.1%      R-Sq(adj) = 92.0%

Analysis of Variance

Source              DF           SS           MS          F          P
Regression           2       927.12       463.56      87.54      0.000
Residual Error      13        68.84         5.30
Total               15       995.95

Source         DF      Seq SS
Horsepwr        1      869.43
Zero60          1       57.68

Unusual Observations
Obs    Horsepwr       Speed         Fit      SE Fit     Residual    St Resid
  2         290     108.000     103.352       1.015        4.648       2.25R
 12         155      84.600      82.747       1.773        1.853       1.26 X

R denotes an observation with a large standardized residual
X denotes an observation whose X value gives it large influence.
```

e.　The standardized residual plot is shown below:

```
       -
SRES   -                                            x
       -
       -
  1.5+
       -   x                                                      x
       -
       -
       -                   2      x              x
  0.0+            x     x                        2
       -                x
       -
       -                  xx
       -
 -1.5+
       -                                  x      x
       -
       -
         ----+---------+---------+---------+---------+---------+--FIT
          84.0      90.0      96.0     102.0     108.0     114.0
```

There is an unusual trend in the plot and one observation appears to be an outlier.

f. The Minitab output indicates that observation 2 is an outlier

g. The Minitab output indicates that observation 12 is an influential observation.

51. a. The Minitab output is shown below:

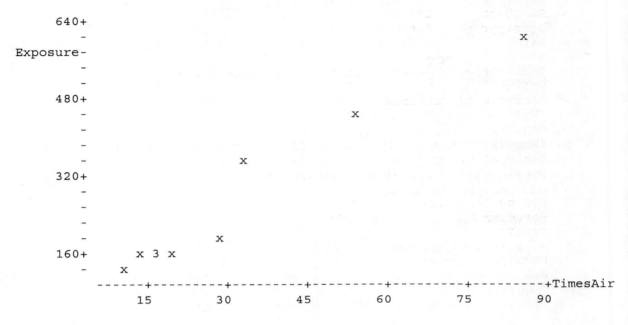

```
640+
   -                                                                      x
Exposure-
   -
   -
480+
   -                                                 x
   -
   -
   -                           x
320+
   -
   -
   -
   -            x
160+      x 3 x
   -    x
     ------+---------+---------+---------+---------+---------+---------+TimesAir
          15        30        45        60        75        90
```

b. The Minitab output is shown below:

```
The regression equation is
Exposure = 53.2 + 6.74 TimesAir

Predictor         Coef        SE Coef            T         P
Constant         53.24          16.53         3.22     0.012
TimesAir        6.7427         0.4472        15.08     0.000

S = 31.70        R-Sq = 96.6%      R-Sq(adj) = 96.2%

Analysis of Variance

Source         DF          SS           MS         F         P
Regression      1      228520       228520    227.36     0.000
Error           8        8041         1005
Total           9      236561
```

Since the *p*-value is 0.000, the relationship is significant.

c. The Minitab output is shown below:

```
The regression equation is
Exposure = 73.1 + 5.04 TimesAir + 101 BigAds
```

```
Predictor          Coef      SE Coef            T          P
Constant         73.063        7.507         9.73      0.000
TimesAir         5.0368       0.3268        15.41      0.000
BigAds           101.11        15.99         6.32      0.000


S = 13.08        R-Sq = 99.5%        R-Sq(adj) = 99.3%


Analysis of Variance


Source        DF          SS          MS          F          P
Regression     2      235363      117682     687.84      0.000
Error          7        1198         171
Total          9      236561
```

d.   The p-value corresponding to the t test for BigAds is 0.000; thus, the dummy variable is significant.

e.   The dummy variable enables us to fit two different lines to the data; this approach is referred to as piecewise linear approximation.

52. a.   The Minitab output is shown below:

```
Resale% = 38.8 +0.000766 Price


Predictor          Coef      SE Coef            T          P
Constant         38.772        4.348         8.92      0.000
Price         0.0007656    0.0001900         4.03      0.000


S = 5.421        R-Sq = 36.7%        R-Sq(adj) = 34.4%


Analysis of Variance


Source            DF          SS          MS          F          P
Regression         1      477.25      477.25      16.24      0.000
Residual Error    28      822.92       29.39
Total             29     1300.17
```

Since the p-value corresponding to $F = 16.24$ is .000 $< \alpha = .05$, there is a significant relationship between Resale% and Price.

b.   R-Sq = 36.7%; not a very good fit.

c.   Let Type1 = 0 and Type2 = 0 if a small pickup; Type1 = 1 and Type2 = 0 if a full-size pickup; and Type1 = 0 and Type2 = 1 if a sport utility.

The Minitab output using Type1, Type2, and Price is shown below:

```
The regression equation is
Resale% = 42.6 + 9.09 Type1 + 7.92 Type2 +0.000341 Price


Predictor          Coef      SE Coef            T          P
Constant         42.554        3.562        11.95      0.000
Type1             9.090        2.248         4.04      0.000
Type2             7.917        2.163         3.66      0.001
Price         0.0003415    0.0001800         1.90      0.069


S = 4.298        R-Sq = 63.1%        R-Sq(adj) = 58.8%
```

```
Analysis of Variance

Source             DF           SS          MS         F         P
Regression          3       819.77      273.26     14.79     0.000
Residual Error     26       480.40       18.48
Total              29      1300.17
```

d. Since the p-value corresponding to $F = 14.79$ is .000 $< \alpha = .05$, there is a significant relationship between Resale% and the independent variables. Note that individually, Price is not significant at the .05 level of significance. If we rerun the regression using just Type1 and Type2 the value of R-Sq (adj) decreases to 54.4%, a drop of only 4%. Thus, it appears that for these data, the type of vehicle is the strongest predictor of the resale value.

Chapter 16
Regression Analysis: Model Building

Learning Objectives

1. Learn how the general linear model can be used to model problems involving curvilinear relationships.

2. Understand the concept of interaction and how it can be accounted for in the general linear model.

3. Understand how an F test can be used to determine when to add or delete one or more variables.

4. Develop an appreciation for the complexities involved in solving larger regression analysis problems.

5. Understand how variable selection procedures can be used to choose a set of independent variables for an estimated regression equation.

6. Know how the Durban-Watson test can be used to test for autocorrelation.

7. Learn how analysis of variance and experimental design problems can be analyzed using a regression model.

Solutions:

1. a. The Minitab output is shown below:

```
The regression equation is
Y = - 6.8 + 1.23 X

Predictor        Coef        Stdev      t-ratio         p
Constant        -6.77        14.17       -0.48        0.658
X               1.2296       0.4697       2.62        0.059

s = 7.269       R-sq = 63.1%      R-sq(adj) = 53.9%

Analysis of Variance

SOURCE        DF           SS          MS         F          p
Regression     1        362.13      362.13      6.85      0.059
Error          4        211.37       52.84
Total          5        573.50
```

b. Since the p-value corresponding to $F = 6.85$ is $0.59 > \alpha = .05$, the relationship is not significant.

c.

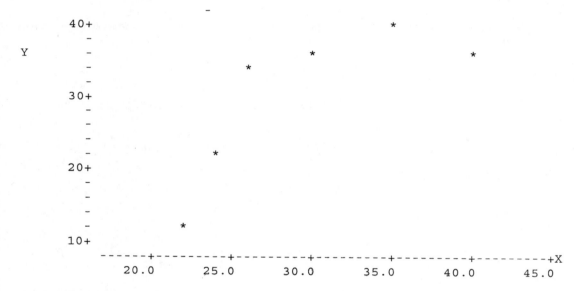

The scatter diagram suggests that a curvilinear relationship may be appropriate.

d. The Minitab output is shown below:

```
The regression equation is
Y = - 169 + 12.2 X - 0.177 XSQ

Predictor        Coef        Stdev      t-ratio         p
Constant       -168.88       39.79       -4.24        0.024
X               12.187        2.663        4.58        0.020
XSQ            -0.17704      0.04290      -4.13        0.026

s = 3.248       R-sq = 94.5%      R-sq(adj) = 90.8%
```

```
Analysis of Variance

SOURCE        DF            SS            MS            F            p
Regression    2         541.85        270.92        25.68        0.013
Error         3          31.65         10.55
Total         5         573.50
```

e. Since the p-value corresponding to $F = 25.68$ is $.013 < \alpha = .05$, the relationship is significant.

f. $\hat{y} = -168.88 + 12.187(25) - 0.17704(25)^2 = 25.145$

2. a. The Minitab output is shown below:

```
The regression equation is
Y = 9.32 + 0.424 X

Predictor         Coef        Stdev       t-ratio           p
Constant         9.315        4.196          2.22       0.113
X               0.4242       0.1944          2.18       0.117

s = 3.531        R-sq = 61.4%      R-sq(adj) = 48.5%

Analysis of Variance

SOURCE        DF            SS            MS            F            p
Regression    1          59.39         59.39         4.76        0.117
Error         3          37.41         12.47
Total         4          96.80
```

The high p-value (.117) indicates a weak relationship; note that 61.4% of the variability in y has been explained by x.

b. The Minitab output is shown below:

```
The regression equation is
Y = - 8.10 + 2.41 X - 0.0480 XSQ

Predictor         Coef        Stdev       t-ratio           p
Constant        -8.101        4.104         -1.97       0.187
X               2.4127       0.4409          5.47       0.032
XSQ           -0.04797      0.01050         -4.57       0.045

s = 1.279        R-sq = 96.6%      R-sq(adj) = 93.2%

Analysis of Variance

SOURCE        DF            SS            MS            F            p
Regression    2         93.529        46.765        28.60        0.034
Error         2          3.271         1.635
Total         4         96.800
```

At the .05 level of significance, the relationship is significant; the fit is excellent.

c. $\hat{y} = -8.101 + 2.4127(20) - 0.04797(20)^2 = 20.965$

3. a. The scatter diagram shows some evidence of a possible linear relationship.

    b. The Minitab output is shown below:

```
The regression equation is
Y = 2.32 + 0.637 X

Predictor         Coef        Stdev      t-ratio          p
Constant         2.322        1.887         1.23      0.258
X               0.6366       0.3044         2.09      0.075

s = 2.054        R-sq = 38.5%      R-sq(adj) = 29.7%

Analysis of Variance

SOURCE          DF          SS           MS          F          p
Regression       1      18.461       18.461       4.37      0.075
Error            7      29.539        4.220
Total            8      48.000
```

    c. The following standardized residual plot indicates that the constant variance assumption is not satisfied.

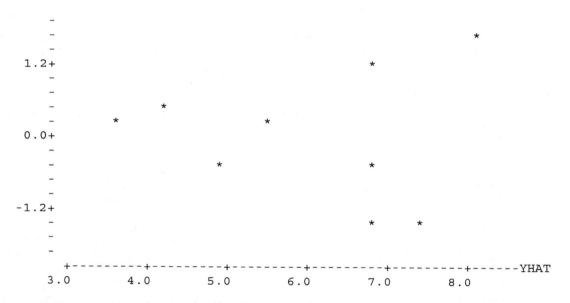

    d. The logarithmic transformation does not appear to eliminate the wedged-shaped pattern in the above residual plot. The reciprocal transformation does, however, remove the wedge-shaped pattern. Neither transformation provides a good fit. The Minitab output for the reciprocal transformation and the corresponding standardized residual pot are shown below.

```
The regression equation is
1/Y = 0.275 - 0.0152 X

Predictor         Coef        Stdev      t-ratio          p
Constant       0.27498      0.04601         5.98      0.000
X            -0.015182     0.007421        -2.05      0.080

s = 0.05009      R-sq = 37.4%      R-sq(adj) = 28.5%
```

```
Analysis of Variance

SOURCE        DF          SS           MS          F         p
Regression    1       0.010501     0.010501      4.19     0.080
Error         7       0.017563     0.002509
Total         8       0.028064


        -                  *
        -
        -
        -
  1.0+           *
        -                                 *
        -
        -
        -                                               *
  0.0+               *
        -
        -
        -                          *            *
        -
 -1.0+
        -    *           *
        -

        --+---------+---------+---------+---------+---------+---------+----YHAT
        0.140     0.160     0.180     0.200     0.220     0.240
```

4.   a.   The Minitab output is shown below:

```
The regression equation is
Y = 943 + 8.71 X

Predictor       Coef      Stdev      t-ratio          p
Constant      943.05      59.38        15.88      0.000
X              8.714       1.544        5.64      0.005

s = 32.29       R-sq = 88.8%      R-sq(adj) = 86.1%

Analysis of Variance

SOURCE        DF          SS           MS          F         p
Regression    1        33223        33223      31.86     0.005
Error         4         4172         1043
Total         5        37395
```

b.   The p-value of $.005 < \alpha = .01$; reject H_0

5.   The Minitab output is shown below:

```
The regression equation is
Y = 433 + 37.4 X - 0.383 1/Y

Predictor        Coef        Stdev      t-ratio          p
Constant        432.6        141.2         3.06      0.055
X              37.429        7.807         4.79      0.017
1/Y           -0.3829       0.1036        -3.70      0.034

s = 15.83       R-sq = 98.0%      R-sq(adj) = 96.7%

Analysis of Variance

SOURCE          DF           SS           MS           F          p
Regression       2        36643        18322       73.15      0.003
Error            3          751          250
Total            5        37395
```

b.   Since the linear relationship was significant (Exercise 4), this relationship must be significant. Note also that since the *p*-value of .005 < α = .05, we can reject H_0.

c.   The fitted value is 1302.01, with a standard deviation of 9.93. The 95% confidence interval is 1270.41 to 1333.61; the 95% prediction interval is 1242.55 to 1361.47.

6.   a.   The scatter diagram is shown below:

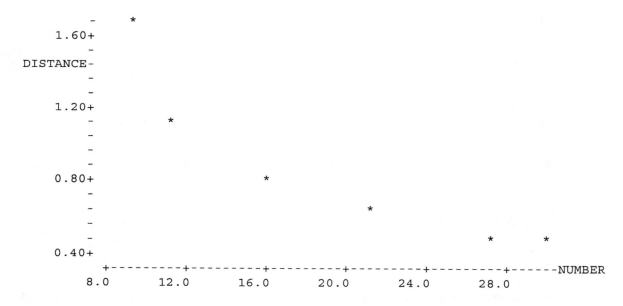

b.   No; the relationship appears to be curvilinear.

c.   Several possible models can be fitted to these data, as shown below:

$\hat{y} = 2.90 - 0.185x + .00351x^2$ $R_a^2 = .91$

$$\hat{y} = -0.0468 + 14.4\left(\frac{1}{x}\right) \qquad R_a^2 = .91$$

7. a. The Minitab output is shown below:

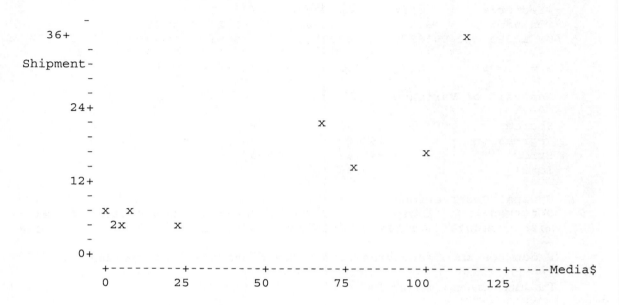

```
       -
  36+                                                      x
       -
Shipment-
       -
       -
  24+
       -                                 x
       -                                          x
       -                              x
  12+
       -
       - x   x
       -    2x          x
       -
   0+
       +---------+---------+---------+---------+---------+-----Media$
       0        25        50        75       100       125
```

b. The Minitab output is shown below:

```
The regression equation is
Shipment = 4.09 + 0.196 Media$

Predictor        Coef      SE Coef           T          P
Constant        4.089        2.168        1.89      0.096
Media$        0.19552      0.03635        5.38      0.000

S = 5.044       R-Sq = 78.3%      R-Sq(adj) = 75.6%

Analysis of Variance

Source          DF          SS           MS          F          P
Regression       1      735.84       735.84      28.93      0.000
Error            8      203.51        25.44
Total            9      939.35

Unusual Observations
Obs     Media$    Shipment      Fit   StDev Fit    Residual     St Resid
  1        120       36.30    27.55        3.30        8.75        2.30R

R denotes an observation with a large standardized residual
```

Simple linear regression appears to do good job in explaining the variability in shipments. However, the scatter diagram in part (a) indicates that a curvilinear relationship may be more appropriate.

c. The Minitab output is shown below:

```
The regression equation is
Shipment = 5.51 + 0.00182 Media$Sq

Predictor          Coef        SE Coef           T          P
Constant          5.506          1.686        3.27      0.011
Media$Sq     0.0018225      0.0002792        6.53      0.000

S = 4.308        R-Sq = 84.2%      R-Sq(adj) = 82.2%

Analysis of Variance

Source         DF            SS            MS          F          P
Regression      1        790.88        790.88      42.62      0.000
Error           8        148.47         18.56
Total           9        939.35

Unusual Observations
Obs   Media$Sq    Shipment       Fit  StDev Fit    Residual      St Resid
  3      10020       15.90     23.77       2.26       -7.87        -2.15R

R denotes an observation with a large standardized residual
```

8. a. The scatter diagram is shown below:

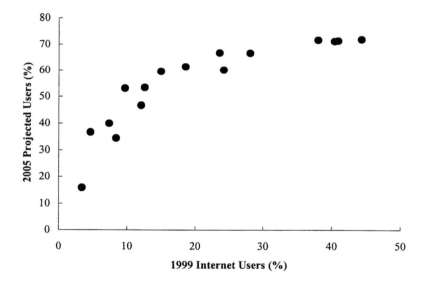

It appears that a simple linear regression model is not appropriate because there is curvature in the plot.

b. The Minitab output is shown below:

```
The regression equation is
2005% = 17.1 + 3.15 1999% - 0.0445 1999%Sq

Predictor          Coef      SE Coef           T          P
Constant         17.099        4.639        3.69      0.003
1999%            3.1462        0.4971        6.33      0.000
1999%Sq         -0.04454      0.01018       -4.37      0.001

S = 5.667       R-Sq = 89.7%      R-Sq(adj) = 88.1%

Analysis of Variance

Source             DF          SS           MS          F          P
Regression          2       3646.3       1823.2      56.78      0.000
Residual Error     13        417.4         32.1
Total              15       4063.8
```

c. The Minitab output is shown below:

```
The regression equation is
Log2000% = 1.17 + 0.449 Log1999%

Predictor          Coef      SE Coef           T          P
Constant        1.17420      0.07468       15.72      0.000
Log1999%        0.44895      0.05978        7.51      0.000

S = 0.08011      R-Sq = 80.1%      R-Sq(adj) = 78.7%

Analysis of Variance

Source             DF          SS           MS          F          P
Regression          1       0.36199      0.36199     56.40      0.000
Residual Error     14       0.08985      0.00642
Total              15       0.45184
```

d. The estimated regression in part (b) is preferred because it explains a higher percentage of the variability in the dependent variable.

9. a. The Minitab output is shown below:

```
The regression equation is
Distance = 268 + 1.52 Wind - 0.0177 WindSq

Predictor          Coef      SE Coef           T          P
Constant        267.841       2.358      113.60      0.000
Wind            1.52143       0.07718      19.71      0.000
WindSq         -0.017698      0.004456     -3.97      0.001

S = 7.073       R-Sq = 95.7%      R-Sq(adj) = 95.3%
```

Analysis of Variance

Source	DF	SS	MS	F	P
Regression	2	20233	10117	202.20	0.000
Error	18	901	50		
Total	20	21134			

b. The estimated distance is $267.841 + 1.52143(-15) - 0.017698(15)^2 = 241.04$.

c. The estimated distance is $267.841 + 1.52143(25) - 0.017698(25)^2 = 269.34$.

10. a. SSR = SST - SSE = 1030

MSR = 1030   MSE = 520/25 = 20.8 F = 1030/20.8 = 49.52

$F_{.05}$ = 4.24 (25 DF)

Since 49.52 > 4.24 we reject H_0: $\beta_1 = 0$ and conclude that x_1 is significant.

b. $F = \dfrac{(520-100)/2}{100/23} = 48.3$

$F_{.05}$ = 3.42 (2 degrees of freedom numerator and 23 denominator)

Since 48.3 > 3.42 the addition of variables x_2 and x_3 is statistically significant

11. a. SSE = SST - SSR = 1805 - 1760 = 45

MSR = 1760/4 = 440   MSE = 45/25 = 1.8

F = 440/1.8 = 244.44

$F_{.05}$ = 2.76 (4 degrees of freedom numerator and 25 denominator)

Since 244.44 > 2.76, variables x_1 and x_4 contribute significantly to the model

b. SSE(x_1, x_2, x_3, x_4) = 45

c. SSE(x_2, x_3) = 1805 - 1705 = 100

d. $F = \dfrac{(100-45)/2}{1.8} = 15.28$

$F_{.05}$ = 3.39 (2 numerator and 25 denominator DF)

Since 15.28 > 3.39 we conclude that x_1 and x_3 contribute significantly to the model.

12. a. The Minitab output is shown below.

The regression equation is
Points = 170 + 6.61 TeamInt

Predictor	Coef	SE Coef	T	P
Constant	170.13	44.02	3.86	0.002
TeamInt	6.613	2.258	2.93	0.013

Regression Analysis: Model Building

```
S = 43.93        R-Sq = 41.7%      R-Sq(adj) = 36.8%

Analysis of Variance

Source              DF          SS         MS          F          P
Regression           1       16546      16546       8.57      0.013
Residual Error      12       23157       1930
Total               13       39703
Unusual Observations
Obs    TeamInt    Points       Fit     SE Fit    Residual     St Resid
 13       33.0     340.0     388.4       34.2       -48.4       -1.75 X

X denotes an observation whose X value gives it large influence.
```

b. The Minitab output is shown below.

```
The regression equation is
Points = 280 + 5.18 TeamInt - 0.0037 Rushing - 3.92 OpponInt

Predictor          Coef      SE Coef          T          P
Constant         280.34        81.42       3.44      0.006
TeamInt           5.176         2.073       2.50      0.032
Rushing        -0.00373       0.03336      -0.11      0.913
OpponInt         -3.918         1.651      -2.37      0.039

S = 37.84        R-Sq = 63.9%      R-Sq(adj) = 53.1%

Analysis of Variance

Source              DF          SS         MS          F          P
Regression           3       25386       8462       5.91      0.014
Residual Error      10       14317       1432
Total               13       39703

Source          DF     Seq SS
TeamInt          1      16546
Rushing          1        776
OpponInt         1       8064
```

c. $$F = \frac{\dfrac{\text{SSE(reduced)} - \text{SSE(full)}}{\text{\# extra terms}}}{\text{MSE(full)}} = \frac{\dfrac{23,157 - 14,317}{2}}{1432} = 3.09$$

$F_{.05} = 4.10$ (2 numerator and 10 denominator DF)

Since $3.09 < 4.10$ the addition of the two independent variables is not significant.

Note: Suppose that we considered adding only the number of interceptions made by the opponents; the corresponding Minitab output is shown below:

```
Points = 274 + 5.23 TeamInt - 3.96 OpponInt

Predictor          Coef      SE Coef          T          P
Constant         273.77        53.81       5.09      0.000
TeamInt           5.227         1.931       2.71      0.020
OpponInt         -3.965         1.524      -2.60      0.025
```

```
S = 36.10         R-Sq = 63.9%      R-Sq(adj) = 57.3%
```

Analysis of Variance

Source	DF	SS	MS	F	P
Regression	2	25368	12684	9.73	0.004
Residual Error	11	14335	1303		
Total	13	39703			

Source	DF	Seq SS
TeamInt	1	16546
OpponInt	1	8822

Unusual Observations

Obs	TeamInt	Points	Fit	SE Fit	Residual	St Resid
10	17.0	312.00	247.64	16.85	64.36	2.02R

R denotes an observation with a large standardized residual

In this case,

$$F = \frac{\dfrac{23{,}157 - 14{,}335}{1}}{1303} = 6.77$$

$F_{.05} = 4.84$ (1 numerator and 11 denominator DF)

Since $6.77 > 4.84$ the addition of the number of interceptions made by the opponents is significant.

13. a.   The Minitab output is shown below:

```
Points = 218 + 0.0252 Passing + 4.39 TeamInt - 4.38 OpponInt
```

Predictor	Coef	SE Coef	T	P
Constant	218.38	69.07	3.16	0.010
Passing	0.02520	0.02039	1.24	0.245
TeamInt	4.387	2.005	2.19	0.053
OpponInt	-4.376	1.525	-2.87	0.017

```
S = 35.26         R-Sq = 68.7%      R-Sq(adj) = 59.3%
```

Analysis of Variance

Source	DF	SS	MS	F	P
Regression	3	27269	9090	7.31	0.007
Residual Error	10	12435	1243		
Total	13	39703			

Source	DF	Seq SS
Passing	1	3416
TeamInt	1	13617
OpponInt	1	10235

```
Unusual Observations
Obs     Passing      Points      Fit      SE Fit      Residual     St Resid
 10        3247      312.00   247.89      16.46         64.11        2.06R
```

R denotes an observation with a large standardized residual

b. The Minitab output is shown below:

```
Points = 235 + 0.0266 Passing + 4.18 TeamInt - 4.26 OpponInt -
0.0115 Rushing

Predictor          Coef      SE Coef           T          P
Constant         235.40        87.52        2.69      0.025
Passing         0.02663      0.02174        1.22      0.252
TeamInt           4.185        2.180        1.92      0.087
OpponInt         -4.256        1.635       -2.60      0.029
Rushing        -0.01145      0.03316       -0.35      0.738

S = 36.93       R-Sq = 69.1%      R-Sq(adj) = 55.4%

Analysis of Variance

Source               DF          SS          MS          F          P
Regression            4       27431        6858       5.03      0.021
Residual Error        9       12272        1364
Total                13       39703

Source          DF      Seq SS
Passing          1        3416
TeamInt          1       13617
OpponInt         1       10235
Rushing          1         163
```

c. $$F = \cfrac{\cfrac{\text{SSE(reduced)} - \text{SSE(full)}}{\text{\# extra terms}}}{\text{MSE(full)}} = \cfrac{\cfrac{12{,}435 - 12{,}272}{1}}{1364} = .1195$$

$F_{.05} = 5.12$ (1 numerator and 9 denominator DF)

Since $.1195 < 5.12$ the addition of Rushing is not significant.

Note: Since only 1 variable was added to the model in part (a), the test can also be performed using the t-ratio for Rushing in the Minitab output.

14. a. The Minitab output is shown below:

```
Risk = - 111 + 1.32 Age + 0.296 Pressure

Predictor          Coef      SE Coef           T          P
Constant        -110.94        16.47       -6.74      0.000
Age              1.3150       0.1733        7.59      0.000
Pressure        0.29640      0.05107        5.80      0.000

S = 6.908       R-Sq = 80.6%      R-Sq(adj) = 78.4%
```

```
Analysis of Variance

Source               DF           SS          MS          F          P
Regression            2       3379.6      1689.8      35.41      0.000
Residual Error       17        811.3        47.7
Total                19       4190.9

Source         DF       Seq SS
Age             1       1772.0
Pressure        1       1607.7

Unusual Observations
Obs       Age      Risk      Fit      SE Fit     Residual     St Resid
 17      66.0      8.00    25.05       1.67       -17.05        -2.54R
```

R denotes an observation with a large standardized residual

b.   The Minitab output is shown below:

```
Risk = - 123 + 1.51 Age + 0.448 Pressure + 8.87 Smoker -
0.00276 AgePress

Predictor         Coef      SE Coef          T          P
Constant       -123.16        56.94      -2.16      0.047
Age             1.5130       0.7796       1.94      0.071
Pressure        0.4483       0.3457       1.30      0.214
Smoker           8.866        3.074       2.88      0.011
AgePress      -0.002756     0.004807      -0.57      0.575

S = 5.881        R-Sq = 87.6%      R-Sq(adj) = 84.3%

Analysis of Variance

Source               DF           SS          MS          F          P
Regression            4      3672.11      918.03      26.54      0.000
Residual Error       15       518.84       34.59
Total                19      4190.95

Source         DF       Seq SS
Age             1      1771.98
Pressure        1      1607.66
Smoker          1       281.10
AgePress        1        11.37

Unusual Observations
Obs       Age      Risk      Fit      SE Fit     Residual     St Resid
 17      66.0      8.00    20.91       2.01       -12.91        -2.34R
```

R denotes an observation with a large standardized residual

c. $$F = \frac{\dfrac{SSE(reduced) - SSE(full)}{\# \text{ extra terms}}}{MSE(full)} = \frac{\dfrac{811.3 - 518.84}{2}}{34.59} = 4.23$$

$F_{.05} = 3.68$ (2 numerator and 15 denominator DF)

Since 4.23 > 3.68 the addition of the two terms is significant.

15. a. Let Pos1 = 0 and Pos2 =0 if player is a guard; Pos1 = 1 and Pos2 =0 if player is an offensive tackle; Pos1 = 0 and Pos2 =1 if player is a wide receiver.

b. The Minitab output is shown below:

```
The regression equation is
Rating = 12.5 + 0.706 Pos1 + 1.92 Pos2 + 0.0242 Weight - 2.63 Speed

Predictor          Coef       SE Coef            T         P
Constant         12.490         4.205         2.97     0.005
Pos1             0.7055        0.2923         2.41     0.021
Pos2             1.9179        0.9211         2.08     0.045
Weight         0.024157      0.007665         3.15     0.003
Speed           -2.6318        0.8600        -3.06     0.004
S = 0.7111       R-Sq = 52.2%      R-Sq(adj) = 46.7%


Analysis of Variance

Source              DF            SS            MS         F         P
Regression           4       19.2999        4.8250      9.54     0.000
Residual Error      35       17.6979        0.5057
Total               39       36.9978
```

c. The p-value corresponding to $F = 9.54$ is $0.000 < \alpha = .05$; thus, the estimated regression equation is significant.

d. The Minitab output using only Weight and Speed is shown below:

```
The regression equation is
Rating = 19.8 + 0.0183 Weight - 3.59 Speed

Predictor          Coef       SE Coef            T         P
Constant         19.839         2.800         7.09     0.000
Weight         0.018297      0.006015         3.04     0.004
Speed           -3.5943        0.8576        -4.19     0.000


S = 0.7763       R-Sq = 39.7%      R-Sq(adj) = 36.5%

Analysis of Variance

Source              DF            SS            MS         F         P
Regression           2       14.7016        7.3508     12.20     0.000
Residual Error      37       22.2961        0.6026
Total               39       36.9978
```

The F statistic used to determine if the addition of Pos1 and Pos2 results in a significant reduction in the error sum of squares is

$$F = \frac{\dfrac{22.2961 - 17.6979}{2}}{.5057} = 4.55$$

The F tables in the appendix do not show a value for two numerator and 35 denominator degrees of freedom. But, the F value for two numerator and 30 denominator degrees of freedom is 3.32 and the *F* value for two numerator and 40 denominator degrees of freedom is 3.23. Thus, the *F* value for two numerator and 35 denominator degrees of freedom is between 3.23 and 3.32. Because the computed *F* exceeds this value, the addition of Pos1 and Pos2 is statistically significant. In other words, position is a significant factor in the player's rating.

16. a. The Minitab output is shown below:

```
The regression equation is
%College = - 26.6 + 0.0970 SATScore

Predictor           Coef      SE Coef            T          P
Constant          -26.61        37.22        -0.72      0.485
SATScore         0.09703       0.03734         2.60      0.019


S = 12.83        R-Sq = 29.7%      R-Sq(adj) = 25.3%

Analysis of Variance

Source               DF           SS           MS          F          P
Regression            1       1110.8       1110.8       6.75      0.019
Residual Error       16       2632.3        164.5
Total                17       3743.1

Unusual Observations
Obs    SATScore    %College      Fit     SE Fit     Residual     St Resid
  3         716       40.00    42.86      10.79        -2.86        -0.41 X

X denotes an observation whose X value gives it large influence.
```

b.

```
Alpha-to-Enter: 0.15   Alpha-to-Remove: 0.15

Response is %College on  5 predictors, with N =    18


        Step          1         2
    Constant     -26.61    -26.93

    SATScore      0.097     0.084
    T-Value        2.60      2.46
    P-Value       0.019     0.026

    %TakeSAT                0.204
    T-Value                  2.21
    P-Value                 0.043

    S             12.8      11.5
    R-Sq         29.68     46.93
    R-Sq(adj)    25.28     39.86
    C-p            6.9       3.8
```

c. Backward elimination procedure:

```
Backward elimination.  Alpha-to-Remove: 0.1

 Response is %College on  5 predictors, with N =    18
```

Step	1	2	3	4
Constant	33.71	17.46	-32.47	-26.93
Size	-1.56	-1.39		
T-Value	-1.43	-1.42		
P-Value	0.179	0.178		
Spending	-0.0024	-0.0026	-0.0019	
T-Value	-1.47	-1.75	-1.31	
P-Value	0.168	0.104	0.212	
Salary	-0.00026			
T-Value	-0.40			
P-Value	0.693			
SATScore	0.077	0.081	0.095	0.084
T-Value	2.06	2.36	2.77	2.46
P-Value	0.062	0.034	0.015	0.026
%TakeSAT	0.285	0.274	0.291	0.204
T-Value	2.47	2.53	2.60	2.21
P-Value	0.029	0.025	0.021	0.043
S	11.2	10.9	11.2	11.5
R-Sq	59.65	59.10	52.71	46.93
R-Sq(adj)	42.83	46.51	42.58	39.86
C-p	6.0	4.2	4.1	3.8

d.

```
Response is %College
```

Vars	R-Sq	R-Sq(adj)	C-p	S	Size	Spending	Salary	SATScore	%TakeSAT
1	29.7	25.3	6.9	12.826				X	
1	25.5	20.8	8.2	13.203					X
2	46.9	39.9	3.8	11.508				X	X
2	38.2	30.0	6.4	12.417	X			X	
3	52.7	42.6	4.1	11.244		X		X	X
3	49.5	38.7	5.0	11.618	X			X	X
4	59.1	46.5	4.2	10.852	X	X		X	X
4	52.8	38.3	6.0	11.660		X	X	X	X
5	59.6	42.8	6.0	11.219	X	X	X	X	X

17. a. The correlation coefficients are as follows:

```
           Wins    Points  Rushing  Passing  TeamInt
Points    -0.664
           0.010

Rushing    0.527   -0.318
           0.053    0.268

Passing    0.206    0.293    0.133
           0.479    0.309    0.651

TeamInt   -0.671    0.646   -0.285    0.290
           0.009    0.013    0.324    0.314

OpponInt   0.506   -0.631    0.312    0.120   -0.276
           0.065    0.015    0.278    0.682    0.340

Cell Contents: Pearson correlation
               P-Value
```

The variable most highly correlated with Wins is TeamInt. The Minitab output for this model using TeamInt to predict Wins is shown below:

```
The regression equation is
Wins = 14.3 - 0.373 TeamInt

Predictor         Coef      SE Coef           T          P
Constant        14.294        2.318        6.17      0.000
TeamInt        -0.3730       0.1189       -3.14      0.009

S = 2.313       R-Sq = 45.1%      R-Sq(adj) = 40.5%

Analysis of Variance

Source            DF           SS           MS          F          P
Regression         1       52.652       52.652       9.84      0.009
Residual Error    12       64.205        5.350
Total             13      116.857

Unusual Observations
Obs    TeamInt    Wins      Fit     SE Fit     Residual    St Resid
  4       15.0   4.000    8.698      0.765       -4.698      -2.15R
 13       33.0   4.000    1.983      1.800        2.017       1.39 X
```

R denotes an observation with a large standardized residual
X denotes an observation whose X value gives it large influence.

b. Stepwise regression procedure:

    Alpha-to-Enter: 0.15 Alpha-to-Remove: 0.15

     Response is   Wins   on 5 predictors, with N =   14

Step	1	2	3
Constant	14.294	7.585	11.199
TeamInt	-0.37	-0.44	-0.28
T-Value	-3.14	-4.14	-2.45
P-Value	0.009	0.002	0.034
Passing		0.00256	0.00288
T-Value		2.27	3.02
P-Value		0.044	0.013
Points			-0.026
T-Value			-2.37
P-Value			0.040
S	2.31	1.99	1.67
R-Sq	45.06	62.63	76.04
R-Sq(adj)	40.48	55.83	68.85
C-p	11.3	6.5	3.3

c. Backward elimination procedure:

     Response is   Wins   on 5 predictors, with N =   14

Step	1	2	3
Constant	8.072	7.827	11.199
Points	-0.024	-0.023	-0.026
T-Value	-1.54	-2.08	-2.37
P-Value	0.163	0.067	0.040
Rushing	0.0018	0.0018	
T-Value	1.13	1.19	
P-Value	0.292	0.263	
Passing	0.00261	0.00257	0.00288
T-Value	2.36	2.65	3.02
P-Value	0.046	0.026	0.013
TeamInt	-0.26	-0.26	-0.28
T-Value	-2.11	-2.30	-2.45
P-Value	0.068	0.047	0.034
OpponInt	-0.01		
T-Value	-0.08		
P-Value	0.939		

```
S                 1.74      1.64      1.67
R-Sq             79.33     79.31     76.04
R-Sq(adj)        66.41     70.12     68.85
C-p               6.0       4.0       3.3
```

d.

```
Response is Wins
```

```
                                                        O
                                            R P T       p
                                          P u a e       p
                                          o s s a       o
                                          i h s m       n
                                          n i i I       I
                                          t n n n       n
 Vars   R-Sq    R-Sq(adj)      C-p      S  s g g t      t

   1    45.1      40.5        11.3   2.3131                  X
   1    44.0      39.4        11.7   2.3344  X
   2    62.6      55.8         6.5   1.9925      X X
   2    61.6      54.7         6.8   2.0187  X   X
   3    76.0      68.9         3.3   1.6732  X   X X
   3    69.3      60.1         5.9   1.8932    X X X
   4    79.3      70.1         4.0   1.6389  X X X X
   4    76.0      65.4         5.3   1.7637  X     X X X
   5    79.3      66.4         6.0   1.7377  X X X X X
```

18. a.   The Minitab output is shown below:

```
The regression equation is
ScoreAvg = 81.4 - 0.147 Green%

Predictor        Coef      SE Coef         T         P
Constant       81.424        1.930     42.20     0.000
Green%        -0.14681      0.02775     -5.29     0.000

S = 0.4380       R-Sq = 60.9%     R-Sq(adj) = 58.7%

Analysis of Variance

Source       DF          SS          MS         F         P
Regression    1       5.3701      5.3701     27.99     0.000
Error        18       3.4537      0.1919
Total        19       8.8238

Unusual Observations
Obs     Green%   ScoreAvg      Fit   StDev Fit    Residual   St Resid
  3      78.6    70.3500  69.8849      0.2723      0.4651      1.36X
 19      69.1    72.1400  71.2797      0.0984      0.8603      2.02R

R denotes an observation with a large standardized residual
X denotes an observation whose X value gives it large influence.
```

b.   The Minitab output is shown below:

```
The regression equation is
ScoreAvg = 58.2 - 0.00996 Distance - 0.152 Green% + 0.869 Putts

Predictor          Coef       SE Coef            T          P
Constant         58.198         6.644         8.76      0.000
Distance      -0.009956      0.009111        -1.09      0.291
Green%         -0.15186       0.02437        -6.23      0.000
Putts            0.8686        0.2251         3.86      0.001

S = 0.3306      R-Sq = 80.2%      R-Sq(adj) = 76.5%

Analysis of Variance

Source          DF            SS            MS           F         P
Regression       3        7.0755        2.3585       21.58     0.000
Error           16        1.7483        0.1093
Total           19        8.8238

Unusual Observations
Obs   Distance    ScoreAvg        Fit   StDev Fit    Residual    St Resid
  3        256     70.3500    69.7369      0.2104      0.6131       2.40R

R denotes an observation with a large standardized residual
```

c.   The estimated regression equation appears to be reasonable; that is, increasing Distance and Green% lowers the average score, whereas increasing Putts increases the average score.

d.   Estimated average score = 58.198 - 0.009956(231.6) - 0.15186(65.2) + 0.8686(30.69) = 72.65.

19.   Let   Health = 1 if health-drugs
              Health = 0 if energy-international or other

```
The regression equation is
P/E = 10.8 + 0.430 Sales% + 10.6 Health

Predictor          Coef       SE Coef            T          P
Constant         10.817         3.143         3.44      0.004
Sales%           0.4297        0.1813         2.37      0.034
Health           10.600         2.750         3.85      0.002

S = 5.012       R-Sq = 55.4%      R-Sq(adj) = 48.5%

Analysis of Variance

Source          DF            SS            MS           F         P
Regression       2        405.69        202.85        8.07     0.005
Error           13        326.59         25.12
Total           15        732.28

Source          DF        Seq SS
Sales%           1         32.36
Health           1        373.33
```

20. See the solution to Exercise 14 in this chapter. The Minitab output using the best subsets regression procedure is shown below:

```
Response is Risk
```

					P r e s s o r A g e e	A g e S m o k e r s	P r e k e r s	A g e P r e s s
Vars	R-Sq	R-Sq(adj)	C-p	S				
1	63.3	61.3	28.5	9.2430				X
1	46.3	43.3	49.1	11.182		X		
2	80.6	78.4	9.5	6.9083	X	X		
2	79.5	77.1	10.8	7.1058	X			X
3	87.3	85.0	3.3	5.7566	X	X	X	
3	86.2	83.7	4.7	6.0051	X		X	X
4	87.6	84.3	5.0	5.8813	X	X	X	X

This output suggests that the model involving Age, Pressure, and Smoker is the preferred model; the Minitab output for this model is shown below:

```
Risk = - 91.8 + 1.08 Age + 0.252 Pressure + 8.74 Smoker
```

Predictor	Coef	SE Coef	T	P
Constant	-91.76	15.22	-6.03	0.000
Age	1.0767	0.1660	6.49	0.000
Pressure	0.25181	0.04523	5.57	0.000
Smoker	8.740	3.001	2.91	0.010

```
S = 5.757        R-Sq = 87.3%     R-Sq(adj) = 85.0%
```

Analysis of Variance

Source	DF	SS	MS	F	P
Regression	3	3660.7	1220.2	36.82	0.000
Residual Error	16	530.2	33.1		
Total	19	4190.9			

Source	DF	Seq SS
Age	1	1772.0
Pressure	1	1607.7
Smoker	1	281.1

Unusual Observations

Obs	Age	Risk	Fit	SE Fit	Residual	St Resid
17	66.0	8.00	21.11	1.94	-13.11	-2.42R

21. a.   The Minitab output is shown below:

```
The regression equation is
P/E = 6.51 + 0.569 %PROFIT

Predictor          Coef      SE Coef            T          p
Constant          6.507        1.509         4.31      0.000
%PROFIT          0.5691       0.1281         4.44      0.000

s = 2.580        R-sq = 53.7%      R-sq(adj) = 51.0%

Analysis of Variance

SOURCE           DF            SS           MS          F          p
Regression        1        131.40       131.40      19.74      0.000
Error            17        113.14         6.66
Total            18        244.54
```

b.   The residual plot as a function of the order in which the data are presented is shown below:

```
RESIDUAL-
        -
        -                                   3
   3.50+                                          6
        -                       8
        -                  7              1
        - 1      3
        -            4                  2
   0.00+                          0                     9
        -     2
        -                                     7
        -                                5
        -           5
        -              6       9
  -3.50+                                      8
        -
        -                            4
        -
        +---------+---------+---------+---------+
        0         5        10        15        20
```

There does not appear to be any pattern indicative of positive autocorrelation.

c.   The Durban-Watson statistic (obtained from Minitab) is $d = 2.34$. At the .05 level of significance, $d_L = 1.18$ and $d_U = 1.39$. Since $d > d_U$ there is no significant positive autocorrelation.

22.   From Minitab, $d = 1.60$. At the .05 level of significance, $d_L = 1.04$ and $d_U = 1.77$. Since $d_L \leq d$, the test is inconclusive.

23.   The dummy variables are defined as follows:

x_1	x_2	x_3	Treatment
0	0	0	A
1	0	0	B
0	1	0	C
0	0	1	D

$$E(y) = \beta_0 + \beta_1 x_1 + \beta_2 x_2 + \beta_3 x_3$$

24.   The dummy variables are defined as follows:

x_1	x_2	Treatment
0	0	1
1	0	2
0	1	3

$x_3 = 0$ if block 1 and 1 if block 2

$$E(y) = \beta_0 + \beta_1 x_1 + \beta_2 x_2 + \beta_3 x_3$$

25.   Factor A

$x_1 = 0$ if level 1 and 1 if level 2

Factor B

x_2	x_3	Level
0	0	1
1	0	2
0	1	3

$$E(y) = \beta_0 + \beta_1 x_1 + \beta_2 x_2 + \beta_3 x_1 x_2 + \beta_4 x_1 x_3$$

26. a.   The dummy variables are defined as follows:

D1	D2	Mfg.
0	0	1
1	0	2
0	1	3

$$E(y) = \beta_0 + \beta_1 D1 + \beta_2 D2$$

b.   The Minitab output is shown below:

```
The regression equation is
TIME = 23.0 + 5.00 D1 - 2.00 D2

Predictor       Coef      SE Coef           T          p
Constant      23.000        1.106       20.80      0.000
D1             5.000        1.563        3.20      0.011
D2            -2.000        1.563       -1.28      0.233

s = 2.211       R-sq = 70.3%      R-sq(adj) = 63.7%

Analysis of Variance

SOURCE        DF           SS          MS          F          p
Regression     2      104.000      52.000      10.64      0.004
Error          9       44.000       4.889
Total         11      148.000
```

c. $H_0 : \beta_1 = \beta_2 = 0$

d.   The p-value of .004 is less than $\alpha = .05$; therefore, we can reject H_0 and conclude that the mean time to mix a batch of material is most the same for each manufacturer.

27. a.   The dummy variables are defined as follows:

D1	D2	D3	Paint
0	0	0	1
1	0	0	2
0	1	0	3
0	0	1	4

The Minitab output is shown below:

```
The regression equation is
TIME = 133 + 6.00 D1 + 3.00 D2 + 11.0 D3

Predictor        Coef      SE Coef           T          p
Constant      133.000        2.941       45.22      0.000
D1              6.000        4.159        1.44      0.168
D2              3.000        4.159        0.72      0.481
D3             11.000        4.159        2.64      0.018

s = 6.576        R-sq = 32.3%      R-sq(adj) = 19.6%

Analysis of Variance

SOURCE       DF          SS           MS          F          p
Regression    3      330.00       110.00       2.54      0.093
Error        16      692.00        43.25
Total        19     1022.00
```

The appropriate hypothesis test is:

$$H_0 : \beta_1 = \beta_2 = \beta_3 = 0$$

The p-value of .093 is greater than $\alpha = .05$; therefore, at the 5% level of significance we can not reject H_0.

b.   Note: Estimating the mean drying for paint 2 using the estimated regression equations developed in part (a) may not be the best approach because at the 5% level of significance, we cannot reject H_0. But, if we want to use the output, we would procede as follows.

D1 = 1 D2 = 0 D3 = 0

TIME = 133 + 6(1) + 3(0) +11(0) = 139

28.   X1 = 0 if computerized analyzer, 1 if electronic analyzer

X2 and X3 are defined as follows:

X2	X3	Car
0	0	1
1	0	2
0	1	3

The complete data set and the Minitab output are shown below:

```
Y    X1   X2   X3

50   0    0    0
55   0    1    0
63   0    0    1
42   1    0    0
44   1    1    0
46   1    0    1
```

```
The regression equation is
Y = 52.0 - 12.0 X1 + 3.50 X2 + 8.50 X3

Predictor          Coef        Stdev      t-ratio         p
Constant         52.000        2.646        19.65      0.003
X1              -12.000        2.646        -4.54      0.045
X2                3.500        3.240         1.08      0.393
X3                8.500        3.240         2.62      0.120

s = 3.240        R-sq = 93.2%       R-sq(adj)  = 83.1%

Analysis of Variance

SOURCE         DF          SS           MS          F          p
Regression      3      289.00        96.33       9.17      0.100
Error           2       21.00        10.50
Total           5      310.00
```

To test for any significant difference between the two analyzers we must test $H_0: \beta_1 = 0$. Since the p-value corresponding to $t = -4.54$ is .045 $< \alpha = .05$, we reject $H_0: \beta_0 = 0$; the time to do a tuneup is not the same for the two analyzers.

29.   X1 = 0 if a small advertisement and 1 if a large advertisement

X2 and X3 are defined as follows:

X2	X3	Design
0	0	A
1	0	B
0	1	C

The complete data set and the Minitab output are shown below:

```
Y    X1   X2   X3   X1X2   X1X3

8    0    0    0     0      0
12   0    0    0     0      0
12   1    0    0     0      0
8    1    0    0     0      0
22   0    1    0     0      0
14   0    1    0     0      0
26   1    1    0     1      0
30   1    1    0     1      0
10   0    0    1     0      0
18   0    0    1     0      0
18   1    0    1     0      1
14   1    0    1     0      1
```

The regression equation is
Y = 10.0 + 0.00 X1 + 8.00 X2 + 4.00 X3 + 10.0 X1X2 + 2.00 X1X3

```
Predictor      Coef      SE Coef        T         p
Constant     10.000      2.828       3.54     0.012
X1            0.000      4.000       0.00     1.000
X2            8.000      4.000       2.00     0.092
X3            4.000      4.000       1.00     0.356
X1X2         10.000      5.657       1.77     0.128
X1X3          2.000      5.657       0.35     0.736
```

s = 4.000   R-sq = 82.4%   R-sq(adj) = 67.6%

Analysis of Variance

```
SOURCE        DF         SS         MS         F        p
Regression     5       448.00      89.60      5.60     0.029
Error          6        96.00      16.00
Total         11       544.00
```

30. a. Let ExS denote the interaction between the expense ratio (%) and the safety rating.

The regression equation is
Perform% = 23.3 + 222 Expense% - 28.9 ExS

```
Predictor      Coef      SE Coef        T         P
Constant      23.32      19.82       1.18     0.256
Expense%     222.43      41.93       5.30     0.000
ExS          -28.869      6.636     -4.35     0.000
```

S = 13.01   R-Sq = 69.0%   R-Sq(adj) = 65.3%

Analysis of Variance

```
Source           DF         SS         MS         F        P
Regression        2       6396.4     3198.2     18.90    0.000
Residual Error    17       2876.6      169.2
Residual Error    35      17.6979       0.5057
Total             39      36.9978
```

The type of fund (load or no load) does not appear to be a significant factor in predicting the one-year performance. The interaction between the expense ratio and the safety rating is significant, and is accounted for by the ExS term in the estimated regression equation.

b. The fit provided by the estimated regression equation shown in part(a) is not bad; R-Sq (adj) = 65.3%

$\hat{y} = 23.2 + 222(1.12) - 28.9[(1.12)(7.6)] = 25.8$; thus, the estimated one-year performance for Acorn International is approximately 26%.

31. a. The Minitab output is shown below:

```
The regression equation is
AUDELAY = 80.4 + 11.9 INDUS - 4.82 PUBLIC - 2.62 ICQUAL - 4.07 INTFIN

Predictor         Coef        Stdev       t-ratio          p
Constant        80.429        5.916        13.60        0.000
INDUS           11.944        3.798         3.15        0.003
PUBLIC          -4.816        4.229        -1.14        0.263
ICQUAL          -2.624        1.184        -2.22        0.033
INTFIN          -4.073        1.851        -2.20        0.035

s = 10.92       R-sq = 38.3%       R-sq(adj) = 31.2%

Analysis of Variance

SOURCE         DF          SS           MS          F          p
Regression      4        2587.7        646.9        5.42        0.002
Error          35        4176.3        119.3
Total          39        6764.0
```

b. The low value of the adjusted coefficient of determination (31.2%) does not indicate a good fit.

c. The scatter diagram is shown below:

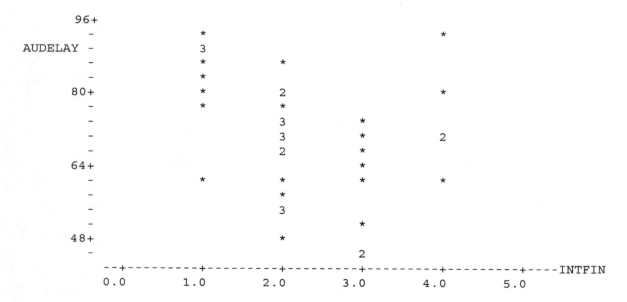

The scatter diagram suggests a curvilinear relationship between these two variables.

d. The output from the stepwise procedure is shown below, where INTFINSQ is the square of INTFIN.

```
Response is AUDELAY  on  5 predictors, with N =   40

        Step             1        2
Constant            112.4    112.8

INDUS                11.5     11.6
T-Value              3.67     3.80
P-Value             0.001    0.001

PUBLIC               -1.0
T-Value             -0.29
P-Value             0.775

ICQUAL              -2.45    -2.49
T-Value             -2.51    -2.60
P-Value             0.017    0.014

INTFIN              -36.0    -36.6
T-Value             -4.61    -4.91
P-Value             0.000    0.000

INTFINSQ             6.5      6.6
T-Value              4.17     4.44
P-Value             0.000    0.000

S                    9.01     8.90
R-Sq                59.15    59.05
R-Sq(adj)           53.14    54.37
C-p                  6.0      4.1
```

32. The computer output is shown below:

```
The regression equation is
AUDELAY = 63.0 + 11.1 INDUS

Predictor        Coef      SE Coef          T          p
Constant       63.000        3.393      18.57      0.000
INDUS          11.074        4.130       2.68      0.011

s = 12.23        R-sq = 15.9%      R-sq(adj) = 13.7%

Analysis of Variance

SOURCE        DF          SS          MS          F          p
Regression     1      1076.1      1076.1       7.19      0.011
Error         38      5687.9       149.7
Total         39      6764.0

Unusual Observations
Obs.    INDUS    AUDELAY       Fit Stdev.Fit   Residual   St.Resid
  5      0.00      91.00     63.00      3.39      28.00      2.38R
 38      1.00      46.00     74.07      2.35     -28.07     -2.34R
```

```
Durban-Watson statistic = 1.55
```

At the .05 level of significance, $d_L = 1.44$ and $d_U = 1.54$. Since $d = 1.55 > d_U$, there is no significant positive autocorrelation.

33. a.   The Minitab output is shown below:

```
The regression equation is
AUDELAY = 70.6 + 12.7 INDUS - 2.92 ICQUAL

Predictor          Coef      SE Coef            T          p
Constant         70.634        4.558        15.50      0.000
INDUS            12.737        3.966         3.21      0.003
ICQUAL           -2.919        1.238        -2.36      0.024

s = 11.56       R-sq = 26.9%      R-sq(adj) = 22.9%

Analysis of Variance

SOURCE          DF            SS           MS          F          p
Regression       2        1818.6        909.3       6.80      0.003
Error           37        4945.4        133.7
Total           39        6764.0

SOURCE          DF        SEQ SS
INDUS            1        1076.1
ICQUAL           1         742.4

Unusual Observations
Obs.    INDUS    AUDELAY        Fit Stdev.Fit    Residual    St.Resid
   5     0.00      91.00      67.71      3.78       23.29       2.13R
  38     1.00      46.00      71.70      2.44      -25.70      -2.27R

R denotes an obs. with a large st. resid.

Durban-Watson statistic = 1.43
```

b. The residual plot as a function of the order in which the data are presented is shown below:

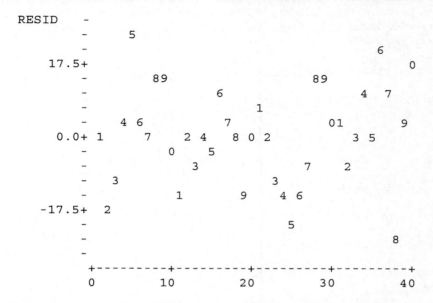

```
   RESID    -
            -      5
            -                                              6
     17.5+                                                      0
            -           89                        89
            -                   6                        4   7
            -                          1
            -      4  6                 7              01           9
     0.0+  1        7      2  4      8  0  2            3  5
            -              0     5
            -                  3                    7     2
            -    3                          3
            -              1           9      4  6
    -17.5+   2
            -                                5
            -                                              8
            -
          +---------+---------+---------+---------+
          0        10        20        30        40
```

There is no obvious pattern in the data indicative of positive autocorrelation.

c. At the .05 level of significance, $d_L = 1.44$ and $d_U = 1.54$. Since $d = 1.43 > d_U$, there is no significant positive autocorrelation.

34. The dummy variables are defined as follows:

D1	D2	Type
0	0	Non
1	0	Light
0	1	Heavy

The Minitab output is shown below:

```
The regression equation is
Score = 4.25 + 1.00 D1 + 1.50 D2


Predictor        Coef       SE Coef            T          p
Constant       4.2500        0.3819        11.13      0.000
D1             1.0000        0.5401         1.85      0.078
D2             1.5000        0.5401         2.78      0.011


s = 1.080       R-sq = 27.6%       R-sq(adj) = 20.7%


Analysis of Variance

SOURCE        DF           SS           MS          F          p
Regression     2        9.333        4.667       4.00      0.034
Error         21       24.500        1.167
Total         23       33.833
```

Since the p-value = .034 is less than α = .05, there are significant differences between comfort levels for the three types of browsers.

35.   First, we will use simple linear regression to estimate the change in the Dow Jones Industrial Average using just party. In the following Minitab output the dummy variable Party is coded as follows: Party = 0 if Democrat, 1 if Republican.

```
The regression equation is
ChangeDJ = 7.13 + 0.92 Party

Predictor          Coef       SE Coef           T         P
Constant          7.125         4.768        1.49     0.146
Party             0.920         6.031        0.15     0.880

S = 16.52        R-Sq = 0.1%        R-Sq(adj) = 0.0%

Analysis of Variance

Source          DF           SS           MS          F         P
Regression       1          6.3          6.3       0.02     0.880
Error           30       8184.3        272.8
Total           31       8190.6

Unusual Observations
Obs      Party    ChangeDJ       Fit   StDev Fit     Residual      St Resid
 10       1.00      -27.60      8.05        3.69       -35.65        -2.21R

R denotes an observation with a large standardized residual
```

The relationship between these two variables is not statistically significant. To model the effect of the year in the presidential term, three dummy variables were used: Year1, Year2, and Year3. These variables were coded as follows: Year1 = 1 if the observation corresponds to the first year in the term of office, 0 otherwise; Year2 = 1 if the observation corresponds to the second year in the term of office, 0 otherwise; and Year3 = 1 if the observation corresponds to the third year in the term of office, 0 otherwise. Using Party, Year1, Year2, and Year3 as independent variables, the only variable that proved to be significant at the .05 level of significance is Year3. The Minitab output is shown below:

```
The regression equation is
ChangeDJ = 4.42 + 13.1 Year3

Predictor          Coef       SE Coef           T         P
Constant          4.425         3.154        1.40     0.171
Year3            13.100         6.307        2.08     0.046

S = 15.45        R-Sq = 12.6%        R-Sq(adj) = 9.7%

Analysis of Variance

Source          DF           SS           MS          F         P
Regression       1       1029.7       1029.7       4.31     0.046
Error           30       7161.0        238.7
Total           31       8190.6

Unusual Observations
Obs      Year3    ChangeDJ       Fit   StDev Fit     Residual      St Resid
 10       0.00      -27.60      4.42        3.15       -32.02        -2.12R

R denotes an observation with a large standardized residual
```

Chapter 17
Index Numbers

Learning Objectives

1. Know how to compute price relatives and understand how they represent price changes over time.

2. Know how to compute aggregate price indexes and understand how the choice of a base period affects the index.

3. Become familiar with the Consumer Price Index, the Producer Price Index and the Dow Jones averages.

4. Learn how to deflate a time series to measure changes over time in constant dollars.

5. Learn how to compute an aggregate quantity index and how to interpret it.

Solutions:

1. a.

Item	Price Relative
A	$103 = (7.75/7.50)$
B	$238 = (1500/630)$

   b. $I_{2001} = \dfrac{7.75 + 1500.00}{7.50 + 630.00}(100) = \dfrac{1507.75}{637.50}(100) = 237$

   c. $I_{2001} = \dfrac{7.75(1500) + 1500.00(2)}{7.50(1500) + 630.00(2)}(100) = \dfrac{14,625.00}{12,510.00}(100) = 117$

   d. $I_{2001} = \dfrac{7.75(1800) + 1500.00(1)}{7.50(1800) + 630.00(1)}(100) = \dfrac{15,450.00}{14,130.00}(100) = 109$

2. a. From the price relative we see the percentage increase was 32%.

   b. Divide the current cost by the price relative and multiply by 100.

   $$1990 \text{ cost} = \dfrac{\$10.75}{132}(100) = \$8.14$$

3. a. Price Relatives
   $A = (6.00 / 5.45)\,100 = 110$

   $B = (5.95 / 5.60)\,100 = 106$

   $C = (6.20 / 5.50)\,100 = 113$

   b. $I_{2001} = \dfrac{6.00 + 5.95 + 6.20}{5.45 + 5.60 + 5.50}(100) = 110$

   c. $I_{2001} = \dfrac{6.00(150) + 5.95(200) + 6.20(120)}{5.45(150) + 5.60(200) + 5.50(120)}(100) = 109$

   9% increase over the two year period.

4. $I_{2001} = \dfrac{16.25(35,000) + 64.00(5,000) + 10.00(60,000)}{15.00(35,000) + 60.00(5,000) + 9.80(60,000)}(100) = 105$

5. $I = \dfrac{.19(500) + 1.80(50) + 4.20(100) + 13.20(40)}{.15(500) + 1.60(50) + 4.50(100) + 12.00(40)}(100) = 104$

   Paasche index

6.

Item	Price Relative	Base Period Price	Base Period Usage	Weight	Weighted Price Relatives
A	150	22.00	20	440	66,000
B	90	5.00	50	250	22,500
C	120	14.00	40	560	67,200
				1250	155,700

$$I = \frac{155,700}{1250} = 125$$

7.   a.   Price Relatives   A = (3.95 / 2.50) 100   = 158

B = (9.90 / 8.75) 100   = 113

C = (.95 /.99) 100   = 96

b.

Item	Price Relatives	Base Price	Quantity	Weight $P_{i0}Q_i$	Weighted Price Relatives
A	158	2.50	25	62.5	9875
B	113	8.75	15	131.3	14837
C	96	.99	60	59.4	5702
				253.2	30414

$$I = \frac{30414}{253.2} = 120$$

Cost of raw materials is up 20% for the chemical.

8.

Stock	Price Relatives	Base Price	Quantity	Weight	Weighted Price Relatives
Holiday	110	15.50	500	7750	852500
NY Electric	109	18.50	200	3700	403300
KY Gas	97	26.75	500	13375	1297375
PQ Soaps	108	42.25	300	12675	1368900
				37500	3922075

$$I = \frac{3922075}{37500} = 105$$

Portfolio up 5%

9.

Item	Price Relatives	Base Price	Quantity	Weight	Weighted Price Relatives
Beer	108	15.00	35,000	525,000	56,700,000
Wine	107	60.00	5,000	300,000	32,100,000
Soft Drink	102	9.80	60,000	588,000	59,976,000
				1,413,000	148,776,000

$$I = \frac{148,776,000}{1,413,000} = 105$$

10. a. Deflated 1980 wages: $\dfrac{\$7.27}{82.4}(100) = \$8.82$

   Deflated 2000 wages: $\dfrac{\$14.36}{172.6}(100) = \$8.32$

   b. $\dfrac{14.36}{7.27}(100) = 197.5$ The percentage increase in actual wages is 97.5%.

   c. $\dfrac{8.32}{8.82}(100) = 94.3$ The change in read wages is a decrease of 5.7%.

11.   1996   11.76 (100/156.9) = 7.49
         1997   12.23 (100/160.5) = 7.62
         1998   12.84 (100/163.0) = 7.88
         1999   13.35 (100/166.6) = 8.01
         2000   13.82 (100/172.6) = 8.01

   $\dfrac{8.01}{7.88} = 1.02$ the increase in real wages and salaries from 1998 to 2000 is 2%.

12. a.   1997   3929 (100/160.5) = 2448
         1998   4052 (100/163.0) = 2486
         1999   4260 (100/166.6) = 2557

   Manufacturers' shipments are increasing slightly in constant dollars when deflated using the CPI.

   b.   1997   3929 (100/131.8) = 2981
         1998   4052 (100/130.7) = 3100
         1999   4260 (100/133.0) = 3203

   c. The PPI is a better deflator since manufacturing shipments reflect prices paid by manufacturers.

13.

Year	Retail Sales ($)	CPI	Deflated Retail Sales ($)
1982	380,000	96.5	393,782
1987	520,000	113.6	457,746
1992	700,000	140.3	498,931
1997	870,000	160.5	542,056
2000	940,000	172.6	544,612

   In terms of constant dollars, the firm's sales are increasing moderately.

14. $I = \dfrac{300(18.00) + 400(4.90) + 850(15.00)}{350(18.00) + 220(4.90) + 730(15.00)}(100) = \dfrac{20,110}{18,328}(100) = 110$

15. $I = \dfrac{95(1200) + 75(1800) + 50(2000) + 70(1500)}{120(1200) + 86(1800) + 35(2000) + 60(1500)}(100) = 99$

   Quantities are down slightly.

16.

Model	Quantity Relatives	Base Quantity	Price ($)	Weight	Weighted Quantity Relatives
Sedan	85	200	15,200	3,040,000	258,400,000
Sport	80	100	17,000	1,700,000	136,000,000
Wagon	80	75	16,800	1,260,000	100,800,000
				6,000,000	495,200,000

$$I = \frac{495,200,000}{6,000,000} = 83$$

17. a/b.

	Price Index	
Year	1996 Base	1997 Base
1996	100.0	95.9
1997	104.3	100.0
1998	108.9	104.5
1999	114.3	109.6

18. a. Price Relatives A = (15.90 / 10.50) (100) = 151

   B = (32.00 / 16.25) (100) = 197

   C = (17.40 / 12.20) (100) = 143

   D = (35.50 / 20.00) (100) = 178

   b. $I = \dfrac{15.90(2000) + 32.00(5000) + 17.40(6500) + 35.50(2500)}{10.50(2000) + 16.25(5000) + 12.20(6500) + 20.00(2500)}(100) = 170$

19. $I = \dfrac{15.90(4000) + 32.00(3000) + 17.40(7500) + 35.50(3000)}{10.50(4000) + 16.25(3000) + 12.20(7500) + 20.00(3000)}(100) = 164$

20. $I_{Jan} = \dfrac{32.75(100) + 59(150) + 42(75) + 16.5(50)}{31.50(100) + 65(150) + 40(75) + 18(50)}(100) = 96$

   $I_{Mar} = \dfrac{32.50(100) + 57.5(150) + 39.5(75) + 13.75(50)}{31.50(100) + 65(150) + 40(75) + 18(50)}(100) = 92$

   Market is down compared to 1999.

21. Price Relatives:

			Jan	Mar
Oil	(32.75 / 31.50) (100)	=	104	103
Computer	(59.00 / 65.00) (100)	=	91	88
Steel	(42.00 / 40.00) (100)	=	105	99
Real Estate	(16.5 / 18.00) (100)	=	92	76

   $I_{Jan} = 96$ $I_{Mar} = 92$

22.

Product	Relatives	Base Price	Quantity	Weight	Weighted Price Relatives
Corn	113	2.30	1427	3282	370,866
Soybeans	123	5.51	350	1929	237,267
				5211	608,133

$$I = \frac{608,133}{5211} = 117$$

23. a.

Fruit	Price Relatives
Bananas	$(.51/.41)\,(100) = 124.4$
Apples	$(.85/.71)\,(100) = 119.7$
Oranges	$(.61/.56)\,(100) = 108.9$
Pears	$(.98/.64)\,(100) = 153.1$

b.

	Weights ($P_{io}Q_{io}$)	Price Relative	Product
	9.963	124.4	1239.3972
	14.129	119.7	1691.2413
	7.784	108.9	847.6776
	2.048	153.1	313.5488
Totals	33.924		4091.8649

$$I = \frac{4091.8649}{33.924} = 120.6$$

Fruit prices have increased by 20.6% over the 10-year period according to the index.

24.   Salaries in constant (1982-84) dollars are computed as follows:

    1970 $14,000 (100 / 38.8)   = $36,082
    1975 $17,500 (100 / 53.8)   = $32,528
    1980 $23,000 (100 / 82.4)   = $27,913
    1985 $37,000 (100 / 107.6) = $34,387
    1990 $53,000 (100 / 130.7) = $40,551
    1995 $65,000 (100 / 152.4) = $42,651
    2000 $80,000 (100 / 172.6) = $46,350

In constant dollar terms, real starting salaries have increased about 28% over this period.

25.   The stock market prices in constant (1982-84) dollars are computed as follows:

    1996 $51.00 (100 / 156.9)   = $32.50
    1997 $54.00 (100 / 160.5)   = $33.64
    1998 $58.00 (100 / 163.0)   = $35.58
    1999 $59.50 (100 / 166.6)   = $35.71
    2000 $59.00 (100 / 172.6)   = $34.18

The value of the stock, in real dollars, is only slightly more in 2000 than it is in 1996. Of course, if the stock paid a high dividend it may still have been a good investment over this period.

26. $$I = \frac{1200(30) + 500(20) + 500(25)}{800(30) + 600(20) + 200(25)}(100) = 143$$

Quantity is up 43%.

Chapter 18
Forecasting

Learning Objectives

1. Understand that the long-run success of an organization is often closely related to how well management is able to predict future aspects of the operation.

2. Know the various components of a time series.

3. Be able to use smoothing techniques such as moving averages and exponential smoothing.

4. Be able to use the least squares method to identify the trend component of a time series.

5. Understand how the classical time series model can be used to explain the pattern or behavior of the data in a time series and to develop a forecast for the time series.

6. Be able to determine and use seasonal indexes for a time series.

7. Know how regression models can be used in forecasting.

8. Know the definition of the following terms:

time series	mean squared error
forecast	moving averages
trend component	weighted moving averages
cyclical component	smoothing constant
seasonal component	seasonal constant
irregular component	

Solutions:

1. a.

Week	Time-Series Value	Forecast	Forecast Error	(Error)^2
1	8			
2	13			
3	15			
4	17	12	5	25
5	16	15	1	1
6	9	16	-7	<u>49</u>
				75

Forecast for week 7 is $(17 + 16 + 9) / 3 = 14$

b. MSE = 75 / 3 = 25

c. Smoothing constant = .3.

Week t	Time-Series Value Y_t	Forecast F_t	Forecast Error $Y_t - F_t$	Squared Error $(Y_t - F_t)^2$
1	8			
2	13	8.00	5.00	25.00
3	15	9.00	6.00	36.00
4	17	10.20	6.80	46.24
5	16	11.56	4.44	19.71
6	9	12.45	-3.45	11.90
				138.85

Forecast for week 7 is $.2(9) + .8(12.45) = 11.76$

d. For the $\alpha = .2$ exponential smoothing forecast MSE = 138.85 / 5 = 27.77. Since the three-week moving average has a smaller MSE, it appears to provide the better forecasts.

e. Smoothing constant = .4.

Week t	Time-Series Value Y_t	Forecast F_t	Forecast Error $Y_t - F_t$	Squared Error $(Y_t - F_t)^2$
1	8			
2	13	8.0	5.0	25.00
3	15	10.0	5.0	25.00
4	17	12.0	5.0	25.00
5	16	14.0	2.0	4.00
6	9	14.8	-5.8	<u>33.64</u>
				112.64

MSE = 112.64 / 5 = 22.53. A smoothing constant of .4 appears to provide better forecasts.

Forecast for week 7 is $.4(9) + .6(14.8) = 12.48$

2. a.

Week	Time-Series Value	4-Week Moving Average Forecast	(Error)^2	5-Week Moving Average Forecast	(Error)^2
1	17				
2	21				
3	19				
4	23				
5	18	20.00	4.00		
6	16	20.25	18.06	19.60	12.96
7	20	19.00	1.00	19.40	0.36
8	18	19.25	1.56	19.20	1.44
9	22	18.00	16.00	19.00	9.00
10	20	19.00	1.00	18.80	1.44
11	15	20.00	25.00	19.20	17.64
12	22	18.75	<u>10.56</u>	19.00	<u>9.00</u>
			77.18		51.84

b. MSE(4-Week) = 77.18 / 8 = 9.65

MSE(5-Week) = 51.84 / 7 = 7.41

c. For the limited data provided, the 5-week moving average provides the smallest MSE.

3. a.

Week	Time-Series Value	Weighted Moving Average Forecast	Forecast Error	(Error)^2
1	17			
2	21			
3	19			
4	23	19.33	3.67	13.47
5	18	21.33	-3.33	11.09
6	16	19.83	-3.83	14.67
7	20	17.83	2.17	4.71
8	18	18.33	-0.33	0.11
9	22	18.33	3.67	13.47
10	20	20.33	-0.33	0.11
11	15	20.33	-5.33	28.41
12	22	17.83	4.17	<u>17.39</u>
				103.43

b. MSE = 103.43 / 9 = 11.49

Prefer the unweighted moving average here.

c. You could always find a weighted moving average at least as good as the unweighted one. Actually the unweighted moving average is a special case of the weighted ones where the weights are equal.

4.

Week	Time-Series Value	Forecast	Error	(Error)^2
1	17			
2	21	17.00	4.00	16.00
3	19	17.40	1.60	2.56
4	23	17.56	5.44	29.59
5	18	18.10	-0.10	0.01
6	16	18.09	-2.09	4.37
7	20	17.88	2.12	4.49
8	18	18.10	-0.10	0.01
9	22	18.09	3.91	15.29
10	20	18.48	1.52	2.31
11	15	18.63	-3.63	13.18
12	22	18.27	3.73	13.91
				101.72

MSE = 101.72 / 11 = 9.25

α = .2 provided a lower MSE; therefore α = .2 is better than α = .1

5. a. $F_{13} = .2Y_{12} + .16Y_{11} + .64(.2Y_{10} + .8F_{10}) = .2Y_{12} + .16Y_{11} + .128Y_{10} + .512F_{10}$

$F_{13} = .2Y_{12} + .16Y_{11} + .128Y_{10} + .512(.2Y_9 + .8F_9) = .2Y_{12} + .16Y_{11} + .128Y_{10} + .1024Y_9 + .4096F_9$

$F_{13} = .2Y_{12} + .16Y_{11} + .128Y_{10} + .1024Y_9 + .4096(.2Y_8 + .8F_8) = .2Y_{12} + .16Y_{11} + .128Y_{10} + .1024Y_9 +$
    $.08192Y_8 + .32768F_8$

b. The more recent data receives the greater weight or importance in determining the forecast. The moving averages method weights the last n data values equally in determining the forecast.

6. a.

Month	Y_t	3-Month Moving Averages Forecast	(Error)^2	$\alpha = 2$ Forecast	(Error)^2
1	80				
2	82			80.00	4.00
3	84			80.40	12.96
4	83	82.00	1.00	81.12	3.53
5	83	83.00	0.00	81.50	2.25
6	84	83.33	0.45	81.80	4.84
7	85	83.33	2.79	82.24	7.62
8	84	84.00	0.00	82.79	1.46
9	82	84.33	5.43	83.03	1.06
10	83	83.67	0.45	82.83	0.03
11	84	83.00	1.00	82.86	1.30
12	83	83.00	0.00	83.09	0.01
			11.12		39.06

MSE(3-Month) = 11.12 / 9 = 1.24

MSE(α = .2) = 39.06 / 11 = 3.55

Use 3-month moving averages.

b. (83 + 84 + 83) / 3 = 83.3

7. a.

Month	Time-Series Value	3-Month Moving Average Forecast	(Error)^2	4-Month Moving Average Forecast	(Error)^2
1	9.5				
2	9.3				
3	9.4				
4	9.6	9.40	0.04		
5	9.8	9.43	0.14	9.45	0.12
6	9.7	9.60	0.01	9.53	0.03
7	9.8	9.70	0.01	9.63	0.03
8	10.5	9.77	0.53	9.73	0.59
9	9.9	10.00	0.01	9.95	0.00
10	9.7	10.07	0.14	9.98	0.08
11	9.6	10.03	0.18	9.97	0.14
12	9.6	9.73	0.02	9.92	0.10
			1.08		1.09

MSE(3-Month) = 1.08 / 9 = .12

MSE(4-Month) = 1.09 / 8 = .14

Use 3-Month moving averages.

b. Forecast = (9.7 + 9.6 + 9.6) / 3 = 9.63

c. For the limited data provided, the 5-week moving average provides the smallest MSE.

8. a.

Month	Time-Series Value	3-Month Moving Average Forecast	(Error)^2	$\alpha = .2$ Forecast	(Error)^2
1	240				
2	350			240.00	12100.00
3	230			262.00	1024.00
4	260	273.33	177.69	255.60	19.36
5	280	280.00	0.00	256.48	553.19
6	320	256.67	4010.69	261.18	3459.79
7	220	286.67	4444.89	272.95	2803.70
8	310	273.33	1344.69	262.36	2269.57
9	240	283.33	1877.49	271.89	1016.97
10	310	256.67	2844.09	265.51	1979.36
11	240	286.67	2178.09	274.41	1184.05
12	230	263.33	1110.89	267.53	1408.50
			17,988.52		27,818.49

MSE(3-Month) = 17,988.52 / 9 = 1998.72

MSE(α = .2) = 27,818.49 / 11 = 2528.95

Based on the above MSE values, the 3-month moving averages appears better. However, exponential smoothing was penalized by including month 2 which was difficult for any method to forecast. Using only the errors for months 4 to 12, the MSE for exponential smoothing is revised to

MSE(α = .2) = 14,694.49 / 9 = 1632.72

Thus, exponential smoothing was better considering months 4 to 12.

b. Using exponential smoothing,

$$F_{13} = \alpha Y_{12} + (1 - \alpha)F_{12} = .20(230) + .80(267.53) = 260$$

9. a. Smoothing constant = .3.

Month t	Time-Series Value Y_t	Forecast F_t	Forecast Error $Y_t - F_t$	Squared Error $(Y_t - F_t)^2$
1	105.0			
2	135.0	105.00	30.00	900.00
3	120.0	114.00	6.00	36.00
4	105.0	115.80	-10.80	116.64
5	90.0	112.56	-22.56	508.95
6	120.0	105.79	14.21	201.92
7	145.0	110.05	34.95	1221.50
8	140.0	120.54	19.46	378.69
9	100.0	126.38	-26.38	695.90
10	80.0	118.46	-38.46	1479.17
11	100.0	106.92	-6.92	47.89
12	110.0	104.85	5.15	26.52
			Total	5613.18

MSE = 5613.18 / 11 = 510.29

Forecast for month 13: $F_{13} = .3(110) + .7(104.85) = 106.4$

b. Smoothing constant = .5

Month t	Time-Series Value Y_t	Forecast F_t	Forecast Error $Y_t - F_t$	Squared Error $(Y_t - F_t)^2$
1	105			
2	135	105	30.00	900.00
3	120	.5(135) + .5(105) = 120	0.00	0.00
4	105	.5(120) + .5(120) = 120	-15.00	225.00
5	90	.5(105) + .5(120) = 112.50	-22.50	506.25
6	120	.5(90) + .5(112.5) = 101.25	18.75	351.56
7	145	.5(120) + .5(101.25) =110.63	34.37	1181.30
8	140	.5(145) + .5(110.63) = 127.81	12.19	148.60
9	100	.5(140) + .5(127.81) = 133.91	-33.91	1149.89
10	80	.5(100) + .5(133.91) = 116.95	-36.95	1365.30
11	100	.5(80) + .5(116.95) = 98.48	1.52	2.31
12	110	.5(100) + .5(98.48) = 99.24	10.76	115.78
				5945.99

MSE = 5945.99 / 11 = 540.55

Forecast for month 13: $F_{13} = .5(110) + .5(99.24) = 104.62$

Conclusion: a smoothing constant of .3 is better than a smoothing constant of .5 since the MSE is less for 0.3.

10. a/b.

Week	Time-Series Value	$\alpha = .2$ Forecast	$(\text{Error})^2$	$\alpha = .3$ Forecast	$(\text{Error})^2$
1	7.35				
2	7.40	7.35	.0025	7.35	.0025
3	7.55	7.36	.0361	7.36	.0361
4	7.56	7.40	.0256	7.42	.0196
5	7.60	7.43	.0289	7.46	.0196
6	7.52	7.46	.0036	7.50	.0004
7	7.52	7.48	.0016	7.51	.0001
8	7.70	7.48	.0484	7.51	.0361
9	7.62	7.53	.0081	7.57	.0025
10	7.55	7.55	.0000	7.58	.0009
			.1548		.1178

c. $\text{MSE}(\alpha = .2) = .1548 / 9 = .0172$

$\text{MSE}(\alpha = .3) = .1178 / 9 = .0131$

Use $\alpha = .3$.

$F_{11} = .3Y_{10} + .7F_{10} = .3(7.55) + .7(7.58) = 7.57$

11. a.

Method	Forecast	MSE
3-Quarter	80.73	2.53
4-Quarter	80.55	2.81

The 3-quarter moving average forecast is better because it has the smallest MSE.

b.

Method	Forecast	MSE
$\alpha = .4$	80.40	2.40
$\alpha = .5$	80.57	2.01

The $\alpha = .5$ smoothing constant is better because it has the smallest MSE.

c. The $\alpha = .5$ is better because it has the smallest MSE.

12. The following values are needed to compute the slope and intercept:

$$\sum t = 15 \quad \sum t^2 = 15 \quad \sum Y_t = 55 \quad \sum tY_t = 186$$

$$b_1 = \frac{\sum tY_t - (\sum t \sum Y_t)/n}{\sum t^2 - (\sum t)^2/n} = \frac{186 - (15)(55)/5}{55 - (15)^2/5} = 2.1$$

$$b_0 = \bar{Y} - b_1\bar{t} = 11 - 2.1(3) = 4.7$$

$$T_t = 4.7 + 2.1t$$

Forecast: $T_6 = 4.7 + 2.1(6) = 17.3$

13. The following values are needed to compute the slope and intercept:

$\Sigma t = 21 \quad \Sigma t^2 = 91 \quad \Sigma Y_t = 1171 \quad \Sigma t Y_t = 4037$

Computation of slope:

$$b_1 = \frac{\Sigma t Y_t - (\Sigma t \Sigma Y_t)/n}{\Sigma t^2 - (\Sigma t)^2/n} = \frac{4037 - (21)(1171)/6}{91 - (21)^2/6} = -3.5143$$

Computation of intercept:

$$b_0 = \bar{Y} - b_1 \bar{t} = 195.1667 - (-3.5143)(3.5) = 207.4668$$

Equation for linear trend: $T_t = 207.467 - 3.514t$

Forecast: $T_6 = 207.467 - 3.514(7) = 182.87$

14. The following values are needed to compute the slope and intercept:

$\Sigma t = 21 \quad \Sigma t^2 = 91 \quad \Sigma Y_t = 117.1 \quad \Sigma t Y_t = 403.7$

Computation of slope:

$$b_1 = \frac{\Sigma t Y_t - (\Sigma t \Sigma Y_t)/n}{\Sigma t^2 - (\Sigma t)^2/n} = \frac{403.7 - (21)(117.1)/6}{91 - (21)^2/6} = -0.3514$$

Computation of intercept:

$$b_0 = \bar{Y} - b_1 \bar{t} = 19.5167 - (-0.3514)(3.5) = 20.7466$$

Equation for linear trend: $T_t = 20.7466 - 0.3514t$

Conclusion: enrollment appears to be decreasing by an average of approximately 351 students per year.

15. The following values are needed to compute the slope and intercept:

$\Sigma t = 28 \quad \Sigma t^2 = 140 \quad \Sigma Y_t = 213,400 \quad \Sigma t Y_t = 865,400$

Computation of slope:

$$b_1 = \frac{\Sigma t Y_t - (\Sigma t \Sigma Y_t)/n}{\Sigma t^2 - (\Sigma t)^2/n} = \frac{865,400 - (28)(213,400)/7}{140 - (28)^2/7} = 421.429$$

Computation of intercept:

$$b_0 = \bar{Y} - b_1 \bar{t} = 30,485.714 - 421.429(4) = 28,800$$

Equation for linear trend: $T_t = 28,800 + 421.429\, t$

16.   A linear trend model is not appropriate. A nonlinear model would provide a better approximation.

17. a. A linear trend appears to be reasonable.

   b. The following values are needed to compute the slope and intercept:

$$\sum t = 36 \quad \sum t^2 = 204 \quad \sum Y_t = 223.8 \quad \sum tY_t = 1081.6$$

Computation of slope:

$$b_1 = \frac{\sum tY_t - (\sum t \sum Y_t)/n}{\sum t^2 - (\sum t)^2/n} = \frac{1081.6 - (36)(223.8)/8}{204 - (36)^2/8} = 1.7738$$

Computation of intercept:

$$b_0 = \bar{Y} - b_1\bar{t} = 27.975 - 1.7738(4.5) = 19.993$$

Equation for linear trend: $T_t = 19.993 + 1.774\,t$

Conclusion: The firm has been realizing an average cost increase of $1.77 per unit per year.

18. a. The following values are needed to compute the slope and intercept:

$$\sum t = 55 \quad \sum t^2 = 385 \quad \sum Y_t = 14.26 \quad \sum tY_t = 94.34$$

Computation of slope:

$$b_1 = \frac{\sum tY_t - (\sum t \sum Y_t)/n}{\sum t^2 - (\sum t)^2/n} = \frac{94.35 - (55)(14.26)/10}{385 - (55)^2/10} = .19297$$

Computation of intercept:

$$b_0 = \bar{Y} - b_1\bar{t} = 1.426 - .19297(5.5) = .365$$

Equation for linear trend: $T_t = .365 + .193\,t$

Forecast: $T_t = .365 + .193(11) = \$2.49$

   b. Over the past ten years the earnings per share have been increasing at the average rate of $.193 per year. Although this is a positive indicator of Walgreen's performance. More information would be necessary to conclude "good investment."

19. a. The following values are needed to compute the slope and intercept:

$$\sum t = 21 \quad \sum t^2 = 91 \quad \sum Y_t = 45.5 \quad \sum tY_t = 160.15$$

Computation of slope:

$$b_1 = \frac{\sum tY_t - (\sum t \sum Y_t)/n}{\sum t^2 - (\sum t)^2/n} = \frac{160.15 - (21)(45.5)/6}{91 - (21)^2/6} = 0.0514$$

Computation of intercept:

$$b_0 = \bar{Y} - b_1\bar{t} = 7.5833 - 0.0514(3.5) = 7.4033$$

Equation for linear trend: $T_t = 7.4033 + 0.0514\,t$

The number of applications is increasing by approximately 1630 per year.

b. 1996: $T_t = 7.4033 + 0.0514(7) = 7.7633$ or about 7.76%

1997: $T_t = 7.4033 + 0.0514(8) = 7.8148$ or about 7.81%

20. a. The following values are needed to compute the slope and intercept:

$$\Sigma t = 55 \quad \Sigma t^2 = 385 \quad \Sigma Y_t = 41841 \quad \Sigma tY_t = 262,923$$

Computation of slope:

$$b_1 = \frac{\Sigma tY_t - (\Sigma t \Sigma Y_t)/n}{\Sigma t^2 - (\Sigma t)^2/n} = \frac{262,923 - (55)(41,841)/10}{385 - (55)^2/10} = 397.545$$

Computation of intercept:

$$b_0 = \bar{Y} - b_1\bar{t} = 4184.1 - 397.545(5.5) = 1997.6$$

Equation for linear trend: $T_t = 1997.6 + 397.545\,t$

b. $T_{11} = 1997.6 + 397.545(11) = 6371$

$T_{12} = 1997.6 + 397.545(12) = 6768$

21. a. The following values are needed to compute the slope and intercept:

$$\Sigma t = 21 \quad \Sigma t^2 = 91 \quad \Sigma Y_t = 118.2 \quad \Sigma tY_t = 549.7$$

Computation of slope:

$$b_1 = \frac{\Sigma tY_t - (\Sigma t \Sigma Y_t)/n}{\Sigma t^2 - (\Sigma t)^2/n} = \frac{549.7 - (21)(118.2)/6}{91 - (21)^2/6} = 7.7714$$

Computation of intercept:

$$b_0 = \bar{Y} - b_1\bar{t} = (118.2/6) - 7.7714(21/6) = -7.5$$

Equation for linear trend: $T_t = -7.5 + 7.7714t$

b. 7.7714 ($M) per year

c. 1998 forecast: $T_8 = -7.5 + 7.7714\,(7) = 46.9$

22. a.

Year	Quarter	Y_t	Four-Quarter Moving Average	Centered Moving Average
1	1	4		
	2	2		
			3.50	
	3	3		3.750
			4.00	
	4	5		4.125
			4.25	
2	1	6		4.500
			4.75	
	2	3		5.000
			5.25	
	3	5		5.375
			5.50	
	4	7		5.875
			6.25	
3	1	7		6.375
			6.50	
	2	6		6.625
			6.75	
	3	6		
	4	8		

b.

Year	Quarter	Y_t	Centered Moving Average	Seasonal-Irregular Component
1	1	4		
	2	2		
	3	3	3.750	0.8000
	4	5	4.125	1.2121
2	1	6	4.500	1.3333
	2	3	5.000	0.6000
	3	5	5.375	0.9302
	4	7	5.875	1.1915
3	1	7	6.375	1.0980
	2	6	6.625	0.9057
	3	6		
	4	8		

Quarter	Seasonal-Irregular Component Values	Seasonal Index	Adjusted Seasonal Index
1	1.3333,1.0980	1.2157	1.2050
2	.60000,.9057	0.7529	0.7463
3	.80000,.9032	0.8651	0.8675
4	1.2121,1.1915	1.2018	1.1912
		4.0355	

Note: Adjustment for seasonal index = 4.000 / 4.0355 = 0.9912

23. a. Four quarter moving averages beginning with

(1690 + 940 + 2625 + 2500) / 4 = 1938.75

Other moving averages are

1966.25	2002.50
1956.25	2052.50
2025.00	2060.00
1990.00	2123.75

b.

Quarter	Seasonal-Irregular Component Values		Seasonal Index	Adjusted Seasonal Index
1	0.904	0.900	0.9020	0.900
2	0.448	0.526	0.4970	0.486
3	1.344	1.453	1.3985	1.396
4	1.275	1.164	1.2195	1.217
			4.0070	

Note: Adjustment for seasonal index = 4.000 / 4.007 = 0.9983

c. The largest seasonal effect is in the third quarter which corresponds to the back-to-school demand during July, August, and September of each year.

24.

Month	Seasonal-Irregular Component Values		Seasonal Index	Adjusted Seasonal Index
1	0.72	0.70	0.71	0.707
2	0.80	0.75	0.78	0.777
3	0.83	0.82	0.83	0.827
4	0.94	0.99	0.97	0.966
5	1.01	1.02	1.02	1.016
6	1.25	1.36	1.31	1.305
7	1.49	1.51	1.50	1.494
8	1.19	1.26	1.23	1.225
9	0.98	0.97	0.98	0.976
10	0.98	1.00	0.99	0.986
11	0.93	0.94	0.94	0.936
12	0.78	0.80	0.79	0.787
			12.05	

Notes: 1. Adjustment for seasonal index = 12 / 12.05 = 0.996

2. The adjustment is really not necessary in this problem since it implies more accuracy than is warranted. That is, the seasonal component values and the seasonal index were rounded to two decimal places.

25. a.   Use a twelve period moving averages. After centering the moving averages, you should obtain the following seasonal indexes:

Hour	Seasonal Index	Hour	Seasonal Index
1	0.771	7	1.207
2	0.864	8	0.994
3	0.954	9	0.850
4	1.392	10	0.647
5	1.571	11	0.579
6	1.667	12	0.504

b.   The hours of July 18 are number 37 to 48 in the time series. Thus the trend component for 7:00 a.m. on July 18 (period 37) would be

$$T_{37} = 32.983 + .3922(37) = 47.49$$

A summary of the trend components for the twelve hours on July 18 is as follows:

Hour	Trend Component	Hour	Trend Component
1	47.49	7	49.85
2	47.89	8	50.24
3	48.28	9	50.63
4	48.67	10	51.02
5	49.06	11	51.42
6	49.46	12	51.81

c.   Multiply the trend component in part b by the seasonal indexes in part a to obtain the twelve hourly forecasts for July 18. For example, 47.49 x (.771) = 36.6 or rounded to 37, would be the forecast for 7:00 a.m. on July 18th.

The seasonally adjusted hourly forecasts for July 18 are as follows:

Hour	Forecast	Hour	Forecast
1	37	7	60
2	41	8	50
3	46	9	43
4	68	10	33
5	77	11	30
6	82	12	26

26. a.   Yes, there is a seasonal effect over the 24 hour period.

Time Period	Seasonal Index
12 - 4 a.m.	1.696
4 - 8 a.m.	1.458
8 - 12	0.711
12 - 4 p.m.	0.326
4 - 8 p.m.	0.448
8 - 12	1.362

b.

Time Period	Forecast
12 - 4 p.m.	166,761.13
4 - 8 p.m.	146,052.99

27. a.

Month	Time-Series Value	3-Month Moving Average Forecast	Forecast Error	(Error)^2
1	34.8750			
2	35.6250			
3	34.6875			
4	33.5625	35.0625	-1.500	2.2500
5	32.6250	34.6250	-2.000	4.0000
6	34.0000	33.6250	0.3750	0.1406
7	33.6250	33.3958	0.2292	0.0525
8	35.0625	33.4167	1.6458	2.7088
9	34.0625	34.2292	-0.1667	0.0278
10	34.1250	34.2500	-0.1250	0.0156
11	33.2500	34.4167	-1.1667	1.3611
12	32.0625	33.8125	-1.7500	3.0625

Note: MSE = 13.6189/9 = 1.51

Forecast for December is (34.1250 + 33.2500 + 32.0625) / 3 = 33.1458

b. The weighted moving average forecasts for months 4-12 are 35.1000, 34.4250, 33.4125, 33.3625, 33.5750, 34.2750, 34.3750, 34.2875 and 33.7625.

Note: MSE = 12.3047/9 = 1.37

Forecast for December is 0.2 (34.125) + 0.4 (33.2500) + 0.4 (32.0625) = 32.9500

c. The exponential smoothing forecasts for months 2-12 are 34.8750, 35.1375, 34.9800, 34.4839, 33.8333, 33.8916, 33.7983, 34.2408, 34.1784, 34.1597 and 33.8413.

Note: MSE = 11.1881 = 1.24

Forecast for December is 0.35 (32.0625) + 0.65 (33.8413) = 33.2187

d.

Method	MSE
Moving Average	1.51
Weighted Moving Average	1.37
Exponential Smoothing	1.24

Exponential Smoothing is the best of the three approaches because it has the smallest MSE.

28. a.

Year	Time-Series Value	$\alpha = 0.1$ Forecast	$\alpha = 0.1$ (Error)^2	$\alpha = 0.2$ Forecast	$\alpha = 0.2$ (Error)^2
1972	55				
1974	38	55.0	289.0	55.0	289.0
1976	54	53.3	0.5	51.6	5.8
1978	37	53.4	268.0	52.1	227.4
1980	53	51.7	1.6	49.1	15.5
1982	40	51.9	140.7	49.9	97.0
1984	53	50.7	5.4	47.9	26.2
1986	36	50.9	222.2	48.9	166.5
1988	50	49.4	0.3	46.3	13.5
1990	37	49.5	155.6	47.1	101.2
1992	55	48.2	45.9	45.0	99.1
1994	39	48.9	98.1	47.0	64.6
1996	49	47.9	1.2	45.4	12.7
	Totals:		1228.4		1118.5

Smoothing Constant	MSE
0.1	1228.4/12 = 102.4
0.2	1118.5/12 = 93.2

A smoothing constant of 0.2 is better.

b. Using $\alpha = 0.2$

Forecast for 1998 = 0.2(49) + 0.8(45.4) = 46.1

29.   a.

Period	Time Series Value	$\alpha = .2$ Forecasts	$\alpha = .3$ Forecasts	$\alpha = .4$ Forecasts
1	28.9			
2	31.0	29.80	29.80	29.80
3	29.9	30.04	30.16	30.28
4	30.1	30.01	30.08	30.13
5	32.2	30.03	30.09	30.12
6	31.5	30.46	30.72	30.95
7	32.0	30.67	30.95	31.17
8	31.9	30.94	31.27	31.50
9	30.0	31.13	31.46	31.66

MSE($\alpha = .2$) = 1.40

MSE($\alpha = .3$) = 1.27

MSE($\alpha = .4$) = 1.23 $\alpha = .4$ provides the best forecast

b. Using $\alpha = .4$, $F_{10} = .4(.30) + .6(31.66) = 31.00$

30.

Week t	Time-Series Value Y_t	Forecast F_t	Forecast Error $Y_t - F_t$	Squared Error $(Y_t - F_t)^2$
1	22			
2	18	22.00	-4.00	16.00
3	23	21.20	1.80	3.24
4	21	21.56	-0.56	0.31
5	17	21.45	-4.45	19.80
6	24	20.56	3.44	11.83
7	20	21.25	-1.25	1.56
8	19	21.00	-2.00	4.00
9	18	20.60	-2.60	6.76
10	21	20.08	0.92	0.85
			Total	64.35

MSE = 64.35 / 9 = 7.15

Forecast for week 11:

$F_{11} = 0.2(21) + 0.8(20.08) = 20.26$

31.

t	Y_t	F_t	$Y_t - F_t$	$(Y_t - F_t)^2$
1	2,750			
2	3,100	2,750.00	350.00	122,500.00
3	3,250	2,890.00	360.00	129,600.00
4	2,800	3,034.00	-234.00	54,756.00
5	2,900	2,940.40	-40.40	1,632.16
6	3,050	2,924.24	125.76	15,815.58
7	3,300	2,974.54	325.46	105,924.21
8	3,100	3,104.73	-4.73	22.37
9	2,950	3,102.84	-152.84	23,260.07
10	3,000	3,041.70	-41.70	1,738.89
11	3,200	3,025.02	174.98	30,618.00
12	3,150	3,095.01	54.99	3,023.90
			Total:	488,991.18

MSE = 488,991.18 / 11 = 44,453.74

Forecast for week 13: $F_{13} = 0.4(3,150) + 0.6(3,095.01) = 3,117.01$

32. a.

Smoothing Constant	MSE
$\alpha = .3$	4,492.37
$\alpha = .4$	2,964.67
$\alpha = .5$	2,160.31

The $\alpha = .5$ smoothing constant is better because it has the smallest MSE.

b. $T_t = 244.778 + 22.088t$

MSE = 357.81

c.   Trend projection provides much better forecasts because it has the smallest MSE. The reason MSE is smaller for trend projection is that sales are increasing over time; as a result, exponential smoothing continuously underestimates the value of sales. If you look at the forecast errors for exponential smoothing you will see that the forecast errors are positive for periods 2 through 18.

33. a. Forecast for July is 236.97

   Forecast for August, using forecast for July as the actual sales in July, is 236.97.

   Exponential smoothing provides the same forecast for every period in the future. This is why it is not usually recommended for long-term forecasting.

   b. $T_t = 149.719 + 18.451t$

   Forecast for July is 278.88

   Forecast for August is 297.33

   c. The proposed settlement is not fair since it does not account for the upward trend in sales. Based upon trend projection, the settlement should be based on forecasted lost sales of $278,880 in July and $297,330 in August.

34. The following values are needed to compute the slope and intercept:

   $$\sum t = 28 \quad \sum t^2 = 140 \quad \sum Y_t = 1575 \quad \sum tY_t = 6491$$

   Computation of slope:

   $$b_1 = \frac{\sum tY_t - (\sum t \sum Y_t)/n}{\sum t^2 - (\sum t)^2/n} = \frac{6491 - (28)(1575)/7}{140 - (28)^2/7} = 6.8214$$

   Computation of intercept:

   $$b_0 = \bar{Y} - b_1\bar{t} = 225 - 6.8214(4) = 197.714$$

   Equation for linear trend: $T_t = 197.714 + 6.821t$

   Forecast: $T_8 = 197.714 + 6.821(8) = 252.28$

   $T_9 = 65.025 + 4.735(9) = 259.10$

35. The following values are needed to compute the slope and intercept:

   $$\sum t = 120 \quad \sum t^2 = 1240 \quad \sum Y_t = 578,400 \quad \sum tY_t = 5,495,900$$

   Computation of slope:

   $$b_1 = \frac{\sum tY_t - (\sum t \sum Y_t)/n}{\sum t^2 - (\sum t)^2/n} = \frac{5,495,900 - (120)(578,400)/15}{1240 - (120)^2/15} = 3102.5$$

   Computation of intercept:

   $$b_0 = \bar{Y} - b_1\bar{t} = (578,400/15) - 3102.5(120/15) = 13,740$$

   Equation for linear trend: $T_t = 13,740 + 3102.5\, t$

b. 1995 forecast: $T_t = 13,740 + 3102.5\,(16) = 60,277.5$

1996 forecast: $T_t = 13,740 + 3102.5\,(17) = 66,482.5$

36. a. A graph of these data shows a linear trend.

b The following values are needed to compute the slope and intercept:

$$\Sigma t = 15 \quad \Sigma t^2 = 55 \quad \Sigma Y_t = 200 \quad \Sigma t Y_t = 750$$

Computation of slope:

$$b_1 = \frac{\Sigma t Y_t - (\Sigma t \Sigma Y_t)/n}{\Sigma t^2 - (\Sigma t)^2/n} = \frac{750 - (15)(200)/5}{55 - (15)^2/5} = 15$$

Computation of intercept:

$$b_0 = \overline{Y} - b_1 \overline{t} = 40 - 15(3) = -5$$

Equation for linear trend: $T_t = -5 + 15t$

Conclusion: average increase in sales is 15 units per year

37. a. Yes, a linear trend appears to exist.

b The following values are needed to compute the slope and intercept:

$$\Sigma t = 28 \quad \Sigma t^2 = 140 \quad \Sigma Y_t = 595 \quad \Sigma t Y_t = 2815$$

Computation of slope:

$$b_1 = \frac{\Sigma t Y_t - (\Sigma t \Sigma Y_t)/n}{\Sigma t^2 - (\Sigma t)^2/n} = \frac{2815 - (28)(595)/7}{140 - (28)^2/7} = 15.5357$$

Computation of intercept:

$$b_0 = \overline{Y} - b_1 \overline{t} = 85 - 15.5357(4) = 22.857$$

Equation for linear trend: $T_t = 22.857 + 15.536t$

c. Forecast: $T_8 = 22.857 + 15.536(8) = 147.15$

38. a. A linear trend appears to be appropriate.

b. $T_2 = 12,899.98 + 2092.066\,t$

c. $2092.066 or $2,092,066

d. 1997: $T_{13} = 12,899.98 + 2092.066\,(13) = 40,096.838$ or $40,096,838

1998: $T_{14} = 12,899.98 + 2092.066\,(14) = 42,188.904$ or $42,188,904

39.   A linear trend does not seem appropriate. The plot indicates some type of curvilinear relationship over time such as

$$T_t = b_0 + b_1 t_t + b_2 t_t^2$$

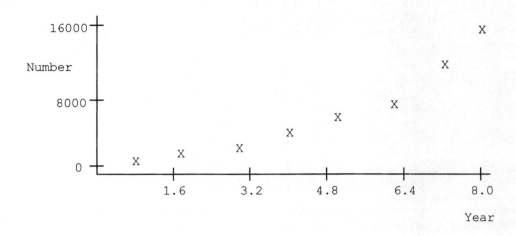

40. a.

t	Sales	Centered Moving Average	Seasonal-Irregular Component
1	6		
2	15		
3	10	9.250	1.081
4	4	10.125	0.395
5	10	11.125	0.899
6	18	12.125	1.485
7	15	13.000	1.154
8	7	14.500	0.483
9	14	16.500	0.848
10	26	18.125	1.434
11	23	19.375	1.187
12	12	20.250	0.593
13	19	20.750	0.916
14	28	21.750	1.287
15	25	22.875	1.093
16	18	24.000	0.750
17	22	25.125	0.876
18	34	25.875	1.314
19	28	26.500	1.057
20	21	27.000	0.778
21	24	27.500	0.873
22	36	27.625	1.303
23	30	28.000	1.071
24	20	29.000	0.690
25	28	30.125	0.929
26	40	31.625	1.265
27	35		
28	27		

b.

Quarter	Seasonal-Irregular Component Values		Seasonal Index
1	0.899, 0.848, 0.916, 0.876, 0.873, 0.929		0.890
2	1.485, 1.434, 1.287, 1.314, 1.303, 1.265		1.348
3	1.081, 1.154, 1.187, 1.093, 1.057, 1.071		1.107
4	0.395, 0.483, 0.593, 0.750, 0.778, 0.690		0.615
		Total	3.960

Quarter	Adjusted Seasonal Index
1	0.899
2	1.362
3	1.118
4	0.621

Note: Adjustment for seasonal index = 4.00 / 3.96 = 1.0101

c. Hudson Marine experiences the largest seasonal increase in quarter 2. Since this quarter occurs prior to the peak summer boating season, this result seems reasonable.

41. a.

t	Sales	Centered Moving Average	Seasonal-Irregular Component
1	4		
2	2		
3	1	3.250	0.308
4	5	3.750	1.333
5	6	4.375	1.371
6	4	5.875	0.681
7	4	7.500	0.533
8	14	7.875	1.778
9	10	7.875	1.270
10	3	8.250	0.364
11	5	8.750	0.571
12	16	9.750	1.641
13	12	10.750	1.116
14	9	11.750	0.766
15	7	13.250	0.528
16	22	14.125	1.558
17	18	15.000	1.200
18	10	17.375	0.576
19	13		
20	35		

Quarter	Seasonal-Irregular Component Values	Seasonal Index
1	1.371, 1.270, 1.116, 1.200	1.239
2	0.681, 0.364, 0.776, 0.576	0.597
3	0.308, 0.533, 0.571, 0.528	0.485
4	1.333, 1.778, 1.641, 1.558	1.578
	Total	3.899

Quarter	Adjusted Seasonal Index
1	1.271
2	0.613
3	0.498
4	1.619

Note: Adjustment for seasonal index = 4 / 3.899 = 1.026

b. The largest effect is in quarter 4; this seems reasonable since retail sales are generally higher during October, November, and December.

42. a. Note: To simplify the calculations the seasonal indexes calculated in problem 40 have been rounded to two decimal places.

Year	Quarter	Sales Y_t	Seasonal Factor S_t	Deseasonalized Sales $Y_t / S_t = T_t I_t$
1	1	6	0.90	6.67
	2	15	1.36	11.03
	3	10	1.12	8.93
	4	4	0.62	6.45
2	1	10	0.90	11.11
	2	18	1.36	13.24
	3	15	1.12	13.39
	4	7	0.62	11.29
3	1	14	0.90	15.56
	2	26	1.36	19.12
	3	23	1.12	20.54
	4	12	0.62	19.35
4	1	19	0.90	21.11
	2	28	1.36	20.59
	3	25	1.12	22.32
	4	18	0.62	29.03
5	1	22	0.90	24.44
	2	34	1.36	25.00
	3	28	1.12	25.00
	4	21	0.62	33.87
6	1	24	0.90	26.67
	2	36	1.36	26.47
	3	30	1.12	26.79
	4	20	0.62	32.26
7	1	28	0.90	31.11
	2	40	1.36	29.41
	3	35	1.12	31.25
	4	27	0.62	43.55

t	Y_t (deseasonalized)	tY_t	t^2
1	6.67	6.67	1
2	11.03	22.06	4
3	8.93	26.79	9
4	6.45	25.80	16
5	11.11	55.55	25
6	13.24	79.44	36
7	13.39	93.73	49
8	11.29	90.32	64
9	15.56	140.04	81
10	19.12	191.20	100
11	20.54	225.94	121
12	19.35	232.20	144
13	21.11	274.43	169
14	20.59	288.26	196
15	22.32	334.80	225
16	29.03	464.48	256
17	24.44	415.48	289
18	25.00	450.00	324
19	25.00	475.00	361
20	33.87	677.40	400
21	26.67	560.07	441
22	26.47	582.34	484
23	26.79	616.17	529
24	32.26	774.24	576
25	31.11	777.75	625
26	29.41	764.66	676
27	31.25	843.75	729
28	43.55	1,219.40	784
406	605.55	10,707.34	7,714

$\bar{t} = 14.5$　　$\bar{Y} = 21.627$　　$b_1 = 1.055$　　$b_0 = 6.329$　　$T_t = 6.329 + 1.055t$

b/c.

t	Trend Forecast
29	36.92
30	37.98
31	39.03
32	40.09

Year	Quarter	Trend Forecast	Seasonal Index	Quarterly Forecast
8	1	36.92	0.90	33.23
	2	37.98	1.36	51.65
	3	29.03	1.12	43.71
	4	40.09	0.62	24.86

43. a   Note: To simplify the calculations the seasonal indexes in problem 40 have been rounded to two decimal places.

Year	Quarter	Sales Y_t	Seasonal Factor S_t	Deseasonalized Sales $Y_t / S_t = T_t I_t$
1	1	4	1.27	3.15
	2	2	0.61	3.28
	3	1	0.50	2.00
	4	5	1.62	3.09
2	1	6	1.27	4.72
	2	4	0.61	6.56
	3	4	0.50	8.00
	4	14	1.62	8.64
3	1	10	1.27	7.87
	2	3	0.61	4.92
	3	5	0.50	10.00
	4	16	1.62	9.88
4	1	12	1.27	9.45
	2	9	0.61	14.75
	3	7	0.50	14.00
	4	22	1.62	13.58
5	1	18	1.27	14.17
	2	10	0.61	16.39
	3	13	0.50	26.00
	4	35	1.62	21.60

t	Y_t (deseasonalized)	tY_t	t^2
1	3.15	3.15	1
2	3.28	6.56	4
3	2.00	6.00	9
4	3.09	12.36	16
5	4.72	23.60	25
6	6.56	39.36	36
7	8.00	56.00	49
8	8.64	69.12	64
9	7.87	70.83	81
10	4.92	49.20	100
11	10.00	110.00	121
12	9.88	118.56	144
13	9.45	122.85	169
14	14.75	206.50	196
15	14.00	210.00	225
16	13.58	217.28	256
17	14.17	240.89	289
18	16.39	295.02	324
19	26.00	494.00	361
20	21.60	432.00	400
210	202.05	2783.28	2870

$\bar{t} = 10.5$ $\bar{Y} = 10.1025$ $b_1 = .995$ $b_0 = -.345$ $T_t = -.345 + .995t$

b.

y	Trend Forecast
21	20.55
22	21.55
23	22.54
24	23.54

c.

Year	Quarter	Trend Forecast	Seasonal Index	Quarterly Forecast
6	1	20.55	1.27	26.10
	2	21.55	0.61	13.15
	3	22.54	0.50	11.27
	4	23.54	1.62	38.13

Chapter 19
Nonparametric Methods

Learning Objectives

1. Learn the difference between parametric and nonparametric methods.

2. Know the particular advantages of nonparametric methods and when they are and when they are not applicable.

3. Learn how to use the sign test for the analysis of paired comparisons.

4. Be able to use the sign test to conduct hypothesis tests about a median.

5. Be able to use the Wilcoxon signed-rank test and the Mann-Whitney-Wilcoxon test to determine whether or not two populations have the same distribution.

6. Be able to use the Kruskal-Wallis tests for the comparison of k populations.

7. Be able to compute the Spearman rank correlation coefficient and test for a significant correlation between two sets of rankings.

Solutions:

1. Binomial Probabilities for $n = 10$, $p = .50$.

x	Probability	x	Probability
0	.0010	6	.2051
1	.0098	7	.1172
2	.0439	8	.0439
3	.1172	9	.0098
4	.2051	10	.0010
5	.2461		

$P(0) + P(1) = .0108$; adding $P(2)$, exceeds .025 required in the tail. Therefore, reject H_0 if the number of plus signs is less than 2 or greater than 8.

Number of plus signs is 7.

Do not reject H_0; conclude that there is no indication that a difference exists.

2. There are $n = 27$ cases in which a value different from 150 is obtained.

Use the normal approximation with $\mu = np = .5(27) = 13.5$ and

$$\sigma = \sqrt{.25n} = \sqrt{.25(27)} = 2.6$$

Use $x = 22$ as the number of plus signs and obtain the following test statistic:

$$z = \frac{x - \mu}{\sigma} = \frac{22 - 13.5}{2.6} = 3.27$$

With $\alpha = .01$, we reject if $z > 2.33$; since $z = 3.27 > 2.33$ we reject H_0.

Conclusion: the median is greater than 150.

3. a. Let p = probability the shares held will be worth more after the split

   H_0: $p \le .50$

   H_a: $p > .50$

   If H_0 cannot be rejected, there is no evidence to conclude stock splits continue to add value to stock holdings.

   b. Let x be the number of plus signs (increases in value).

   Use the binomial probability tables with $n = 18$ (there were 2 ties in the 20 cases)

   $P(x > 12) = .0482$

   Reject H_0 if the number of + signs is greater than 12.

   c. With $x = 14$, we reject H_0. The results support the conclusion that stock splits are beneficial for shareholders.

4.   We need to determine the number who said better and the number who said worse. The sum of the two is the sample size used for the study.

$$n = .34(1253) + .29(1253) = 789.4$$

Use the large sample test using the normal distribution. This means the value of n ($n = 789.4$ above) need not be integer. Hence,

$$\mu = .5\, n = .5(789.4) = 394.7$$

$$\sigma = \sqrt{.25n} = \sqrt{.25(789.4)} = 14.05$$

Let p = proportion of adults who feel children will have a better future.

H_0: $p \le .50$

H_a: $p > .50$

With $x = .34(1253) = 426$

$$z = \frac{x - \mu}{\sigma} = \frac{426 - 394.7}{14.05} = 2.23$$

With $\alpha = .05$, we reject H_0 if $z > 1.645$

Since $z = 2.23 > 1.645$, we reject H_0

Conclusion: more than half of the adults feel their children will have a better future.

5. $n = 185 + 165 = 350$

$$\mu = 0.5\, n = 0.5(350) = 175$$

$$\sigma = \sqrt{.25n} = \sqrt{.25(350)} = 9.35$$

Reject H_0 if $z < -1.96$ or if $z > 1.96$

$$z = \frac{185 - 175}{9.35} = 1.07$$

Do not reject H_0; cannot conclude there is a difference in preference for the two shows.

6. $n = 202 + 158 = 360$

$$\mu = 0.5\, n = 0.5(360) = 180$$

$$\sigma = \sqrt{.25n} = \sqrt{.25(360)} = 9.49$$

Reject H_0 if $z < -1.96$ or if $z > 1.96$

$$z = \frac{202 - 180}{9.49} = 2.32$$

Reject H_0; conclude Packard Bell and Compaq have different market shares.

7. $\mu = 0.5\ n = 0.5(300) = 150$

    $\sigma = \sqrt{.25n} = \sqrt{.25(300)} = 8.66$

    $z = \dfrac{165 - 150}{8.66} = 1.73$

    p-value $= 2(.5000 - .4582) = .0836$

    Do not reject H_0; we are unable to conclude that the median annual income differs.

8. $\mu = .5\ n = .5(150) = 75$

    $\sigma = \sqrt{.25n} = \sqrt{.25(150)} = 6.12$

    One tailed test: reject H_0 if $z > 1.645$

    For 98 + signs

    $z = \dfrac{98 - 75}{6.12} = 3.76$

    Reject H_0; conclude that a home team advantage exists.

9. H_0: Median ≤ 15

    H_a: Median > 15

    Use binomial probabilities with $n = 8$ and $p = .50$:

    One tail test with $\alpha = .05$,

    $$P(8\ +\text{'s}) = .0039$$
    $$P(7\ +\text{'s}) = \underline{.0312}$$
    $$.0351$$

    $$P(6\ +\text{'s}) = .1094$$

    Reject H_0 if 7 or 8 +'s. With 7 +'s in the sample, reject H_0. Data does enable us to conclude that there has been an increase in the median number of part-time employees.

10. H_0: Median $= 152$

    H_a: Median $\neq 152$

    $\mu = .5n = .5(225) = 112.5$

    $\sigma = \sqrt{.25n} = \sqrt{.25(225)} = 7.5$

    Reject H_0 if $z < -1.96$ or if $z > 1.96$

For 122 cases

$$z = \frac{122 - 112.5}{7.5} = 1.27$$

Do not reject H_0; we are unable to conclude that the median annual income needed differs from that reported in the survey.

11. $n = 50$

$$\mu = 0.5n = 0.5(50) = 25$$

$$\sigma = \sqrt{.25n} = \sqrt{.25(50)} = 3.54$$

Reject H_0 if $z > 1.645$

33 had wages greater than \$585

$$z = \frac{33 - 25}{3.54} = 2.26$$

Reject H_0; conclude that the median weekly wage is greater than \$585.

12. H_0: The populations are identical

H_a: The populations are not identical

Additive 1	Additive 2	Difference	Absolute Value	Rank	Signed Rank
20.12	18.05	2.07	2.07	9	+9
23.56	21.77	1.79	1.79	7	+7
22.03	22.57	-.54	.54	3	-3
19.15	17.06	2.09	2.09	10	+10
21.23	21.22	.01	.01	1	+1
24.77	23.80	.97	.97	4	+4
16.16	17.20	-1.04	1.04	5	-5
18.55	14.98	3.57	3.57	12	+12
21.87	20.03	1.84	1.84	8	+8
24.23	21.15	3.08	3.08	11	+11
23.21	22.78	.43	.43	2	+2
25.02	23.70	1.32	1.32	6	+6

Total 62

$$\mu_T = 0$$

$$\sigma_T = \sqrt{\frac{n(n+1)(2n+1)}{6}} = \sqrt{\frac{12(13)(25)}{6}} = 25.5$$

$$z = \frac{T - \mu_T}{\sigma_T} = \frac{62 - 0}{25.5} = 2.43$$

Two-tailed test. Reject H_0 if $z < -1.96$ or if $z > 1.96$

Since $z = 2.43 > 1.96$ we reject H_0.

Conclusion: there is a significant difference in the additives.

13.

Without Relaxant	With Relaxant	Difference	Rank of Absolute Difference	Signed Rank
15	10	5	9	9
12	10	2	3	3
22	12	10	10	10
8	11	-3	6.5	-6.5
10	9	1	1	1
7	5	2	3	3
8	10	-2	3	-3
10	7	3	6.5	6.5
14	11	3	6.5	6.5
9	6	3	6.5	6.5
				Total 36

$\mu_T = 0$

$$\sigma_T = \sqrt{\frac{n(n+1)(2n+1)}{6}} = \sqrt{\frac{10(11)(21)}{6}} = 19.62$$

$$z = \frac{T - \mu_T}{\sigma_T} = \frac{36}{19.62} = 1.83$$

One-tailed test. Reject H_0 if $z > 1.645$

Since $z = 1.83 > 1.645$ we reject H_0.

Conclusion: there is a significant difference in favor of the relaxant.

14.

Airport	Difference	Absolute Difference	Signed Rank
Boston Logan	0.19	0.19	10
Chicago Midway	-0.02	0.02	-3.5
Chicago O'Hare	0.05	0.05	6
Denver	0.04	0.04	5
Fort Lauderdale	-0.01	0.01	-1.5
Los Angeles	0.06	0.06	7
Miami	0.02	0.02	3.5
New York (JFK)	0.09	0.09	8
Orange County (CA)	0.16	0.16	9
Washington (Dulles)	0.01	0.01	1.5
			T = 45

$$\sigma_T = \sqrt{\frac{n(n+1)(2n+1)}{6}} = \sqrt{\frac{10(11)(21)}{6}} = 19.62$$

$$z = \frac{T - \mu_T}{\sigma_T} = \frac{45 - 0}{19.62} = 2.29$$

Reject H_0 if $z < -1.96$ or if $z > 1.96$.

Reject H_0; conclude a difference exists with Avis higher.

15.

Service #1	Service #2	Difference	Rank of Absolute Difference	Signed Rank
24.5	28.0	-3.5	7.5	-7.5
26.0	25.5	0.5	1.5	1.5
28.0	32.0	-4.0	9.5	-9.5
21.0	20.0	1.0	4	4.0
18.0	19.5	-1.5	6	-6.0
36.0	28.0	8.0	11	11.0
25.0	29.0	-4.0	9.5	-9.5
21.0	22.0	-1.0	4	-4.0
24.0	23.5	0.5	1.5	1.5
26.0	29.5	-3.5	7.5	-7.5
31.0	30.0	1.0	4	4.0
				$T = -22.0$

$\mu_T = 0$

$$\sigma_T = \sqrt{\frac{n(n+1)(2n+1)}{6}} = \sqrt{\frac{11(12)(23)}{6}} = 22.49$$

$$z = \frac{T - \mu_T}{\sigma_T} = \frac{-22}{22.49} = -.98$$

Reject H_0 if $z < -1.96$ or if $z > 1.96$. Since $z = -.98$, do not reject H_0; there is no significant difference.

16.

1997 P/E Ratio	Est. 1998 P/E Ratio	Difference	Rank	Signed Rank
40	32	8	9	9
24	22	2	2.5	2.5
21	23	-2	2.5	-2.5
30	23	7	8	8
25	19	6	6.5	6.5
19	19	0	0	0
20	17	3	4	4
29	19	10	10	10
35	20	15	11	11
17	18	-1	1	-1
33	27	6	6.5	6.5
20	16	4	5	5
				$T = 59$

$n = 11$ (discarding the 0)

$\mu_T = 0$

$$\sigma_T = \sqrt{\frac{n(n+1)(2n+1)}{6}} = \sqrt{\frac{11(12)(23)}{6}} = 22.49$$

Reject H_0 if $z < -1.96$ or if $z > 1.96$

$$z = \frac{59 - 0}{22.49} = 2.62$$

Reject H_0; conclude a difference exists between the 1997 P/E ratios and the estimated 1998 P/E ratios.

17.

Precampaign	Postcampaign	Difference	Rank of Absolute Difference	Signed Rank
130	160	-30	10	-10
100	105	-5	2.5	-2.5
120	140	-20	9	-9
95	90	5	2.5	2.5
140	130	10	4.5	4.5
80	82	-2	1	-1
65	55	10	4.5	4.5
90	105	-15	7.5	-7.5
140	152	-12	6	-6
125	140	-15	7.5	-7.5
				T = -32

$\mu_T = 0$

$$\sigma_T = \sqrt{\frac{n(n+1)(2n+1)}{6}} = \sqrt{\frac{10(11)(21)}{6}} = 19.62$$

$$z = \frac{T - \mu_T}{\sigma_T} = \frac{-32}{19.62} = -1.63$$

Reject H_0 if $z < -1.63$

Do not reject H_0; the difference is not significant at the $\alpha = .05$ level.

18.   Rank the combined samples and find the rank sum for each sample.

This is a small sample test since $n_1 = 7$ and $n_2 = 9$

Additive 1		Additive 2	
MPG	Rank	MPG	Rank
17.3	2	18.7	8.5
18.4	6	17.8	4
19.1	10	21.3	15
16.7	1	21.0	14
18.2	5	22.1	16
18.6	7	18.7	8.5
17.5	3	19.8	11
	34	20.7	13
		20.2	12
			102

T = 34

With $\alpha = .05$, $n_1 = 7$ and $n_2 = 9$

$T_L = 41$ and $T_U = 7(7 + 9 + 1) - 41 = 78$

Since $T = 34 < 41,$ we reject H_0

Conclusion: there is a significant difference in gasoline mileage

19. a.

Public Accountant	Rank		Financial Planner	Rank
25.2	5		24.0	2
33.8	19		24.2	3
31.3	16		28.1	10
33.2	18		30.9	15
29.2	13		26.9	8.5
30.0	14		28.6	11
25.9	6		24.7	4
34.5	20		28.9	12
31.7	17		26.8	7
26.9	8.5		23.9	1
	136.5			73.5

$$\mu_T = \frac{1}{2} n_1 (n_1 + n_2 + 1) = \frac{1}{2} 10(10 + 10 + 1) = 105$$

$T = 136.5$

$$\sigma_T = \sqrt{\frac{1}{12} n_1 n_2 (n_1 + n_2 + 1)} = \sqrt{\frac{1}{12}(10)(10)(21)} = 13.23$$

Reject H_0 if $z < -1.96$ or if $z > 1.96$

$$z = \frac{136.5 - 105}{13.23} = 2.38$$

Reject H_0; salaries differ significantly for the two professions.

b. Public Accountant: $30,200

Financial Planner: $26,700

Conclusion: there is a significant difference in starting salaries

20. a. Median → 4th salary for each

Men 49.9   Women 35.4

b.

Men	Rank	Women	Rank
30.6	4	44.5	8
75.5	14	35.4	5
45.2	9	27.9	3
62.2	13	40.5	7
38.2	6	25.8	2
49.9	11	47.5	10
55.3	12	24.8	1
			$T = 36$

From Tables $T_L = 37$

$T < T_L$ Reject H_0; Conclude populations differ. Men show higher salaries.

21.   Sum of ranks (Model 1) = 185.5

        Sum of ranks (Model 2) = 114.5

        Use T = 185.5

$$\mu_T = \frac{1}{2} n_1(n_1 + n_2 + 1) = \frac{1}{2} 12(12 + 12 + 1) = 150$$

$$\sigma_T = \sqrt{\frac{1}{12} n_1 n_2 (n_1 + n_2 + 1)} = \sqrt{\frac{1}{12}(12)(12)(25)} = 17.32$$

$$z = \frac{T - \mu_T}{\sigma_T} = \frac{185.5 - 150}{17.32} = 2.05$$

        Reject H_0 if z > 1.645

        Since $z = 2.05 > 1.645$ we reject H_0

        Conclusion: there is a significant difference between the populations.

22. H_0: There is no difference in the distributions of P/E ratios

        H_a: There is a difference between the distributions of P/E ratios

        We will reject H_0 if $z < -2.33$ or $z > 2.33$

Japan				United States		
Company	P/E Ratio	Rank		Company	P/E Ratio	Rank
Sumitomo Corp.	153	20		Gannet	19	6
Kinden	21	8		Motorola	24	11.5
Heiwa	18	5		Schlumberger	24	11.5
NCR Japan	125	19		Oracle Systems	43	16
Suzuki Motor	31	13		Gap	22	10
Fuji Bank	213	21		Winn-dixie	14	2
Sumitomo Chemical	64	17		Ingersoll-Rand	21	8
Seibu Railway	666	22		Am. Elec. Power	14	2
Shiseido	33	14		Hercules	21	8
Toho Gas	68	18		Times Mirror	38	15
	Total	157		WellPoint Health	15	4
				No. States Power	14	2
					Total	96

$$\mu_T = \frac{1}{2} n_1(n_1 + n_2 + 1) = \frac{1}{2} 10(10 + 12 + 1) = 115$$

$$\sigma_T = \sqrt{\frac{1}{12} n_1 n_2 (n_1 + n_2 + 1)} = \sqrt{\frac{1}{12}(10)(12)(10 + 12 + 1)} = 15.17$$

T = 157

$$z = \frac{157 - 115}{15.17} = 2.77$$

Since $z = 2.77 > 2.33$, reject H_0.

We conclude that there is a significant difference in P/E ratios for the two countries.

23.   Sum of ranks (Winter) = 71.5

Sum of ranks (Summer) = 138.5

Use T = 71.5

$$\mu_T = \frac{1}{2} n_1 (n_1 + n_2 + 1) = \frac{1}{2} 10(21) = 105$$

$$\sigma_T = \sqrt{\frac{1}{12} n_1 n_2 (n_1 + n_2 + 1)} = \sqrt{\frac{1}{12}(10)(10)(21)} = 13.23$$

$$z = \frac{T - \mu_T}{\sigma_T} = \frac{71.5 - 105}{13.23} = -2.53$$

Reject H_0 if $z < -1.96$ or if $z > 1.96$

Reject H_0; there is a significant difference

24.   Sum of ranks (Dallas) = 116   Sum of ranks (San Antonio) = 160

Use T = 116

$$\mu_T = \frac{1}{2} n_1 (n_1 + n_2 + 1) = \frac{1}{2} 10(24) = 120$$

$$\sigma_T = \sqrt{\frac{1}{12} n_1 n_2 (n_1 + n_2 + 1)} = \sqrt{\frac{1}{12}(10)(13)(24)} = 16.12$$

$$z = \frac{T - \mu_T}{\sigma_T} = \frac{116 - 120}{16.12} = -.25$$

Reject H_0 if $z < -1.96$ or if $z > 1.96$

Do not reject H_0; there is not significant evidence to conclude that there is a difference.

25.

Kitchen	Rank	Master Bedroom	Rank
25,200	16	18,000	4
17,400	2	22,900	11
22,800	10	26,400	17
21,900	9	24,800	15
19,700	5.5	26,900	18
23,000	12	17,800	3
19,700	5.5	24,600	14
16,900	1	21,000	7
21,800	8		89
23,600	13		
	82		

From Appendix B,

$T_L = 73$ $\qquad$ $T_U = n_1 (n_1 + n_2 + 1) - T_L$
$\qquad\qquad\qquad\qquad = 10 (10 + 8 + 1) - 73 = 117$

Reject H_0 if $T < 73$ or if $T > 117$

Since $T = 82$, do not reject

There is no significant difference between the costs.

26.

A	B	C
4	11	7
8	14	2
10	15	1
3	12	6
9	13	5
34	65	21

$$W = \frac{12}{(15)(16)}\left[\frac{(34)^2}{5} + \frac{(65)^2}{5} + \frac{(21)^2}{5}\right] - 3(16) = 10.22$$

$\chi^2_{.05} = 5.99147$ (2 degrees of freedom)

Reject H_0; conclude that the ratings for the products differ.

27.

A	B	C
11.5	5.0	17.0
2.5	11.5	20.0
8.0	2.5	15.0
10.0	4.0	8.0
8.0	6.0	16.0
18.0	1.0	19.0
	13.0	14.0
58.0	43.0	109.0

$$W = \frac{12}{(20)(21)}\left[\frac{(58)^2}{6} + \frac{(43)^2}{7} + \frac{(109)^2}{7}\right] - 3(21) = 9.06$$

$\chi^2_{.01} = 9.21034$ (2 degrees of freedom)

Do not reject H_0; we cannot conclude that there is a significant difference in test preparation programs.

28.

Swimming	Rank		Tennis	Rank		Cycling	Rank
408	8		415	9		385	5
380	4		485	14		250	1
425	11		450	13		295	3
400	6		420	10		402	7
427	12		530	15		268	2
Sum	41			61			18

$$W = \frac{12}{(15)(15+1)}\left[\frac{(41)^2}{5} + \frac{(61)^2}{5} + \frac{(18)^2}{5}\right] - 3(15+1) = 9.26$$

$\chi^2_{.05} = 5.99147$

Since $9.26 > 5.99147$, reject H_0; conclude that there is a significant difference in calories among the three activities.

29.

A	B	C
2	2	12
7	4.5	14
4.5	9	10.5
2	7	13
7	10.5	15
22.5	33	64.5

$$W = \frac{12}{(15)(16)}\left[\frac{(22.5)^2}{5} + \frac{(33)^2}{5} + \frac{(64.5)^2}{5}\right] - 3(16) = 9.555$$

$\chi^2_{.05} = 5.99147$ (2 degrees of freedom)

Since $9.555 > 5.99147$ we reject H_0 and conclude that there is a significant difference in gas mileage among the three automobiles.

30.

Course 1	Course 2	Course 3	Course 4
3	2	19	20
14	7	16	4
10	1	9	15
12	5	18	6
13	11	17	8
52	26	79	53

$$W = \frac{12}{(20)(21)} \left[\frac{(52)^2}{5} + \frac{(26)^2}{5} + \frac{(79)^2}{5} + \frac{(53)^2}{5} \right] - 3(21) = 8.03$$

$\chi^2_{.05} = 7.81473$ (3 degrees of freedom)

Since $8.03 > 7.81473$, we reject H_0 and conclude that there is a significant difference in the quality of courses offered by the four management development centers.

31.

M&Ms	Kit Kat	Milky Way II
10.5	9	3
7	5	6
13	14	4
15	12	2
10.5	8	1
56	48	16

$$W = \frac{12}{(15)(16)} \left[\frac{(56)^2}{5} + \frac{(48)^2}{5} + \frac{(16)^2}{5} \right] - 3(16) = 8.96$$

$\chi^2_{.05} = 5.99147$ (2 degrees of freedom)

Since $8.96 > 5.99147$ we reject H_0

There are significant differences in calorie content among the three candies.

32. a. $\Sigma d_i^2 = 52$

$$r_s = 1 - \frac{6 \Sigma d_i^2}{n(n^2 - 1)} = 1 - \frac{6(52)}{10(99)} = .68$$

b. $\sigma_{r_s} = \sqrt{\frac{1}{n-1}} = \sqrt{\frac{1}{9}} = .33$

$$z = \frac{r_s - 0}{\sigma_{r_s}} = \frac{.68}{.33} = 2.06$$

Reject if $z < -1.96$ or if $z > 1.96$

Since $z = 2.06 > 1.96$, we reject H_0.

Conclude that significant rank correlation exists.

33. Case 1:

$\Sigma d_i^2 = 0$

$$r_s = 1 - \frac{6 \Sigma d_i^2}{n(n^2 - 1)} = 1 - \frac{6(0)}{6(36 - 1)} = 1$$

Case 2:

$\Sigma d_i^2 = 70$

$$r_s = 1 - \frac{6\Sigma d_i^2}{n(n^2 - 1)} = 1 - \frac{6(70)}{6(36 - 1)} = -1$$

With perfect agreement, $r_s = 1$.

With exact opposite ranking, $r_s = -1$.

34. $\Sigma d_i^2 = 250$

$$r_s = 1 - \frac{6\Sigma d_i^2}{n(n^2 - 1)} = 1 - \frac{6(250)}{11(120)} = -.136$$

$$\sigma_{r_s} = \sqrt{\frac{1}{n-1}} = \sqrt{\frac{1}{10}} = .32$$

$$z = \frac{r_s - 0}{\sigma_{r_s}} = \frac{-.136}{.32} = -.425$$

Reject if $z < -1.96$ or if $z > 1.96$

Since $z = -.425$, we cannot reject H_0.

Conclude that there is not a significant relationship between the rankings.

35. a. $\Sigma d_i^2 = 54$

$$r = 1 - \frac{6\Sigma d_i^2}{n(n^2 - 1)} = 1 - \frac{6(54)}{10(10^2 - 1)} = .67$$

b. $H_0 : p_r \leq 0$

$H_a : p_r > 0$

$$\sigma_{r_s} = \sqrt{\frac{1}{n-1}} = \sqrt{\frac{1}{10-1}} = .3333$$

$$z = \frac{r_s - \mu_{r_s}}{\sigma_{r_s}} = \frac{.67 - 0}{.3333} = 2.02$$

p-value $= .5000 - .4783 = .0217$

c.   Reject H_0: Conclude a significant positive rank correlation.

36.

Driving Distance	Putting	d_i	d_i^2
1	5	-4	16
5	6	-1	1
4	10	-6	36
9	2	7	49
6	7	-1	1
10	3	7	49
2	8	-6	36
3	9	-6	36
7	4	3	9
8	1	7	49
			$\Sigma d_i^2 = 282$

$$r_s = 1 - \frac{6\Sigma d_i^2}{n(n^2 - 1)} = 1 - \frac{6(282)}{10(100 - 1)} = -.709$$

$$\mu_{r_s} = 0$$

$$\sigma_{r_s} = \sqrt{\frac{1}{n-1}} = \sqrt{\frac{1}{9}} = .333$$

Reject H_0 if $z < -1.645$ or if $z > 1.645$

$$z = \frac{-.709 - 0}{.333} = -2.13$$

Reject H_0; there is a significant negative rank correlation between driving distance and putting.

37. $\Sigma d_i^2 = 38$

$$r_s = 1 - \frac{6\Sigma d_i^2}{n(n^2 - 1)} = 1 - \frac{6(38)}{10(99)} = .77$$

$$\mu_{r_s} = 0$$

$$\sigma_{r_s} = \sqrt{\frac{1}{n-1}} = \sqrt{\frac{1}{9}} = .3333$$

Reject H_0 if $z < -1.645$ or if $z > 1.645$

$$z = \frac{r_s - 0}{\sigma_{r_s}} = \frac{.77}{.3333} = 2.31$$

Reject H_0; there is a significant rank correlation between current students and recent graduates.

38. $n = 905 + 1045 = 1950$

$\mu = .5n = .5(1950) = 975$

$\sigma = \sqrt{.25n} = \sqrt{.25(1950)} = 22.01$

Reject H_0 if $z < -1.96$ or if $z > 1.96$

$$z = \frac{905 - 975}{22.01} = -3.17$$

Reject H_0; the difference in the favor-oppose opinion is significant.

39. a. $n = 11 + 32 = 43$

H_0: Median $\geq$ \$118,000

H_a: Median $<$ \$118,000

$\mu = .5n = .5(43) = 21.5$

$\sigma = \sqrt{.25n} = \sqrt{.25(43)} = 3.2787$

$$z = \frac{x - \mu}{\sigma} = \frac{11 - 21.5}{3.2787} = -3.20$$

Since $z = -3.20 < -1.645$, reject H_0.

We conclude that the median resale price for homes in Houston, Texas is below the national median.

b. $n = 27 + 13 = 40$

H_0: Median $\leq$ \$118,000

H_a: Median $>$ \$118,000

$\mu = .5 n = .5(40) = 20$

$\sigma = \sqrt{.25n} = \sqrt{.25(40)} = 3.1623$

$$z = \frac{x - \mu}{\sigma} = \frac{27 - 20}{3.1623} = 2.21$$

Since $z = 2.21 > 1.645$, reject H_0.

We conclude that the median resale price for homes in Boston, Massachusetts is above the national median.

40.   Use the Wilcoxon Signed Rank Test

Homemaker	Difference	Signed Rank
1	-250	-11
2	40	2
3	50	3
4	-150	-6
5	-330	-12
6	-180	-7
7	-190	-8.5
8	-230	-10
9	-100	-5
10	-190	-8.5
11	-90	-4
12	20	1
		T = -66

$\mu_T = 0$

$$\sigma_T = \sqrt{\frac{n(n+1)(2n+1)}{6}} = \sqrt{\frac{12(13)(25)}{6}} = 25.5$$

Reject H_0 if $z < -1.96$ or if $z > 1.96$

$$z = \frac{T - \mu_T}{\sigma_T} = \frac{-66}{25.5} = -2.59$$

Reject H_0; conclude that the models differ in terms of selling prices.

41.

Difference	Rank of Absolute Difference	Signed Rank
1.5	10	10.0
1.2	9	9.0
-.2	2.5	-2.5
0	—	—
.5	4	4.0
.7	6	6.0
.8	7	7.0
1.0	8	8.0
0	—	—
.6	5	5.0
.2	2.5	2.5
-.01	1	-1.0
		T = 48

$$\sigma_T = \sqrt{\frac{n(n+1)(2n+1)}{6}} = \sqrt{\frac{10(11)(21)}{6}} = 19.62$$

Reject H_0 if $z > 1.645$

$$z = \frac{T - \mu_T}{\sigma_T} = \frac{48}{19.62} = 2.45$$

Reject H_0; conclude that there is a significant weight gain.

42.   Use the MWW test.

Sum of ranks (line 1) = 70

Sum of ranks (line 2) = 183

T = 70

$$\mu_T = \frac{1}{2} n_1(n_1 + n_2 + 1) = \frac{1}{2} 10(23) = 115$$

$$\sigma_T = \sqrt{\frac{1}{12} n_1 n_2 (n_1 + n_2 + 1)} = \sqrt{\frac{1}{12}(10)(12)(23)} = 15.17$$

Reject H_0 if z < -1.645 or if z > 1.645

$$z = \frac{T - \mu_T}{\sigma_T} = \frac{70 - 115}{15.17} = -2.97$$

Reject H_0; conclude that the weights differ for the two production lines.

43.

Method 1	Method 2	Method 3
8.5	4.5	2.0
15.0	14.0	7.0
6.0	16.0	10.0
17.0	8.5	1.0
18.0	12.5	3.0
12.5	11.0	4.5
77.0	66.5	27.5

$$W = \frac{12}{(18)(19)} \left[\frac{(77)^2}{6} + \frac{(66.5)^2}{6} + \frac{(27.5)^2}{6} \right] - 3(19) = 7.956$$

$\chi^2_{.05} = 5.99147$ (3 degrees of freedom)

Since 7.956 > 5.99147, we reject H_0 and conclude that there is a significant difference among the methods.

44.

No Program	Company Program	Off Site Program
16	12	7
9	20	1
10	17	4
15	19	2
11	6	3
13	18	8
	14	5
74	106	30

$$W = \frac{12}{(20)(21)}\left[\frac{(74)^2}{6} + \frac{(106)^2}{7} + \frac{(30)^2}{7}\right] - 3(21) = 12.61$$

$\chi^2_{.05} = 7.37776$ (2 degrees of freedom)

Since $12.61 > 7.37776$, we reject H_0; there is a significant difference among the programs.

45.

Black	Jennings	Swanson	Wilson
22.5	20.5	22.5	9.5
9.5	27.0	6.0	17.5
8.0	7.0	2.5	1.0
2.5	17.5	12.5	5.0
26.0	28.5	17.5	24.0
4.0	28.5	12.5	20.5
	17.5	15.0	
	25.0	14.0	
		11.0	
72.5	171.5	113.5	77.5

$$W = \frac{12}{(29)(30)}\left[\frac{(72.5)^2}{6} + \frac{(171.5)^2}{8} + \frac{(113.5)^2}{9} + \frac{(77.5)^2}{6}\right] - 3(30) = 6.344$$

$\chi^2_{.05} = 7.81473$ (3 degrees of freedom)

Since $6.344 < 7.81473$ we cannot reject H_0. We cannot conclude that there is a significant difference among the course evaluation ratings for the 4 instructors.

46. $\Sigma d_i^2 = 136$

$$r_s = 1 - \frac{6\Sigma d_i^2}{n(n^2 - 1)} = 1 - \frac{6(136)}{15(224)} = .76$$

$$\sigma_{r_s} = \sqrt{\frac{1}{n-1}} = \sqrt{\frac{1}{14}} = .2673$$

Reject H_0 if $z < -1.645$ or if $z > 1.645$

$$z = \frac{r_s - \mu_{r_s}}{\sigma_{r_s}} = \frac{.76}{.2673} = 2.84$$

Reject H_0; conclude that there is a significant rank correlation between the two exams.

Chapter 20
Statistical Methods for Quality Control

Learning Objectives

1. Learn about the importance of quality control and how statistical methods can assist in the quality control process.

2. Learn about acceptance sampling procedures.

3. Know the difference between consumer's risk and producer's risk.

4. Be able to use the binomial probability distribution to develop acceptance sampling plans.

5. Know what is meant by multiple sampling plans.

6. Be able to construct quality control charts and understand how they are used for statistical process control.

7. Know the definitions of the following terms:

producer's risk	assignable causes
consumer's risk	common causes
acceptance sampling	control charts
acceptable criterion	upper control limit
operating characteristic curve	lower control limit

Solutions:

1. a. For $n = 4$

$$UCL = \mu + 3(\sigma / \sqrt{n}) = 12.5 + 3(.8 / \sqrt{4}) = 13.7$$
$$LCL = \mu - 3(\sigma / \sqrt{n}) = 12.5 - 3(.8 / \sqrt{4}) = 11.3$$

   b. For $n = 8$

$$UCL = \mu + 3(.8 / \sqrt{8}) = 13.35$$
$$LCL = \mu - 3(.8 / \sqrt{8}) = 11.65$$

   For $n = 16$

$$UCL = \mu + 3(.8 / \sqrt{16}) = 13.10$$
$$LCL = \mu - 3(.8 / \sqrt{16}) = 11.90$$

   c. UCL and LCL become closer together as n increases. If the process is in control, the larger samples should have less variance and should fall closer to 12.5.

2. a. $\mu = \dfrac{677.5}{25(5)} = 5.42$

   b.
$$UCL = \mu + 3(\sigma / \sqrt{n}) = 5.42 + 3(.5 / \sqrt{5}) = 6.09$$
$$LCL = \mu - 3(\sigma / \sqrt{n}) = 5.42 - 3(.5 / \sqrt{5}) = 4.75$$

3. a. $p = \dfrac{135}{25(100)} = 0.0540$

   b. $\sigma_{\bar{p}} = \sqrt{\dfrac{p(1-p)}{n}} = \sqrt{\dfrac{0.0540(0.9460)}{100}} = 0.0226$

   c.
$$UCL = p + 3\,\sigma_{\bar{p}} = 0.0540 + 3(0.0226) = 0.1218$$
$$LCL = p - 3\,\sigma_{\bar{p}} = 0.0540 - 3(0.0226) = -0.0138$$

   Use LCL $= 0$

4. R Chart:
$$UCL = \bar{R}D_4 = 1.6(1.864) = 2.98$$
$$LCL = \bar{R}D_3 = 1.6(0.136) = 0.22$$

   $\bar{x}$ Chart:
$$UCL = \bar{\bar{x}} + A_2\bar{R} = 28.5 + 0.373(1.6) = 29.10$$
$$LCL = \bar{\bar{x}} - A_2\bar{R} = 28.5 - 0.373(1.6) = 27.90$$

5. a.
$$UCL = \mu + 3(\sigma / \sqrt{n}) = 128.5 + 3(.4 / \sqrt{6}) = 128.99$$
$$LCL = \mu - 3(\sigma / \sqrt{n}) = 128.5 - 3(.4 / \sqrt{6}) = 128.01$$

b. $\bar{x} = \Sigma x_i / n = \dfrac{772.4}{6} = 128.73$ in control

c. $\bar{x} = \Sigma x_i / n = \dfrac{774.3}{6} = 129.05$ out of control

6.   Process Mean $= \dfrac{20.12 + 19.90}{2} = 20.01$

$$\text{UCL} = \mu + 3(\sigma / \sqrt{n}) = 20.01 + 3(\sigma / \sqrt{5}) = 20.12$$

Solve for σ:

$$\sigma = \frac{(20.12 - 20.01)\sqrt{5}}{3} = 0.082$$

7.

Sample Number	Observations			$\bar{x}_i$	R_i
1	31	42	28	33.67	14
2	26	18	35	26.33	17
3	25	30	34	29.67	9
4	17	25	21	21.00	8
5	38	29	35	34.00	9
6	41	42	36	39.67	6
7	21	17	29	22.33	12
8	32	26	28	28.67	6
9	41	34	33	36.00	8
10	29	17	30	25.33	13
11	26	31	40	32.33	14
12	23	19	25	22.33	6
13	17	24	32	24.33	15
14	43	35	17	31.67	26
15	18	25	29	24.00	11
16	30	42	31	34.33	12
17	28	36	32	32.00	8
18	40	29	31	33.33	11
19	18	29	28	25.00	11
20	22	34	26	27.33	12

$\bar{R} = 11.4$ and $\bar{\bar{x}} = 29.17$

R Chart:

$$\text{UCL} = \bar{R}D_4 = 11.4(2.575) = 29.35$$
$$\text{LCL} = \bar{R}D_3 = 11.4(0) = 0$$

$\bar{x}$ Chart:

$$\text{UCL} = \bar{\bar{x}} + A_2\bar{R} = 29.17 + 1.023(11.4) = 40.8$$
$$\text{LCL} = \bar{\bar{x}} - A_2\bar{R} = 29.17 - 1.023(11.4) = 17.5$$

R Chart:

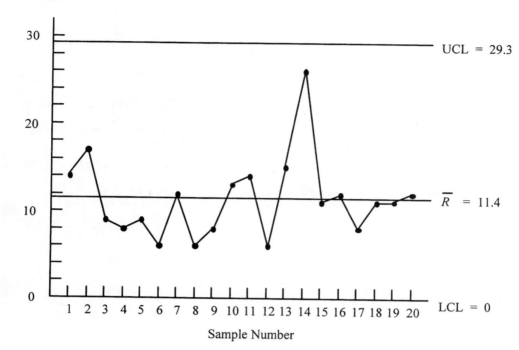

$\bar{x}$ Chart:

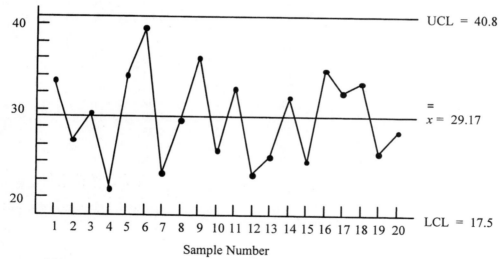

8. a. $p = \dfrac{141}{20(150)} = 0.0470$

b. $\sigma_{\bar{p}} = \sqrt{\dfrac{p(1-p)}{n}} = \sqrt{\dfrac{0.0470(0.9530)}{150}} = 0.0173$

$$\text{UCL} = p + 3\,\sigma_{\bar{p}} = 0.0470 + 3(0.0173) = 0.0989$$
$$\text{LCL} = p - 3\,\sigma_{\bar{p}} = 0.0470 - 3(0.0173) = -0.0049$$

Use LCL = 0

c. $\bar{p} = \dfrac{12}{150} = 0.08$

Process should be considered in control.

d. $p = .047, n = 150$

$$UCL = np + 3\sqrt{np(1-p)} = 150(0.047) + 3\sqrt{150(0.047)(0.953)} = 14.826$$
$$LCL = np - 3\sqrt{np(1-p)} = 150(0.047) - 3\sqrt{150(0.047)(0.953)} = -0.726$$

Thus, the process is out of control if more than 14 defective packages are found in a sample of 150.

e. Process should be considered to be in control since 12 defective packages were found.

f. The np chart may be preferred because a decision can be made by simply counting the number of defective packages.

9. a. Total defectives: 165

$$p = \dfrac{165}{20(200)} = 0.0413$$

b. $\sigma_{\bar{p}} = \sqrt{\dfrac{p(1-p)}{n}} = \sqrt{\dfrac{0.0413(0.9587)}{200}} = 0.0141$

$$UCL = p + 3\sigma_{\bar{p}} = 0.0413 + 3(0.0141) = 0.0836$$
$$LCL = p - 3\sigma_{\bar{p}} = 0.0413 + 3(0.0141) = -0.0010$$

Use LCL = 0

c. $\bar{p} = \dfrac{20}{200} = 0.10$ \quad Out of control

d. $p = .0413, n = 200$

$$UCL = np + 3\sqrt{np(1-p)} = 200(0.0413) + 3\sqrt{200(0.0413)(0.9587)} = 16.702$$
$$LCL = np - 3\sqrt{np(1-p)} = 200(0.0413) - 3\sqrt{200(0.0413)(0.9587)} = 0.1821$$

e. The process is out of control since 20 defective pistons were found.

10. $f(x) = \dfrac{n!}{x!(n-x)!} p^x (1-p)^{n-x}$

When $p = .02$, the probability of accepting the lot is

$$f(0) = \dfrac{25!}{0!(25-0)!}(0.02)^0 (1-0.02)^{25} = 0.6035$$

When $p = .06$, the probability of accepting the lot is

$$f(0) = \frac{25!}{0!(25-0)!}(0.06)^0(1-0.06)^{25} = 0.2129$$

11. a. Using binomial probabilities with $n = 20$ and $p_0 = .02$.

P (Accept lot) $= f(0) = .6676$

Producer's risk: $\alpha = 1 - .6676 = .3324$

b. P (Accept lot) $= f(0) = .2901$

Producer's risk: $\alpha = 1 - .2901 = .7099$

12. At $p_0 = .02$, the $n = 20$ and $c = 1$ plan provides

P (Accept lot) $= f(0) + f(1) = .6676 + .2725 = .9401$

Producer's risk: $\alpha = 1 - .9401 = .0599$

At $p_0 = .06$, the $n = 20$ and $c = 1$ plan provides

P (Accept lot) $= f(0) + f(1) = .2901 + .3703 = .6604$

Producer's risk: $\alpha = 1 - .6604 = .3396$

For a given sample size, the producer's risk decreases as the acceptance number c is increased.

13. a. Using binomial probabilities with $n = 20$ and $p_0 = .03$.

P(Accept lot) $= f(0) + f(1)$

$\qquad = .5438 + .3364 = .8802$

Producer's risk: $\alpha = 1 - .8802 = .1198$

b. With $n = 20$ and $p_1 = .15$.

P(Accept lot) $= f(0) + f(1)$

$\qquad = .0388 + .1368 = .1756$

Consumer's risk: $\beta = .1756$

c. The consumer's risk is acceptable; however, the producer's risk associated with the $n = 20, c = 1$ plan is a little larger than desired.

14.

	c	P (Accept) $p_0 = .05$	Producer's Risk α	P (accept) $p_1 = .30$	Consumer's Risk β
($n = 10$)	0	.5987	.4013	.0282	.0282
	1	.9138	.0862	.1493	.1493
	2	.9884	.0116	.3828	.3828
($n = 15$)	0	.4633	.5367	.0047	.0047
	1	.8291	.1709	.0352	.0352
	2	.9639	.0361	.1268	.1268
	3	.9946	.0054	.2968	.2968
($n = 20$)	0	.3585	.6415	.0008	.0008
	1	.7359	.2641	.0076	.0076
	2	.9246	.0754	.0354	.0354
	3	.9842	.0158	.1070	.1070

The plan with $n = 15$, $c = 2$ is close with $\alpha = .0361$ and $\beta = .1268$. However, the plan with $n = 20$, $c = 3$ is necessary to meet both requirements.

15. a. P (Accept) shown for p values below:

c	$p = .01$	$p = .05$	$p = .08$	$p = .10$	$p = .15$
0	.8179	.3585	.1887	.1216	.0388
1	.9831	.7359	.5169	.3918	.1756
2	.9990	.9246	.7880	.6770	.4049

The operating characteristic curves would show the P (Accept) versus p for each value of c.

b. P (Accept)

c	At $p_0 = .01$	Producer's Risk	At $p_1 = .08$	Consumer's Risk
0	.8179	.1821	.1887	.1887
1	.9831	.0169	.5169	.5169
2	.9990	.0010	.7880	.7880

16. a. $\mu = \dfrac{\Sigma \bar{x}}{20} = \dfrac{1908}{20} = 95.4$

b.

$$\text{UCL} = \mu + 3(\sigma / \sqrt{n}) = 95.4 + 3(.50 / \sqrt{5}) = 96.07$$
$$\text{LCL} = \mu - 3(\sigma / \sqrt{n}) = 95.4 - 3(.50 / \sqrt{5}) = 94.73$$

c. No; all were in control

17. a. For $n = 10$

$$\text{UCL} = \mu + 3(\sigma / \sqrt{n}) = 350 + 3(15 / \sqrt{10}) = 364.23$$
$$\text{LCL} = \mu - 3(\sigma / \sqrt{n}) = 350 - 3(15 / \sqrt{10}) = 335.77$$

For $n = 20$

$$UCL = 350 + 3(15 / \sqrt{20}) = 360.06$$
$$LCL = 350 - 3(15 / \sqrt{20}) = 339.94$$

For $n = 30$

$$UCL = 350 + 3(15 / \sqrt{30}) = 358.22$$
$$LCL = 350 - 3(15 / \sqrt{30}) = 343.78$$

b. Both control limits come closer to the process mean as the sample size is increased.

c. The process will be declared out of control and adjusted when the process is in control.

d. The process will be judged in control and allowed to continue when the process is out of control.

e. All have $z = 3$ where area $= .4986$

$$P \text{ (Type I)} = 1 - 2 (.4986) = .0028$$

18. R Chart:

$$UCL = \overline{R}D_4 = 2(2.115) = 4.23$$
$$LCL = \overline{R}D_3 = 2(0) = 0$$

$\overline{x}$ Chart:

$$UCL = \overline{\overline{x}} + A_2\overline{R} = 5.42 + 0.577(2) = 6.57$$
$$LCL = \overline{\overline{x}} - A_2\overline{R} = 5.42 - 0.577(2) = 4.27$$

Estimate of Standard Deviation:

$$\hat{\sigma} = \frac{\overline{R}}{d_2} = \frac{2}{2.326} = 0.86$$

19. $\overline{R} = 0.665 \quad \overline{\overline{x}} = 95.398$

$\overline{x}$ Chart:

$$UCL = \overline{\overline{x}} + A_2\overline{R} = 95.398 + 0.577(0.665) = 95.782$$
$$LCL = \overline{\overline{x}} - A_2\overline{R} = 95.398 - 0.577(0.665) = 95.014$$

R Chart:

$$UCL = \overline{R}D_4 = 0.665(2.115) = 1.406$$
$$LCL = \overline{R}D_3 = 0.665(0) = 0$$

The R chart indicated the process variability is in control. All sample ranges are within the control limits. However, the process mean is out of control. Sample 11 ($\overline{x} = 95.80$) and Sample 17 ($\overline{x} = 94.82$) fall outside the control limits.

20. $\overline{R} = .053$ $\overline{\overline{x}} = 3.082$

$\overline{x}$ Chart:

$$UCL = \overline{\overline{x}} + A_2\overline{R} = 3.082 + 0.577(0.053) = 3.112$$
$$LCL = \overline{\overline{x}} - A_2\overline{R} = 3.082 - 0.577(0.053) = 3.051$$

R Chart:

$$UCL = \overline{R}D_4 = 0.053(2.115) = 0.1121$$
$$LCL = \overline{R}D_3 = 0.053(0) = 0$$

All data points are within the control limits for both charts.

21. a.

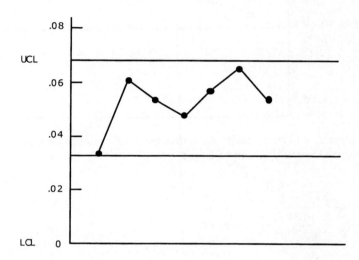

Warning: Process should be checked. All points are within control limits; however, all points are also greater than the process proportion defective.

b.

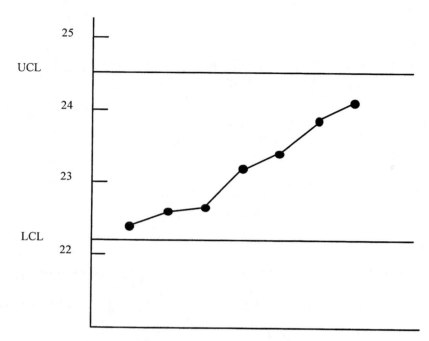

Warning: Process should be checked. All points are within control limits yet the trend in points show a movement or shift toward UCL out-of-control point.

22. a. $p = .04$

$$\sigma_{\bar{p}} = \sqrt{\frac{p(1-p)}{n}} = \sqrt{\frac{0.04(0.96)}{200}} = 0.0139$$

$$\text{UCL} = p + 3\,\sigma_{\bar{p}} = 0.04 + 3(0.0139) = 0.0817$$
$$\text{LCL} = p - 3\,\sigma_{\bar{p}} = 0.04 - 3(0.0139) = -0.0017$$

Use LCL $= 0$

b.

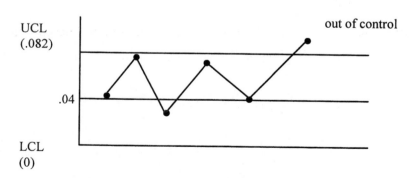

For month 1 $\bar{p} = 10/200 = 0.05$. Other monthly values are .075, .03, .065, .04, and .085. Only the last month with $\bar{p} = 0.085$ is an out-of-control situation.

23. a. Use binomial probabilities with $n = 10$.

   At $p_0 = .05$,

   $P(\text{Accept lot}) = f(0) + f(1) + f(2)$

   $\qquad\qquad\qquad\quad = .5987 + .3151 + .0746 = .9884$

   Producer's Risk: $\alpha = 1 - .9884 = .0116$

   At $p_1 = .20$,

   $P(\text{Accept lot}) = f(0) + f(1) + f(2)$

   $\qquad\qquad\qquad\quad = .1074 + .2684 + .3020 = .6778$

   Consumer's risk: $\beta = .6778$

   b. The consumer's risk is unacceptably high. Too many bad lots would be accepted.

   c. Reducing c would help, but increasing the sample size appears to be the best solution.

24. a. P (Accept) are shown below: (Using $n = 15$)

	$p = .01$	$p = .02$	$p = .03$	$p = .04$	$p = .05$
$f(0)$	.8601	.7386	.6333	.5421	.4633
$f(1)$	.1303	.2261	.2938	.3388	.3658
	.9904	.9647	.9271	.8809	.8291
$\alpha = 1 - P$ (Accept)	.0096	.0353	.0729	.1191	.1709

   Using $p_0 = .03$ since α is close to .075. Thus, .03 is the fraction defective where the producer will tolerate a .075 probability of rejecting a good lot (only .03 defective).

   b.

	$p = .25$
$f(0)$	.0134
$f(1)$	.0668
$\beta =$	.0802

25. a. P (Accept) when $n = 25$ and $c = 0$. Use the binomial probability function with

$$f(x) = \frac{n!}{x!(n-x)!} p^x (1-p)^{n-x}$$

   or

$$f(0) = \frac{25!}{0!25!} p^0 (1-p)^{25} = (1-p)^{25}$$

If	$f(0)$
$p = .01$	.7778
$p = .03$	.4670
$p = .10$	.0718
$p = .20$	.0038

b.

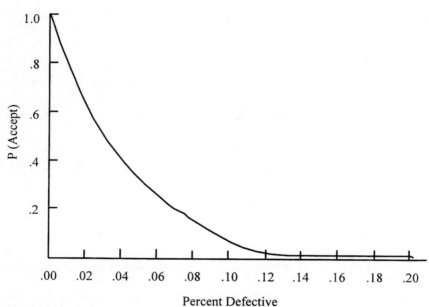

Percent Defective

c. $1 - f(0) = 1 - .778 = .222$

26. a. $\mu = np = 250(.02) = 5$

$$\sigma = \sqrt{np(1-p)} = \sqrt{250(0.02)(0.98)} = 2.21$$

$P(\text{Accept}) = P(x \le 10.5)$

$$z = \frac{10.5 - 5}{2.21} = 2.49$$

$P(\text{Accept}) = .5000 + .4936 = .9936$

Producer's Risk: $\alpha = 1 - .9936 = .0064$

b. $\mu = np = 250(.08) = 20$

$$\sigma = \sqrt{np(1-p)} = \sqrt{250(0.08)(0.92)} = 4.29$$

$P(\text{Accept}) = P(x \le 10.5)$

$$z = \frac{10.5 - 5}{4.29} = -2.21$$

$P(\text{Accept}) = 1 - .4864 = .0136$

Consumer's Risk: $\beta = .0136$

c. The advantage is the excellent control over the producer's and the consumer's risk. The disadvantage is the cost of taking a large sample.

Chapter 21
Sample Survey

Learning Objectives

1. Learn what a sample survey is and how it differs from an experiment as a method of collecting data.

2. Know about the methods of data collection for a survey.

3. Know the difference between sampling and nonsampling error.

4. Learn about four sample designs: (1) simple random sampling, (2) stratified simple random sampling, (3) cluster sampling, and (4) systematic sampling.

5. Lean how to estimate a population mean, a population total, and a population proportion using the above sample designs.

6. Understand the relationship between sample size and precision.

7. Learn how to choose the appropriate sample size using stratified and simple random sampling.

8. Learn how to allocate the total sample to the various strata using stratified simple random sampling.

Solutions:

1. a. $\bar{x} = 215$ is an estimate of the population mean.

    b. $s_{\bar{x}} = \dfrac{20}{\sqrt{50}}\sqrt{\dfrac{800-50}{800}} = 2.7386$

    c. $215 \pm 2(2.7386)$ or 209.5228 to 220.4772

2. a. Estimate of population total $= N\bar{x} = 400(75) = 30,000$

    b. Estimate of Standard Error $= Ns_{\bar{x}}$

    $$Ns_{\bar{x}} = 400\left(\dfrac{8}{\sqrt{80}}\right)\sqrt{\dfrac{400-80}{400}} = 320$$

    c. $30,000 \pm 2(320)$ or $29,360$ to $30,640$

3. a. $\bar{p} = .30$ is an estimate of the population proportion

    b. $s_{\bar{p}} = \sqrt{\left(\dfrac{1000-100}{1000}\right)\left(\dfrac{(.3)(.7)}{99}\right)} = .0437$

    c. $.30 \pm 2(.0437)$ or $.2126$ to $.3874$

4. $B = 15$

    $$n = \dfrac{(70)^2}{\dfrac{(15)^2}{4}+\dfrac{(70)^2}{450}} = \dfrac{4900}{67.1389} = 72.9830$$

    A sample size of 73 will provide an approximate 95% confidence interval of width 30.

5. a. $\bar{x} = 149,670$ and $s = 73,420$

    $$s_{\bar{x}} = \sqrt{\dfrac{771-50}{771}}\left(\dfrac{73,420}{\sqrt{50}}\right) = 10,040.83$$

    <u>approximate 95% confidence interval</u>

    $149,670 \pm 2(10,040.83)$
    or
    $\$129,588.34$ to $\$169,751.66$

    b. $\widehat{X} = N\bar{x} = 771(149,670) = 115,395,570$

    $s_{\hat{x}} = Ns_{\bar{x}} = 771(10,040.83) = 7,741,479.93$

approximate 95% confidence interval

$$115,395,770 \pm 2(7,741,479.93)$$

or

$$\$99,912,810.14 \text{ to } \$130,878,729.86$$

c. $\bar{p} = 18/50 = 0.36$ and $s_{\bar{p}} = \sqrt{\left(\dfrac{771-50}{771}\right)\left(\dfrac{(.36)(.64)}{49}\right)} = .0663$

approximate 95% confidence interval

$$0.36 \pm 2(0.0663)$$

or

$$0.2274 \text{ to } 0.4926$$

This is a rather large interval; sample sizes must be rather large to obtain tight confidence intervals on a population proportion.

6. $B = 5000/2 = 2500$ Use the value of s for the previous year in the formula to determine the necessary sample size.

$$n = \frac{(31.3)^2}{\dfrac{(2.5)^2}{4} + \dfrac{(31.3)^2}{724}} = \frac{979.69}{2.9157} = 336.0051$$

A sample size of 337 will provide an approximate 95% confidence interval of width no larger than $5000.

7. a.   Stratum 1: = 138

Stratum 2: $\bar{x}_2 = 103$

Stratum 3: $\bar{x}_3 = 210$

b.   Stratum 1

$\bar{x}_1 = 138$

$$s_{\bar{x}_1} = \left(\frac{30}{\sqrt{20}}\right)\sqrt{\frac{200-20}{200}} = 6.3640$$

$$138 \pm 2(6.3640)$$

or

$$125.272 \text{ to } 150.728$$

Stratum 2

$\bar{x}_2 = 103$

$$s_{\bar{x}_2} = \left(\frac{25}{\sqrt{30}}\right)\sqrt{\frac{250-30}{250}} = 4.2817$$

$$103 \pm 2(4.2817)$$
$$\text{or}$$
$$94.4366 \text{ to } 111.5634$$

Stratum 3

$$\bar{x}_3 = 210$$

$$s_{\bar{x}_3} = \left(\frac{50}{\sqrt{25}}\right)\sqrt{\frac{100-25}{100}} = 8.6603$$

$$210 \pm 2(8.6603)$$
$$\text{or}$$
$$192.6794 \text{ to } 227.3206$$

c. $$\bar{x}_{st} = \left(\frac{200}{550}\right)138 + \left(\frac{250}{550}\right)103 + \left(\frac{100}{550}\right)210$$

$$= 50.1818 + 46.8182 + 38.1818$$
$$= 135.1818$$

$$s_{\bar{x}_{st}} = \sqrt{\left(\frac{1}{(550)^2}\right)\left(200(180)\frac{(30)^2}{20} + 250(220)\frac{(25)^2}{30} + 100(75)\frac{(50)^2}{25}\right)}$$

$$= \sqrt{\left(\frac{1}{(550)^2}\right)3,515,833.3} = 3.4092$$

approximate 95% confidence interval

$$135.1818 \pm 2(3.4092)$$
$$\text{or}$$
$$128.3634 \text{ to } 142.0002$$

8.   a.   Stratum 1: $N_1\bar{x}_1 = 200(138) = 27,600$

Stratum 2: $N_2\bar{x}_2 = 250(103) = 25,750$

Stratum 3: $N_3\bar{x}_3 = 100(210) = 21,000$

b. $N\,\bar{x}_{st} = 27,600 + 25,750 + 21,000 = 74,350$

Note: the sum of the estimate for each stratum total equals $N\,\bar{x}_{st}$

c. $N\,\bar{x}_{st} = 550(3.4092) = 1875.06$ (see 7c)

approximate 95% confidence interval

$$74,350 \pm 2(1875.06)$$
$$\text{or}$$
$$70,599.88 \text{ to } 78,100.12$$

9. a. Stratum 1

$\overline{p}_1 = .50$

$$s_{\overline{p}_1} = \sqrt{\left(\frac{200-20}{200}\right)\left(\frac{(.50)(.50)}{19}\right)} = .1088$$

$$50 \pm 2(.1088)$$
$$\text{or}$$
$$.2824 \text{ to } .7176$$

Stratum 2

$\overline{p}_2 = .78$

$$s_{\overline{p}_2} = \sqrt{\left(\frac{250-30}{250}\right)\left(\frac{(.78)(.22)}{29}\right)} = .0722$$

$$.78 \pm 2(.0722)$$
$$\text{or}$$
$$.6356 \text{ to } .9244$$

Stratum 3

$\overline{p}_3 = .21$

$$s_{\overline{p}_3} = \sqrt{\left(\frac{100-25}{100}\right)\left(\frac{(.21)(.79)}{24}\right)} = .0720$$

$$.21 \pm 2(.0720)$$
$$\text{or}$$
$$.066 \text{ to } .354$$

b. $\overline{p}_{st} = \dfrac{200}{550}(.50) + \dfrac{250}{550}(.78) + \dfrac{100}{550}(.21) = .5745$

c. $s_{\overline{p}_{st}} = \sqrt{\left(\dfrac{1}{(550)^2}\right)\left(200(180)\dfrac{(.5)(.5)}{19} + 250(220)\dfrac{(.78)(.22)}{29} + 100(75)\dfrac{(.21)(.79)}{24}\right)}$

$$= \sqrt{\left(\frac{1}{(550)^2}\right)(473.6842 + 325.4483 + 51.8438)} = .0530$$

d. approximate 95% confidence interval

$$.5745 \pm 2(.0530)$$
$$\text{or}$$
$$.4685 \text{ to } .6805$$

10. a. $n = \dfrac{\left[300(150) + 600(75) + 500(100)\right]^2}{(1400)^2 \left(\dfrac{(20)^2}{2}\right) + \left[300(150) + 600(75)^2 + 500(100)^2\right]} = \dfrac{(140,000)^2}{196,000,000 + 15,125,000} = 92.8359$

Rounding up we choose a total sample of 93.

$n_1 = 93\left(\dfrac{300(150)}{140,000}\right) = 30$

$n_2 = 93\left(\dfrac{600(75)}{140,000}\right) = 30$

$n_3 = 93\left(\dfrac{500(100)}{140,000}\right) = 33$

b. With $B = 10$, the first term in the denominator in the formula for n changes.

$n = \dfrac{(140,000)^2}{(1400)^2 \left(\dfrac{(10)^2}{4}\right) + 15,125,000} = \dfrac{(140,000)^2}{49,000,000 + 15,125,000} = 305.6530$

Rounding up, we see that a sample size of 306 is needed to provide this level of precision.

$n_1 = 306\left(\dfrac{300(150)}{140,000}\right) = 98$

$n_2 = 306\left(\dfrac{600(75)}{140,000}\right) = 98$

$n_3 = 306\left(\dfrac{500(100)}{140,000}\right) = 109$

Due to rounding, the total of the allocations to each strata only add to 305. Note that even though the sample size is larger, the proportion allocated to each stratum has not changed.

$n = \dfrac{(140,000)^2}{\dfrac{(15,000)^2}{4} + 15,125,000} = \dfrac{(140,000)^2}{56,250,000 + 15,125,000} = 274.6060$

Rounding up, we see that a sample size of 275 will provide the desired level of precision.

The allocations to the strata are in the same proportion as for parts a and b.

$n_1 = 275\left(\dfrac{300(150)}{140,000}\right) = 98$

$$n_2 = 275\left(\frac{600(75)}{140,000}\right) = 88$$

$$n_3 = 275\left(\frac{500(100)}{140,000}\right) = 98$$

Again, due to rounding, the stratum allocations do not add to the total sample size. Another item could be sampled from, say, stratum 3 if desired.

11. a. $\bar{x}_1 = 29.5333$ $\qquad\qquad$ $\bar{x}_2 = 64.775$

$\bar{x}_3 = 45.2125$ $\qquad\qquad$ $\bar{x}_4 = 53.0300$

b. <u>Indianapolis</u>

$$29.533 \pm 2\left(\frac{13.3603}{\sqrt{6}}\right)\sqrt{\frac{38-6}{38}}$$

$29.533 \pm 10.9086(.9177)$
or
19.5222 to 39.5438

<u>Louisville</u>

$$64.775 \pm 2\left(\frac{25.0666}{\sqrt{8}}\right)\sqrt{\frac{45-8}{45}}$$

$64.775 \pm 17.7248(.9068)$
or
48.7022 to 80.8478

<u>St. Louis</u>

$$45.2125 \pm 2\left(\frac{19.4084}{\sqrt{8}}\right)\sqrt{\frac{80-8}{80}}$$

$45.2125 \pm (13.7238)(.9487)$
or
32.1927 to 58.2323

<u>Memphis</u>

$$53.0300 \pm 2\left(\frac{29.6810}{\sqrt{10}}\right)\sqrt{\frac{70-10}{70}}$$

$53.0300 \pm 18.7719(.9258)$
or
35.6510 to 70.4090

c. $\bar{p}_{st} = \left(\frac{38}{233}\right)\left(\frac{1}{6}\right) + \left(\frac{45}{233}\right)\left(\frac{5}{8}\right) + \left(\frac{80}{233}\right)\left(\frac{3}{8}\right) + \left(\frac{70}{233}\right)\left(\frac{5}{10}\right) = .4269$

d. $N_1(N_1-n_1)\dfrac{\overline{p}_1(1-\overline{p}_1)}{n_1-1}=38(32)\dfrac{\left(\frac{1}{6}\right)\left(\frac{5}{6}\right)}{5}=33.7778$

$N_2(N_2-n_2)\dfrac{\overline{p}_2(1-\overline{p}_2)}{n_2-1}=45(37)\dfrac{\left(\frac{5}{8}\right)\left(\frac{3}{8}\right)}{7}=55.7478$

$N_3(N_3-n_3)\dfrac{\overline{p}_3(1-\overline{p}_3)}{n_3-1}=80(72)\dfrac{\left(\frac{3}{8}\right)\left(\frac{5}{8}\right)}{7}=192.8571$

$N_4(N_4-n_4)\dfrac{\overline{p}_4(1-\overline{p}_4)}{n_4-1}=70(60)\dfrac{\left(\frac{5}{10}\right)\left(\frac{5}{10}\right)}{9}=116.6667$

$s_{\overline{p}_{st}}=\sqrt{\left(\dfrac{1}{(233)^2}\right)[33.7778+55.7478+192.8571+116.6667]}=\sqrt{\dfrac{1}{(233)^2}(399.0494)}=.0857$

<u>approximate 95% confidence interval</u>

$.4269\ \pm\ 2(.0857)$

or

$.2555$ to $.5983$

12. a. St. Louis total = $N_1\overline{x}_1$ = 80 (45.2125) = 3617

In dollars: $3,617,000

b. Indianapolis total = $N_1\overline{x}_1$ = 38 (29.5333) = 1122.2654

In dollars: $1,122,265

c. $\overline{x}_{st}=\left(\dfrac{38}{233}\right)29.5333+\left(\dfrac{45}{233}\right)64.775+\left(\dfrac{80}{233}\right)45.2125+\left(\dfrac{70}{233}\right)53.0300=48.7821$

$N_1(N_1-n_1)\dfrac{s_1^2}{n_1}=38(32)\dfrac{(13.3603)^2}{6}=36,175.517$

$N_2(N_2-n_2)\dfrac{s_2^2}{n_2}=45(37)\dfrac{(25.0666)^2}{8}=130,772.1$

$N_3(N_3-n_3)\dfrac{s_3^2}{n_3}=80(72)\dfrac{(19.4084)^2}{8}=271,213.91$

$N_4(N_4-n_4)\dfrac{s_4^2}{n_4}=70(60)\dfrac{(29.6810)^2}{10}=370,003.94$

$$s_{\bar{x}_{st}} = \sqrt{\left(\frac{1}{(233)^2}\right)\left[36,175.517 + 130,772.1 + 271,213.91 + 370,003.94\right]}$$

$$= \sqrt{\frac{1}{(233)^2}(808,165.47)} = 3.8583$$

<u>approximate 95% confidence interval</u>

$$\bar{x}_{st} \pm 2s_{\bar{x}_{st}}$$
$$48.7821 \pm 2(3.8583)$$
or
$$41.0655 \text{ to } 56.4987$$

In dollars: \$41,066 to \$56,499

d.

<u>approximate 95% confidence interval</u>

$$N\bar{x}_{st} \pm 2Ns_{\bar{x}_{st}}$$

$$233(48.7821) \pm 2(233)(3.8583)$$

$$11,366.229 \pm 1797.9678$$
or
$$9,568.2612 \text{ to } 13,164.197$$

In dollars: \$9,568,261 to \$13,164,197

13. $$n = \frac{\left[50(80) + 38(150) + 35(45)\right]^2}{(123)^2\left(\frac{(30)^2}{4}\right) + \left[50(80)^2 + 38(150)^2 + 35(45)^2\right]} = \frac{(11,275)^2}{3,404,025 + 1,245,875} = 27.3394$$

Rounding up we see that a sample size of 28 is necessary to obtain the desired precision.

$$n_1 = 28\left(\frac{50(80)}{11,275}\right) = 10$$

$$n_2 = 28\left(\frac{38(150)}{11,275}\right) = 14$$

$$n_3 = 28\left(\frac{35(45)}{11,275}\right) = 4$$

b. $$n = \frac{\left[50(100) + 38(100) + 35(100)\right]^2}{(123)^2\left(\frac{(30)^2}{4}\right) + \left[50(100)^2 + 38(100)^2 + 35(100)^2\right]} = \frac{\left[123(100)\right]^2}{3,404,025 + 123(100)^2} = 33$$

$$n_1 = 33\left(\frac{50(100)}{12,300}\right) = 13$$

$$n_2 = 33 \left(\frac{38(100)}{12,300} \right) = 10$$

$$n_3 = 33 \left(\frac{35(100)}{12,300} \right) = 9$$

This is the same as proportional allocation. Note that for each stratum

$$n_h = n \left(\frac{N_h}{N} \right)$$

14. a. $\bar{x}_c = \dfrac{\sum x_i}{\sum M_i} = \dfrac{750}{50} = 15$

$\widehat{X} = M \bar{x}_c = 300(15) = 4500$

$\bar{p}_c = \dfrac{\sum a_i}{\sum M_i} = \dfrac{15}{50} = .30$

b. $\sum (x_i - \bar{x}_c M_i)^2 \quad = [\, 95 - 15\,(7)\,]^2 + [\, 325 - 15\,(18)\,]^2 + [\, 190 - 15\,(15)\,]^2 + [\, 140 - 15\,(10)]^2$

$\qquad\qquad\qquad\quad = (-10)^2 + (55)^2 + (-35)^2 + (-10)^2$

$\qquad\qquad\qquad\quad = 4450$

$$s_{\bar{x}_c} = \sqrt{ \left(\frac{25-4}{(25)(4)(12)^2} \right) \left(\frac{4450}{3} \right) } = 1.4708$$

$s_{\widehat{X}} = M s_{\bar{x}_c} = 300(1.4708) = 441.24$

$\sum (a_i - \bar{p}_c M_i)^2 \quad = [\, 1 - .3\,(7)\,]^2 + [\, 6 - .3\,(18)\,]^2 + [\, 6 - .3\,(15)\,]^2 + [\, 2 - .3\,(10)\,]^2$

$\qquad\qquad\qquad\quad = (-1.1)^2 + (.6)^2 + (1.5)^2 + (-1)^2$

$\qquad\qquad\qquad\quad = 4.82$

$$s_{\bar{p}_c} = \sqrt{ \left(\frac{25-4}{(25)(4)(12)^2} \right) \left(\frac{4.82}{3} \right) } = .0484$$

c. approximate 95% confidence
Interval for Population Mean:

15 ± 2(1.4708)
or
12.0584 to 17.9416

d. approximate 95% confidence
Interval for Population Total:

4500 ± 2(441.24)
or
3617.52 to 5382.48

e. approximate 95% confidence
    Interval for Population Proportion:

    .30 ± 2(.0484)
    or
    .2032 to .3968

15. a. $\bar{x}_c = \dfrac{10,400}{130} = 80$

    $\widehat{X} = M\,\bar{x}_c = 600(80) = 48,000$

    $\bar{p}_c = \dfrac{13}{130} = .10$

b. $\sum (x_i - \bar{x}_c M_i)^2 = [\,3500 - 80\,(35)\,]^2 + [\,965 - 80\,(15)\,]^2 + [\,960 - 80\,(12)\,]^2$
    $+ [\,2070 - 80\,(23)\,]^2 + [\,1100 - 80\,(20)\,]^2 + [\,1805 - 80\,(25)\,]^2$
    $= (700)^2 + (-235)^2 + (0)^2 + (230)^2 + (-500)^2 + (-195)^2$
    $= 886,150$

    $s_{\bar{x}_c} = \sqrt{\left(\dfrac{30-6}{(30)(6)(20)^2}\right)\left(\dfrac{886,150}{5}\right)} = 7.6861$

    approximate 95% confidence
    Interval for Population Mean:

    80 ± 2(7.6861)
    or
    64.6278 to 95.3722

c. $s_{\widehat{X}} = 600(7.6861) = 4611.66$

    approximate 95% confidence
    Interval for Population Total:

    48,000 ± 2(4611.66)
    or
    38,776.68 to 57,223.32

    $\sum (a_i - \bar{p}_c M_i)^2 = [\,3 - .1\,(35)\,]^2 + [\,0 - .1\,(15)\,]^2 + [\,1 - .1\,(12)\,]^2 + [\,4 - .1\,(23)\,]^2$
    $+ [\,3 - .1\,(20)\,]^2 + [\,2 - .1\,(25)\,]^2$
    $= (-.5)^2 + (-1.5)^2 + (-.2)^2 + (1.7)^2 + (1)^2 + (-.5)^2$
    $= 6.68$

    $s_{\bar{p}_c} = \sqrt{\left(\dfrac{30-6}{(30)(6)(20)^2}\right)\left(\dfrac{6.68}{5}\right)} = .0211$

    approximate 95% confidence

Interval for Population Proportion:

.10 ± 2(.0211)
or
.0578 to .1422

16. a. $\bar{x}_c = \dfrac{2000}{50} = 40$

Estimate of mean age of mechanical engineers: 40 years

b. $\bar{p}_c = \dfrac{35}{50} = .70$

Estimate of proportion attending local university: .70

c. $\sum(x_i - \bar{x}_c M_i)^2$ $= [\,520 - 40\,(12)\,]^2 + \cdots + [\,462 - 40\,(13)\,]^2$
$= (40)^2 + (-7)^2 + (-10)^2 + (-11)^2 + (30)^2 + (9)^2 + (22)^2 + (8)^2 + (-23)^2$
$+ (-58)^2$
$= 7292$

$s_{\bar{x}_c} = \sqrt{\left(\dfrac{120-10}{(120)(10)(50/12)^2}\right)\left(\dfrac{7292}{9}\right)} = 2.0683$

approximate 95% confidence
Interval for Mean age:

40 ± 2(2.0683)
or
35.8634 to 44.1366

d. $\sum(a_i - \bar{p}_c M_i)^2$ $= [\,8 - .7\,(12)\,]^2 + \cdots + [\,12 - .7\,(13)\,]^2$
$= (-.4)^2 + (-.7)^2 + (-.4)^2 + (.3)^2 + (-1.2)^2 + (-.1)^2 + (-1.4)^2 + (.3)^2$
$+ (.7)^2 + (2.9)^2$
$= 13.3$

$s_{\bar{p}_c} = \sqrt{\left(\dfrac{120-10}{(120)(10)(50/12)^2}\right)\left(\dfrac{13.3}{9}\right)} = .0883$

approximate 95% confidence
Interval for Proportion Attending Local University:

.70 ± 2(.0883)
or
.5234 to .8766

17. a. $\bar{x}_c = \dfrac{17(37)+35(32)+\cdots+57(44)}{17+35+\cdots+57} = \dfrac{11,240}{304} = 36.9737$

Estimate of mean age: 36.9737 years

b. Proportion of College Graduates: $128 / 304 = .4211$

Proportion of Males: $112 / 304 = .3684$

c. $\Sigma(x_i - \overline{x}_c M_i)^2 = [\ 17\ (37) - (36.9737)\ (17)\ ]^2 + \cdots + [\ 57\ (44) - (36.9737)\ (44)\ ]^2$

$= (.4471)^2 + (-174.0795)^2 + (-25.3162)^2 + (-460.2642)^2 + (173.1309)^2$
$+ (180.3156)^2 + (-94.7376)^2 + (400.4991)^2$
$= 474,650.68$

$$s_{\overline{x}_c} = \sqrt{\left(\frac{150-8}{(150)(8)(40)^2}\right)\left(\frac{474,650.68}{7}\right)} = 2.2394$$

approximate 95% confidence
Interval for Mean Age of Agents:

$36.9737 \pm 2(2.2394)$
or
32.4949 to 41.4525

d. $\Sigma(a_i - \overline{p}_c M_i)^2 = [\ 3 - .4211\ (17)\ ]^2 + \cdots + [\ 25 - .4211\ (57)\ ]^2$

$= (-4.1587)^2 + (-.7385)^2 + (-2.9486)^2 + (10.2074)^2 + (-.1073)^2 + (-3.0532)^2$
$+ (-.2128)^2 + (.9973)^2$
$= 141.0989$

$$s_{\overline{p}_c} = \sqrt{\left(\frac{150-8}{(150)(8)(40)^2}\right)\left(\frac{141.0989}{7}\right)} = .0386$$

approximate 95% confidence

Interval for Proportion of Agents that are College Graduates:

$.4211 \pm 2(.0386)$
or
$.3439$ to $.4983$

e. $\Sigma(a_i - \overline{p}_c M_i)^2 = [\ 4 - .3684\ (17)\ ]^2 + \cdots + [\ 26 - .3684\ (57)\ ]^2$

$= (-2.2628)^2 + (-.8940)^2 + (-2.5784)^2 + (3.6856)^2 + (-3.8412)^2 + (1.5792)^2$
$+ (-.6832)^2 + (5.0012)^2$
$= 68.8787$

$$s_{\overline{p}_c} = \sqrt{\left(\frac{150-8}{(150)(8)(40)^2}\right)\left(\frac{68.8787}{7}\right)} = .0270$$

approximate 95% confidence
Interval for Proportion of Agents that are Male:

$.3684 \pm 2(.0270)$
or
$.3144$ to $.4224$

18. a. $\bar{p} = 0.19$

$$s_{\bar{p}} = \sqrt{\frac{(0.19)(0.81)}{363}} = 0.0206$$

Approximate 95% Confidence Interval:

$0.19 \pm 2(0.0206)$
or
0.1488 to 0.2312

b. $\bar{p} = 0.31$

$$s_{\bar{p}} = \sqrt{\frac{(0.31)(0.69)}{363}} = 0.0243$$

Approximate 95% Confidence Interval:

$0.31 \pm 2(0.0243)$
or
0.2615 to 0.3585

c. $\bar{p} = 0.17$

$$s_{\bar{p}} = \sqrt{\frac{(0.17)(0.83)}{373}} = 0.0197$$

Approximate 95% Confidence Interval:

$0.17 \pm 2(0.0197)$
or
0.1306 to 0.2094

d.   The largest standard error is when $\bar{p} = .50$.

At $\bar{p} = .50$, we get

$$s_{\bar{p}} = \sqrt{\frac{(0.5)(0.5)}{363}} = 0.0262$$

Multiplying by 2, we get a bound of $B = 2(.0262) = 0.0525$

For a sample of 363, then, they know that in the worst case ($\bar{p} = 0.50$), the bound will be approximately 5%.

e.   If the poll was conducted by calling people at home during the day the sample results would only be representative of adults not working outside the home. It is likely that the Louis Harris organization took precautions against this and other possible sources of bias.

19. a. Assume $(N - n) / N \approx 1$

$\bar{p} = .55$

$$s_{\bar{p}} = \sqrt{\frac{(0.55)(0.45)}{504}} = 0.0222$$

b. $\bar{p} = .31$

$$s_{\bar{p}} = \sqrt{\frac{(0.31)(0.69)}{504}} = 0.0206$$

c. The estimate of the standard error in part (a) is larger because $\bar{p}$ is closer to .50.

d. Approximate 95% Confidence interval:

.55 ± 2(.0222)
or
.5056 to .5944

e. Approximate 95% Confidence interval:

.31 ± 2(.0206)

.2688 to .3512

20. a. $s_{\bar{x}} = \sqrt{\frac{3000 - 200}{3000}} \frac{3000}{\sqrt{200}} = 204.9390$

Approximate 95% Confidence Interval for Mean Annual Salary:

23,200 ± 2(204.9390)
or
$22,790 to $23,610

b. $N\bar{x} = 3000\,(23,200) = 69,600,000$

$s_{\bar{x}} = 3000\,(204.9390) = 614,817$

Approximate 95% Confidence Interval for Population Total Salary:

69,600,000 ± 2(614,817)
or
$68,370,366 to $70,829,634

c. $\bar{p} = .73$

$$s_{\bar{p}} = \sqrt{\left(\frac{3000 - 200}{3000}\right)\left(\frac{(.73)(.27)}{199}\right)} = .0304$$

Approximate 95% Confidence Interval for Proportion that are Generally Satisfied:

.73 ± 2(.0304)
or
.6692 to .7908

d. If management administered the questionnaire and anonymity was not guaranteed we would expect a definite upward bias in the percent reporting they were " generally satisfied" with their job. A procedure for guaranteeing anonymity should reduce the bias.

21. a. $\bar{p} = 1/3$

$$s_{\bar{p}} = \sqrt{\left(\frac{380-30}{380}\right)\left(\frac{(1/3)(2/3)}{29}\right)} = .0840$$

Approximate 95% Confidence Interval:

.3333 ± 2(.0840)
or
.1653 to .5013

b. $\widehat{X}_2 = 760\,(19/45) = 320.8889$

c. $\bar{p} = 19/45 = .4222$

$$s_{\bar{p}} = \sqrt{\left(\frac{760-45}{760}\right)\left(\frac{(19/45)(26/45)}{44}\right)} = .0722$$

Approximate 95% Confidence Interval:

.4222 ± 2(.0722)
or
.2778 to .5666

d. $\bar{p}_{st} = \left(\frac{380}{1400}\right)\left(\frac{10}{30}\right) + \left(\frac{760}{1400}\right)\left(\frac{19}{45}\right) + \left(\frac{260}{1400}\right)\left(\frac{7}{25}\right) = .3717$

$$\sum N_h (N_h - n_h)\left[\frac{\bar{p}_h(1-\bar{p}_h)}{n_h - 1}\right] = 380(350)\frac{(1/3)(2/3)}{29}$$

$$+760(715)\frac{(19/45)(26/45)}{44} + 260(235)\frac{(7/25)(18/25)}{24}$$

$$= 1019.1571 + 3012.7901 + 513.2400 = 4545.1892$$

$$s_{\bar{p}_{st}} = \sqrt{\left(\frac{1}{(1400)^2}\right)4545.1892} = .0482$$

Approximate 95% Confidence Interval:

.3717 ± 2(.0482)
or
.2753 to .4681

22. a. $\widehat{X} = 380\,(9\,/\,30) + 760\,(12\,/\,45) + 260\,(11\,/\,25) = 431.0667$

Estimate approximately 431 deaths due to beating.

b. $\overline{p}_{st} = \left(\dfrac{380}{1400}\right)\left(\dfrac{9}{30}\right) + \left(\dfrac{760}{1400}\right)\left(\dfrac{12}{45}\right) + \left(\dfrac{260}{1400}\right)\left(\dfrac{11}{25}\right) = .3079$

$\sum N_h (N_h - n_h) \dfrac{\left[\overline{p}_h (1 - \overline{p}_h)\right]}{n_h - 1}$

= (380) (380 - 30) (9 / 30) (21 / 30) / 29 + (760) (760 - 45) (12 / 45) (33 / 45) / 44 +
    (260) (260 - 25)(11 / 25) (14 / 25) / 24

= 4005.5079

$s_{\overline{p}_{st}} = \sqrt{\left(\dfrac{1}{(1400)^2}\right) 4005.5079} = .0452$

Approximate 95% Confidence Interval:

.3079 ± 2(.0452)
or
.2175 to .3983

c. $\overline{p}_{st} = \left(\dfrac{380}{1400}\right)\left(\dfrac{21}{30}\right) + \left(\dfrac{760}{1400}\right)\left(\dfrac{34}{45}\right) + \left(\dfrac{260}{1400}\right)\left(\dfrac{15}{25}\right) = .7116$

$\sum N_h (N_h - n_h) \dfrac{\left[\overline{p}_h (1 - \overline{p}_h)\right]}{n_h - 1}$

= (380) (380 - 30) (21 / 30) (9 / 30) / 29 + (760) (760 - 45) (34 / 45) (11 / 45) / 44 +
    (260) (260 - 25) (15 / 25) (10 / 25) / 24

= 3855.0417

$s_{\overline{p}_{st}} = \sqrt{\left(\dfrac{1}{(1400)^2}\right) 3855.0417} = .0443$

Approximate 95% Confidence Interval:

.7116 ± 2(.0443)
or
.6230 to .8002

d. $\widehat{X} = 1400\,(.7116) = 996.24$

Estimate of total number of black victims ≈ 996

23. a. $n = \dfrac{\left[3000(80) + 600(150) + 250(220) + 100(700) + 50(3000)\right]^2}{(4000)^2\left(\dfrac{(20)^2}{4}\right) + 3000(80)^2 + 600(150)^2 + 250(220)^2 + 100(700)^2 + 50(3000)^2}$

$= \dfrac{366,025,000,000}{1,600,000,000 + 543,800,000} = 170.7365$

Rounding up, we need a sample size of 171 for the desired precision.

$n_1 = 171\left(\dfrac{3000(80)}{605,000}\right) = 68$

$n_2 = 171\left(\dfrac{600(150)}{605,000}\right) = 25$

$n_3 = 171\left(\dfrac{250(220)}{605,000}\right) = 16$

$n_4 = 171\left(\dfrac{100(700)}{605,000}\right) = 20$

$n_5 = 171\left(\dfrac{50(3000)}{605,000}\right) = 42$

24. a. $\bar{x}_c = \dfrac{14(61) + 7(74) + 96(78) + 23(69) + 71(73) + 29(84)}{14 + 7 + 96 + 23 + 71 + 29} = \dfrac{18,066}{240} = 75.275$

Estimate of mean age is approximately 75 years old.

b. $\bar{p}_c = \dfrac{12 + 2 + 30 + 8 + 10 + 22}{14 + 7 + 96 + 23 + 71 + 29} = \dfrac{84}{240} = .35$

$\begin{aligned}
\Sigma(a_i - \bar{p}_c M_i)^2 &= [12 - .35\,(14)\,]^2 + [\,2 - .35\,(7)\,]^2 + [30 - .35\,(96)\,]^2 \\
&\quad + [\,8 - .35\,(23)\,]^2 + [\,10 - .35\,(71)\,]^2 + [\,22 - .35\,(29)\,]^2 \\
&= (7.1)^2 + (-.45)^2 + (-3.6)^2 + (-.05)^2 + (-14.85)^2 + (11.85)^2 \\
&= 424.52
\end{aligned}$

$s_{\bar{p}_c} = \sqrt{\left(\dfrac{100 - 6}{(100)(6)(48)^2}\right)\left(\dfrac{424.52}{5}\right)} = .0760$

Approximate 95% Confidence Interval:

.35 ± 2(.0760)
or
.198 to .502

$\widehat{X} = 4800\ (.35) = 1680$

Estimate of total number of Disabled Persons is 1680.